WINTERING OF PLANTS

АКАДЕМИЯ НАУК СССР

И. М. ВАСИЛЬЕВ

ЗИМОВКА РАСТЕНИЙ

ИЗДАТЕЛЬСТВО АКАДЕМИИ НАУК СССР

Москва · 1956

Wintering of Plants

by I. M. Vasil'yev

Editor of English Translation

JACOB LEVITT

———

Translated from the Russian by

ROYER and ROGER, Inc.

AMERICAN INSTITUTE OF BIOLOGICAL SCIENCES

WASHINGTON 6, D. C.

STECHERT-HAFNER SERVICE AGENCY, INC.
31 EAST 10th STREET
NEW YORK 3, N. Y.

FOREWORD

The present volume represents the first of what is planned as a series of translations of recent contributions to Plant Science published in the Russian language. Two years ago, the Botanical Society of America appointed a committee to survey the Russian publications, particularly those of monographic type, and to consider which of them would be most useful to English-speaking readers. It was desired to select books in fields in which Russian progress has been most active, books whose content would be otherwise inaccessible to non-Russian readers, and books whose translation would not be wholly impracticable. To this end, our Russian colleagues were extensively circularized by the Committee, and their recommendations considered in parallel with the Committee's own selections and with those requests and recommendations for translations which had been received from American and English botanists. The American Institute of Biological Sciences has collaborated wholeheartedly in this venture. The members of the Botanical Society's Committee have, in turn, selected the books, supervised the translation, and edited the final form. The Committee consists of Helen P. Sorokin, Chairman, E. K. Akamine, C. J. Alexopoulos, Katherine Esau, J. Levitt, H. J. Oosting, R. C. Rollins, R. C. Starr, and G. L. Stebbins. It is believed that English-speaking botanists the world over will owe them a considerable debt of gratitude.

Kenneth V. Thimann
Past President
Botanical Society of America

THE AMERICAN INSTITUTE OF BIOLOGICAL SCIENCES AND WHAT IT DOES

American biologists, seeking to harness pressure for modernization and coordination, created the American Institute of Biological Sciences to administer programs in behalf of all biology.

Protection of traditional areas of concentration has remained inherent in the Institute, although it serves all disciplines. Scientists in research, teaching or applied fields may propose and sponsor creative exploration of frontier areas or search for solutions to perennial problems.

Through the Institute, too, biologists stimulate scholarly and administrative interchanges to current information. Last year more than 800 biologists found their professional life enriched and their personal satisfactions deepened by active participation in AIBS-managed undertakings.

Biologists now direct more than 100 separate Institute projects. Some are massive, long-term concerns with the future of science, such as the Biological Sciences Curriculum Study and the Biological Sciences Communication Project. Others are short-lived but productive attacks on vital specific targets.

Through steadily increasing resources, the AIBS provides sound, full-time management for biology-centered activities. Among these are advance preparation and operation of conferences and symposia, enlisting and attracting public and private understanding and support, placement services for individual biologists, and translation, publishing, editorial and business services for learned societies.

In these and other ways, AIBS "minds the store" and serves as the eyes, ears, voice and strong right arm of 85,000 professional biologists in this country and around the world.

EDITOR'S PREFACE

In no country is the winter survival of crop plants a more important problem than in the U.S.S.R. For this reason, there have probably been more papers published on this subject during recent years in the Russian language than in all other languages combined. This is well illustrated by a conference on "The Physiology of the Hardiness of Plants" held in March of 1959 and published soon after in Moscow. Over 100 papers were presented on winter hardiness. The investigator of this problem therefore cannot possibly be thoroughly familiar with the literature in his field unless he knows the Russian work.

In 1940, the well-known Soviet scientist I.I. Tumanov published a book on winter hardiness. Unfortunately for the investigator who does not read Russian, this book has never been translated (at least into the Western European languages). Fortunately, this error has not been repeated with Vasil'yev's book. Coming 16 years later, it includes a large number of investigations made since publication of Tumanov's book, and is, therefore, particularly valuable to anyone who wishes to familiarize himself with the recent Russian literature. The non-Russian literature is also included, though it is of course covered less thoroughly. The author, in fact, points out that he is not attempting to review the literature exhaustively.

But Vasil'yev's book is much more than a literature review. It gives a clear idea of the aims, concepts, and methods of plant scientists in the U.S.S.R. As indicated by the author, the objective of all the Russian investigations of winter hardiness is a practical solution to the problem. His tremendous practical experience has well fitted him to this task. As has been shown over and over again in scientific investigations, what are originally practical problems may nevertheless lead to information of value to more basic general problems in science. The non-agriculturist can, therefore, expect to find considerable information of interest to him in this book.

On behalf of all the scientists interested in this field, the editor would like to thank the AIBS Committee on Translations (Donald P. de Sylva, Kenneth C. Kates, Chauncey Leake, Foster E. Mohrhardt, J. Levitt, and Fred R. Cagle, Chairman) for approving the translation of this monograph, as well as Francis C. Harwood, Director of Publications, together with all his staff, for their dedicated and efficient supervision of the publication. They have performed a real service to the scientific world. We are indebted to the National Science Foundation for granting the funds to make this publication possible.

Jacob Levitt
Editor

June, 1961

The Cyrillic transliteration system used in the preparation of
WINTERING OF PLANTS is that recommended by the Board on
Geographical Names, U. S. Department of the Interior.

Alphabet		transliteration	Alphabet		transliteration
А	а	a	П	п	p
Б	б	b	Р	р	r
В	в	v	С	с	s
Г	г	g	Т	т	t
Д	д	d	У	у	u
Е	е	e, ye	Ф	ф	f
Ё	ё	ë, yë	Х	х	kh
Ж	ж	zh	Ц	ц	ts
З	з	z	Ч	ч	ch
И	и	i	Ш	ш	sh
Й	й	y	Щ	щ	shch
К	к	k	Ъ	ъ	"
Л	л	l	Ы	ы	y'
М	м	m	Ь	ь	'
Н	н	n	Э	э	e
О	о	o	Ю	ю	yu
			Я	я	ya

TABLE OF CONTENTS

PART II

PHYSIOLOGY OF WINTER RESISTANCE IN PLANTS

PART III

DEVELOPMENT OF WINTER-RESISTANT FORMS OF PLANTS

SCIENCE IS CALLED ON TO MAKE THE
FARMER'S TASK MORE PRODUCTIVE.

— K. A. Timiryazev

FOREWORD

The purpose of this book is to provide an up-to-date scientific account of plant wintering in connection with practical problems in plant growing. The book is based chiefly on experimental research and observations on cultivated plants ranging over many years. The research was conducted in different years in accordance with the instructions of the USSR and RSFSR ministries of agriculture and local agencies.

The author was able to study the wintering of plants in a great variety of climatic and soil zones: in Moscow and Kursk oblasts, in the Ukraine, Belorussia, Latvia, Leningrad and Rostov oblasts, Krasnodarsk and Stavropol krays, the Black Sea coast from Batum to Sochi, in the Volga region, Mordovian Automonous Republic, in the Urals, Siberia, the Far East, Sakhalin, and in Central Asia. The experimental findings were regularly compared with observations in the field and in agricultural practice.

These materials have been supplemented with data from the literature. The author did not set out to give an exhaustive summary of the items pertaining to the individual chapters, for the sheer bulk of the reports on the various topics made this impossible. However, it was deemed necessary to survey the development of research on the main problems.

The most important published source was the works of Ivan Vladimirovich Michurin who was the first to explain many phenomena related to the wintering of plants and outline methods of planned modification of the nature of wintering plants to meet agricultural requirements. He furnished our country with more than 300 winter-hardy varieties of fruit and other plants and made it possible to grow grapes, etc. in the far north. Michurin's greatest contribution was to lay a genuinely scientific foundation for successful solution of the problems involved in the wintering of plants.

The book was examined in manuscript by many experts whose comments were gratefully received. The author is particularly indebted to his late teacher Academician N. A. Maksimov and to Academicians N. V. Tsitsin and A. L. Kursanov, associate member I. I. Tumanov of the Academy of Sciences USSR, Professor P. A. Genkel', and Chairman I. I. Gunar of the Department of Plant Physiology at the Timiryazev Agricultural Academy.

1

INJURY TO AND DEATH OF PLANTS
DURING THE WINTERING PERIOD

INTRODUCTION

Winter is a very difficult time of the year for plants because they are exposed to many adverse conditions. The main cause of death may be: winterkilling; "cold" — death of heat-loving plants due to cold; heaving, deflation, and washing out caused by exposure of the subsurface parts of plants; damping-off from fungi under snow; soaking from prolonged stagnation of water in and on the soil; desiccation after prolonged absence of snow and strong winds.

As a rule, none of the injurious factors acts on plants by itself. Injury and death are usually caused by a combination of things, the most important being frost. Frost injury is a precondition of the subsequent lethal effect of other factors, but not infrequently it is the immediate cause of death. It is appropriate, therefore, that we begin with a discussion of the injurious effect of frost.

CHAPTER 1

HISTORICAL REVIEW OF THE DEVELOPMENT
OF CONCEPTS ABOUT WINTERKILLING OF PLANTS

The devastation wrought by frost in fields, gardens, and orchards late in the fall, winter, and early spring has always been a concern of man. Our oldest documents contain references to it. For example, the Novgorod chronicles for 1127 A.D. noted: "That year water was abundant in the Volkhov River and the snow lay on the ground until the days of Yakovlev, and in the fall frost killed the winter crops." Such phenomena attracted the attention of scientific minded people from ancient times. We find descriptions of plant injury and death in seventeenth century scientific writings on the eve of the birth of botany as a science. The number of studies on the problem has been growing steadily since then.

1. EARLY IDEAS ON WINTERKILLING

One of the earliest to describe winterkilling was Bobart (1683), director of the Oxford Botanical Gardens and a leading botanist of his time. Bobart described various kinds of frost clefts formed on the branches, trunks, and roots of trees, mentioning the differences in resistance shown by individual plants.

The damage done to plants during the winter of 1708-1709, when the temperature dropped to 40°C below zero* (unusually severe for Western Europe), attracted the attention of scientists. Numerous accounts of the effect of the cold on plants and animals were published. The famous climatologist Deghem (1709) was one of those who described the winter and detailed many facts on plant injury and death.

We also find a full description of the external symptoms of frost action on plants (cracks on tree trunks and dying off of succulent shoots) in the works of the well-known French scientists Buffon and Duhamel (1737). The authors noted that there was less damage with dry frost than with moist frost. Frost after a thaw, they found, was particularly injurious.

Snow and windbreaks have been regarded from ancient times as means of protecting plants from unfavorable winter conditions. The article of G. Ya. Ekleben (1766) "The Great Usefulness of the Siberian Acacia" is very instructive in this respect. The article was published in the first number of the earliest agricultural journal in Russia, founded in 1765, Trudy Vol'nogo ekonomicheskogo obshchestva k pooshchreniyu v Rossii zemledeliya i domostroitel'stva [Transactions of the Volniy Economics Society for the Encouragement of Agriculture and Home-Building in Russia]. Ekleben wrote: "Enclosing fields with these trees to protect them from the severe northeast winds is useful as well as necessary. The yield will undoubtedly be double that of the ordinary unprotected field and, in addition, the grain will ripen sooner" (p. 68).

No less interesting are the "Notes on Gardening in Vladimir Province" published by I. Belin in the periodical Sadovodstvo [Horticulture] (1861). "Vladimir, Suzdal', Vyazniki, and Murom," Belin wrote, "were long famous for their apple and cherry orchards. Orchards were so numerous in Vladimir principality in the thirteenth century that there was no limit to the amount of fruit that they consumed. This is not true of our modern orchards. Some 20 to 40 years ago we had wonderful protection from the bitter hard frosts — the forests in Vladimir, Tversk, and Novgorod provinces up to Lake Ladoga. But now there is no such protection because the forests have been destroyed" (p. 292).

We could quote many more similar observations.

The early investigators found no difficulty in explaining why plants were injured by frost and died: if water freezes in the cracks of rocks and causes them to disintegrate, it is not surprising then that ice forming in plants ruptures woody tissue, particularly the delicate cells of succulent plants. These were the ideas on winterkilling of plants current in seventeenth and eighteenth century literature.

In 1830 Göppert revolutionized these ideas which were based solely on superficial observations and physical analogies. This scientist had set out to determine whether plant death from frost was actually due to rupture of the cells and he examined under the microscope tissues from a great variety of

---

*Unless noted to the contrary, all temperature readings will hereafter refer to centigrade.

plants, both frozen and thawed. In neither case did Göppert find any cells ruptured by ice. All the cells, surviving as well as dead, appeared to be intact; the cell walls looked completely uninjured. The only difference between the dead and living cells was that the former had lost their ability to retain water so that the cell sap penetrated the intercellular spaces while the cell wall lost its characteristic tension and became flabby.

Göppert's studies laid the foundation for a profound investigation of the phenomenon of winterkilling, which was aided by the widespread introduction of the microscope into scientific research. However, the German scientist also played an important negative role by endorsing the vitalistic interpretation of winterkilling. According to his thinking, plants are killed by frost because their inherent "vital force" is overcome. All the external and internal changes caused by frost, said Göppert, take place after the plants die and are not responsible for their death. This view of winterkilling reflects the idealistic world outlook then prevailing in science, particularly in Germany.

The question of whether plants die when they are actually frozen or when they thaw greatly influenced the course of thought on winterkilling. Göppert believed that low temperature was the direct and specific cause of winterkilling. However, this did not explain the very common and more severe injury inflicted by fall frosts on grain crops growing on the sunnier southern slopes and parts of trees facing south.

A new attempt to explain winterkilling was made by Treviranus (1838) who showed that the harmful effect of frost could be markedly reduced or even completely eliminated if the frozen portions were thawed as slowly as possible. Treviranus cited his own experiments in which frozen apples thawing in water with ice retained their original appearance, color, odor, and taste, whereas they became spoiled when allowed to thaw in the usual way in the air. This idea of the positive value of slow thawing was developed by the well-known German physiologist Sachs (1860; quotations from the second edition, 1892) and used in his "theory of thawing."

Sachs began the experimental part of his research with microscopic observations of ice in plants. Confirming the previously established view that ice does not form inside the cells, as was once thought (Schacht, 1856-1859), but in the intercellular spaces, Sachs found that the origin and growth of ice crystals largely depends on the rate at which the temperature falls: with rapid freezing ice forms in the intercellular spaces everywhere, with slow freezing ice crystals form only here and there and appear to be interspersed in the tissue, but are larger than the surrounding cells. After examining the structure of these crystals, Sachs discovered that they were virtually pure, slightly acidified water. The dry residue after thawing and evaporation did not exceed several tenths of one per cent. Ice formation, according to Sachs, begins with the appearance of thin hexagonal flakes on the surface of single cells. As the temperature drops, the flakes thicken and change into tall ice prisms. Each prism grows because of the water coming in from adjacent cells which become dehydrated during the freezing process, shrink, and lose turgor.

While studying the thawing of frozen plant tissues, Sachs found that the effect of freezing depends wholly on the rate of thawing: if slow, all the water formed from the ice is absorbed by the cells and they resume their former condition unimpaired; if rapid, the ice water fills the intercellular spaces and the cells lose the capacity to absorb the water while experiencing great difficulty in retaining their sap, which flows out at the slightest pressure. Sachs formulated his main finding (1892) this way: "My ideas of winterkilling differ from Göppert's in that he sees the center of gravity in the freezing process, whereas I consider freezing harmless. I regard as the sole cause of death of frozen plants the conditions under which they thaw" (p. 35).

Sachs' contention that plants die not from freezing, but from thawing, particularly when rapid, was widely supported, chiefly by horticulturists, for it accorded with well-known facts. It was difficult to refute because there were no external indications to judge the death of plants while frozen. Death always occurred after thawing alone. Nevertheless, objections were soon raised. Göppert (1871) managed to find plants whose death coincided with freezing — the indigo orchids Phajus grandifolia and Calanthe veratrifoiia whose petals turn blue on death regardless of the cause. They also turn blue as soon as the temperature drops below a given point. Göppert concluded on the basis of these facts that "death occurs during freezing and not during thawing or as a result of thawing" (p. 402).

Another equally strong criticism came from one of Sachs' students Müller-Thurgau (1880, 1886) who also started his research by studying the formation of ice in freezing plants and confirming the basic views of his teacher. He then made the important discovery that plants do not freeze immediately but do so only after some supercooling, which exerts a protective influence. Supercooled plants can safely tolerate frost that is lethal for frozen plants. For example, supercooled potatoes tolerated temperatures to -4° but died as soon as they became chilled, although the temperature rose to -1° in the process.

Müller-Thurgau also checked Sachs' experiments on thawing frozen plants and discovered an error in method. Comparing the thawing of the leaves of rape, beet, tobacco, and other plants as well as bits of beet root and squash fruit in cold water and in the air, Sachs thought that thawing proceeded more slowly in water than in the air. Müller-Thurgau actually found the reverse to be true. This led him to reject Sachs' theory and conclude that plants die during freezing rather than during thawing.

However, neither Müller-Thurgau nor Göppert succeeded in demolishing Sachs' position, for there were too many facts in favor of slow thawing, as even Müller-Thurgau himself later had to admit (1894) in connection with his investigation of the thawing of frozen fruit. Frozen apples and pears, he found, remained intact if thawed slowly, but were injured or died if thawed rapidly. Müller-Thurgau was forced to change his mind on Sachs' view of thawing, conceding that it was correct, at least in individual cases.

Although Göppert and Müller-Thurgau both opposed Sachs, they differed on what constituted the direct cause of death in plants exposed to frost. The former maintained that it was the specific effect of low temperature, whereas the latter linked it to the formation of ice in the plants.

Göppert's reasoning was purely deductive. He performed no experiments to provide direct arguments against Müller-Thurgau who had extensive experimental data at his disposal. Besides his research on the phenomena caused by supercooling and subsequent freezing, which confirmed the significance of ice formation in winterkilling, Müller-Thurgau relied on other studies. His experiments on freezing the leaves of such hardy plants as Phajus, begonia, corn, and grape were particularly instructive. After thawing, all the cells directly adjacent to accumulations of ice were found to be dead.

6

Remote cells remained alive even though exposed to the same temperature. According to Müller-Thurgau, this was incontestable proof of the fact that it is ice formation near the cells rather than low temperature that is the cause of death.

A new discussion of the problem arose early in the twentieth century. Méz (1905) supported Göppert, while N.A. Maksimov (1913) backed Müller-Thurgau. Mez proved that ice formation in plants is a helpful rather than deleterious phenomenon because heat is released during the freezing of water and crystallization of substances dissolved in the cell sap. This heat tends to warm up the plants and check the onset of the specific temperature minimum that is fatal to them. Supercooling, on the other hand, is harmful and plants protect themselves from it by forming oils in the cells which decrease or even prevent supercooling. Cell dehydration, Mez contended, is an insignificant factor in winterkilling because the entire cell sap freezes when the temperature is in the 0 to -6° range; when the temperature is lower there is no further dehydration, and the sap experiences only the specific effect of falling temperature.

Maksimov tested these views experimentally and after critical analysis found that they were "the fruit of theoretically erroneous assumptions and incorrect interpretation of the experimental data" (Maksimov, 1913, pp. 131-132). Maksimov's studies opened a new era in research on the winterkilling of plants.

2. EARLY IDEAS ON INTERCELLULAR CHANGES IN WINTERKILLING

Regardless of point of view on winterkilling, the question always arises: what internal changes take place in the plant during the process? The earliest idea on the rupture of the cell by ice was not derived from accurate observations, but was based wholly on physical analogy to the expansion of water on freezing. This was abandoned after Göppert's research. The same fate met the views based on ideas relating to the resemblance between plants and animals. For example, Schulz (1823) argued that the foundation of plant life is the continuous movement of their sap, just as the movement of blood is the foundation of animal life. Frost causes the sap to congeal, which kills the plants. In tune with the ideas of his time regarding the harmful effect of air on skin burns, Hoffman (1857) claimed that air has the same effect on thawing plants by penetrating the cells due to freezing of the cell sap.

Sachs (1860, 1860a) was the first to explain winterkilling on the basis of experimental data. He thought that the direct cause of cell death was "disorganization" of the cell wall due to rapid thawing. The wall becomes porous, he argued, and the sap readily filters into the intercellular spaces and evaporates, while air enters the cell and oxidizes its contents. The process of disintegration ends with the coalescing of cell elements previously kept distinct (acid sap with alkaline sap) and subsequent destruction of the cell. Sachs' theory apparently constituted the scientific foundation for the idea prevalent at the time that slow thawing could prevent winterkilling. However, the theory was far from perfect. The underlying assumption, namely, that "disorganization" of the cell wall takes place during thawing, was lacking in firm proof. The conception of the cell wall as an apparatus associated with cell impermeability was clearly erroneous.

The impossibility of reconciling this theory with the available data on winterkilling regardless of thawing conditions predetermined its fate. Frank's Plant Diseases (1880, 1895) devotes a small section to Sachs' theory, while considering the phenomenon of winterkilling from another point of view. According to Frank, plants die as a result of actual freezing. The ice forming in the intercellular spaces apparently sucks water from the cells, thus killing them. As proof he cites the drying of leaves after prolonged frost when ice evaporates from the intercellular spaces and the leaves come to resemble hay.

Müller-Thurgau used Frank's idea for his "theory of dehydration." However, Müller-Thurgau too failed to show how the harmful effect of cell dehydration is manifested. This task was undertaken by Molisch (1897) who enlarged the theory of dehydration and became its co-author.

Molisch started his research by studying microscopically the effect of freezing on different kinds of colloids, emulsions, pigments, and salt solutions. The freezing of colloids and salt solutions is apparently always accompanied by dehydration and structural changes in the substance. For example, initially homogeneous gelatin becomes sponge-like when frozen. Turning to living objects, Molisch found that ice does not form outside the cells of all plants. In certain fungi and Tradescantia ice forms within the cells, in the protoplasm. However, regardless of where ice forms, the invariable consequence of cell freezing is dehydration and ensuing contraction and shriveling of the protoplasm. Molisch concluded that the cause of cell death was disruption of protoplasmic structure as was the case with the freezing of inert colloids. "Living substance does not, as a rule, tolerate strong dehydration, and the molecular structure and architecture of protoplasm are destroyed when there are abnormal losses of water" (p. 72).

Müller-Thurgau and Molisch's theory equated winterkilling with the desiccation of plants in a drought. The cause of death in both, said the authors, is dehydration of protoplasm. However, this did not accord with the facts and Pfeffer (1904) for one was highly critical of the theory, correctly observing that some plants capable of withstanding 20, 30, or even 50° below zero cannot tolerate drying. On the other hand, swollen seeds can withstand total desiccation but are winterkilled even by slight frosts.

Gorke (1907) approached the problem in a different way. He set out to determine the chemical changes in plants caused by winterkilling and began to study the proteins dissolved in the sap squeezed from plants. He discovered that a substantial part of the proteins coagulates when plants freeze and that the sap of frost-killed plants contains less proteins than do living plants. Moreover, the proteins of hardier speciments are precipitated at lower temperatures. These plants also contain less soluble salts in their sap. These observations were the basis for Gorke's "chemical theory of winterkilling": as a result of ice formation and associated dehydration the cell sap becomes more concentrated with increased acidity, thus causing the proteins and other soluble colloids to coagulate; if the coagulation exceeds certain limits and becomes irreversible, the cells die.

Gorke's theory stimulated extensive research on the chemistry winterkilling, which was aided by the rapid development of physical and colloid chemistry and the eagerness of investigators to apply the findings to plants. A typical work of the time was Fischer's (1911) in which changes in the condition of inert colloids exposed to frost were compared with changes observed in connection with the winterkilling of living protoplasm in animal and plant cells. His own research along with published reports led Fischer to conclude that freezing subjects colloids to irreversible changes and loss of the capacity to swell. These changes occur at different temperatures in various colloids, even in the same colloid depending on the conditions surrounding the colloid prior to freezing and on its age. A colloid kept before freezing at a low temperature becomes "acclimatized" to frost and develops greater resistance. A freshly prepared "young" colloid is hardier than an "old" colloid.

Comparing these data with findings on winterkilling, Fischer concluded that frost has the same effect on living protoplasm that it has on inert colloids. Irreversible changes in colloids show up in the inability of frost-killed cells to retain water. The difference in the temperature at which irreversible changes appear in individual colloids accounts for the difference in hardiness shown by individual plants as well as by individual cells and cell elements. The low-temperature "acclimatization" of colloids to frost agrees with the established facts on the increased hardiness of plants under similar conditions. And, finally, the greater hardiness of freshly prepared "young" colloids as compared with that of "old" colloids in complete accord with published reports on the greater degree of frost resistance exhibited by young plant tissues.

The resemblance between changes in the water-holding capacity of inert colloids and living protoplasm as noted by Fischer could not, of course, fully explain the nature of plant and animal winterkilling because living protoplasm, not to mention cells with their varied content, is a much more complicated formation than any colloid. Fischer wrote in a foreword to his work that "the processes taking place in every animal and plant organism are interrelated and interdependent. And if the rate at which these processes take place changes in varying degree with falling temperatures, the existing balance in the organism is impaired and its life endangered" (1911, p. 134). However, the author failed to follow through on this significant idea and contented himself with purely external analogies.

3. MAIN INVESTIGATIONS OF WINTERKILLING IN LATER YEARS

A new stage in the thinking on winterkilling began with the publication of N.A. Maksimov's studies (1913). Maksimov laid the foundation for widespread Russian research in this major field of plant physiology.

Maksimov first studied winterkilling and hardiness in the lower plants, but he soon turned to the higher cultivated plants which he investigated for many years. Let us sum up the findings of his master's thesis (1913).

Although he championed Müller-Thurgau and Molisch's dehydration theory against the attacks of Mez, Maksimov was by no means an all-out adherent, for there were too many facts that it did not explain. His own research showed that winterkilling results in injury to the external layer of protoplasm which had been known since Pfeffer's time as the source of the cell's osmotic properties. When experimental objects were chilled in various kinds of solutions that prevent freezing, the tissues were not adversely affected by the cold. The protective effect of the solutions showed up after simple contact with the protoplasm. From this flowed the logical conclusion that the direct cause of injury and destruction of protoplasm following the formation

9

of ice on the surface of cells is the ice itself. This raised the question of the precise way in which ice injures the external layer of protoplasm. Maksimov assumed that mechanical pressure of ice on this layer was the key factor. "The ice forming when plants freeze," he concluded, "has both a water-removing and a mechanically coagulating effect on the colloidal substance of protoplasm" (1913, p. 305).

Maksimov's theory of mechanical pressure of ice on protoplasm greatly influenced almost all investigators of winterkilling although in time it was naturally modified by new data. It was particularly developed by I.I. Tumanov (1940) who linked the harmful effect of mechanical pressure of ice on protoplasm to its intense dehydration. Tumanov's experiments demonstrated that after water is injected into intercellular spaces ice has no effect on the protoplasm even if large masses freeze in the intercellular spaces. Ice affects only protoplasm that has lost a substantial quantity of water, such as occurs when plants freeze naturally and their cells become intensely dehydrated. Under these circumstances ice pressure, primarily on the surface layer of protoplasm, is harmful. This layer becomes damaged and permeable to ice crystals. As a result crystals form throughout the protoplasm and destroy it.

Thus, according to Tumanov, cell death from cold is caused by the formation of ice within protoplasm. This was confirmed by the experiments of M.F. Bugayevskiy (1939, 1939a). After chilling under the microscope achlorophyllous tissue from the tillering nodes of young winter wheat, Bugayevskiy observed that when the temperature dropped to -3 or -7° ice formed on the surface of the cells enlarging as the temperature continued to drop without the cells suffering any injury or dying. When, however, the temperature reached -15 or -18°, the appearance of the cell contents changed instantaneously, and ice crystals developed all over the protoplasm. The crystals "proliferated and not only deformed the delicate protoplasm, crushing and dehydrating it, but also cut the protoplasm in different directions as they grew in size" (1939, p. 133). After the cells thus frozen were thawed, the protoplasm appeared to be dead.

The idea of mechanical injury of protoplasm by frost was interpreted somewhat differently by W.S. Iljin (1930, 1933, 1934, 1935) who investigated the effect on protoplasm of changes in the water content of cells. Iljin compared dehydration under drought conditions with freezing and thawing after preliminary plasmolysis and without it. He discovered that plasmolyzed cells are highly resistant both to desiccation and to freezing. Such cells can be brought to an air-dried condition and even kept for some time over sulfuric acid. Red cabbage cells normally winterkilled at -4 or -5° survive in a plasmolyzed state at -21.2, -33.6, and even at -80°. The same results were also achieved by plazmolyzing cells during the thawing period.

Iljin advanced the following hypothesis by way of explanation. When the cell is dehydrated because of evaporation or freezing, the size of its vacuole decreases and the surrounding protoplasm contracts. If the cell is not plasmolyzed, the protoplasm is prevented from contracting by the cell wall whose capacity to stretch and contract is limited. But since the protoplasm cannot break away from the wall in the absence of a plasmolytic, strong tension builds up and it ruptures. If the plasmolyzed cell is dehydrated, the protoplasm not adhering to the wall contracts freely and remains intact. As water enters the dehydrated cell, the wall, sharply retracted with the cell, absorbs the water before the protoplasm does, becomes quickly smoothed out, and returns to its normal condition. The protoplasm takes longer to become smoothed out so that tension builds up quickly and it bursts from the cell. This naturally does not happen in the plasmolyzed cell.

Rupture is an extreme expression of the deformation of protoplasm. Protoplasm usually incurs injuries that cannot be seen under the microscope. These are the most frequent cause of death of cells exposed to drought or frost. Restoration of the vacuole in the dehydrated cell is particularly dangerous, for if the process is rapid, it inevitably destroys the protoplasm. Careful, gradual saturation of the cell with water can significantly reduce the damage caused by vacuole restoration. Hence, thawing conditions are frequently crucial to the survival of frozen plants.

Iljin's theory is highly interesting, but his experimental data are faulty. The main weakness is that the experiments were on tissue sections, and Iljin judged surviving cells from their capacity for deplasmolysis without carrying the process through to the end. This method of determining cell viability may well be a source of errors, as was evidently the case in evaluating the findings of experiments involving the freezing of tissue at very low temperatures. It is also possible that the basic mass of protoplasm died with only the tonoplast remaining unharmed due to the protection afforded by the concentrated solution of vacuolar cell sap washing it. This was established in Maksimov's investigations mentioned above. Deplasmolysis was assured by the presence of the intact tonoplast. However, this could scarcely be the criterion of viability of protoplasm which died sooner or later. That is why the main point of interest in Iljin's work is the underlying idea.

Scarth (1941) echoed Iljin's thinking on mechanical injury of protoplasm following changes in water content of the cell, although he did not mention Iljin by name. Scarth studied physicochemical changes in protoplasm in connection with the dehydration and subsequent saturation of cells with water, focussing on the external layer of protoplasm — the ectoplasm. Like Iljin he employed the plasmolysis method and found that ectoplasm thickens, becomes brittle, and readily breaks during severe and abrupt cell dehydration, especially when dehydrated protoplasm is supplied with water. In the latter case the swelling protoplasm breaks through the delicate crust enveloping it and dies. In normal winterkilling when ice forms in the intercellular spaces, the bursting out of protoplasm is the direct cause of cell death. Thawing is unusually dangerous.

Since Scarth's work is a partial continuation of Iljin's research, it has the defects associated with use of the plasmolysis method. Brittleness of the ectoplasm, as mentioned by Scarth, was undoubtedly the result both of dehydration of the protoplasm and of the action of the plasmolytic on it. This can be seen in the fact, noted by the author himself, that the ectoplasm increased in brittleness the longer the cell remained in the plasmolytic.

Stiles gave a novel explanation of winterkilling (1930). He attributed the death of plant cells after frost to intracellular freezing. Ice crystals forming in protoplasm change the space between its constituents, thereby destroying the characteristic "architecture" of the protoplasm. The larger the ice crystals, the more destructive they are. If small crystals form, as is the case when cells are chilled quickly, freezing need not entail the destruction of protoplasm. Thus, quick chilling enables the cells to survive even at very low temperatures. By way of confirmation Stiles cites earlier publications of his in which he describes experiments in freezing colloidal solutions of chlorophyll as well as fish and meat. The chlorophyll hydrosols remained unchanged after rapid freezing, but coagulated after slow freezing. Slow freezing of meat spoiled it.

The chemical emphasis in research on winterkilling was reflected in the work of E. Schaffnit and his colleagues (Schaffnit, 1910; Schander and Schaffnit, 1919; Schaffnit and Lüdtke, 1932; Schaffnit and Wilhelm, 1933). Schaffnit carried out systematic studies of a great number of compounds found in plants, particularly proteins, carbohydrates, and enzymes. He showed that low temperatures cause complex proteins to become transformed into simple but stable forms. At the same time sugar and other compounds accumulate and prevent the proteins from coagulating. However, other changes occur in the chemical composition of plants that injure protoplasm. Disturbed metabolism, chiefly impaired coordination in the activity of the enzymes, is a precondition of these changes. Enzymes are generally less sensitive to frost than the complex protein compounds of protoplasm, although they vary in degree of sensitivity, e.g., with freezing in the cell sap at -10° the activity of amylase and protease decreases, whereas the activity of peroxydase actually increases.

Disturbed metabolism, according to Schaffnit, is the initial link in the chain of modifications that lead to the injury and eath of plants upon freezing, even before freezing in the case of heat-loving plants. Coagulation is the final link in the chain of modifications caused by frost. As the water turns into ice the cell sap becomes increasingly concentrated and acid. This, in turn, results in injury to the internal layer of protoplasm lining the vacuole. Electrolytes and acids now freely penetrate the protoplasm and it coagulates. The cell as a whole then dies.

CONCLUSION

This, in brief, is the history of ideas on winterkilling of plants. A more detailed analysis of the modern view will be given in the following chapters. Now, however, we should like to offer some general observations.

We have seen the variety of theories advanced to account for the phenomenon along with continuing and at times bitter discussions. Some of them, e.g., theory of the specific minimum, theory of dehydration, theory of thawing, were quickly rejected but later found new supporters who used better research techniques.

The ideological struggle in science clearly affected the course of development of the problem. For example, the investigations of the French scientists Buffon and Duhamel were patently materialistic in character. These men tried to treat winterkilling as a simple physical phenomenon in conformity with the mechanistic philosophy prevailing at the time. The clash between Sachs and Göppert had ideological implications together with its specifically scientific aspects. Göppert was a vitalist, although not a consistent one. Sachs, on the other hand, was a materialist who tried to place a materialistic foundation under the phenomenon of winterkilling. The ideological struggle naturally continued in the twentieth century. Materialism has steadily gained the upper hand, but echoes of idealism in science, now loud, now muffled, could always be heard, as they still can.

CHAPTER 2

MODERN IDEAS ON THE WINTERKILLING OF PLANTS

Winterkilling has much in common with other processes causing plants to die, but it has several peculiarities of its own depending on internal factors. Let us first consider the nature of frost injury and then the individual factors conducive to winterkilling.

1. GENERAL PICTURE OF PLANT INJURY
AND DEATH FROM FROST

In grasses injury always begins with dying off of the oldest leaves and parts (Fig. 1). In woody plants frost affects primarily the young and "immature" shoots which are less protected by surface tissue (Fig. 2).

Frost-killed plants usually but not necessarily turn black. Grasses brought indoors frequently remain green for some time after which they turn yellow and die. Plants brought into the greenhouse in the winter may shrivel after being thawed and retain their color as in the case of drought. A very common symptom of frost injury is the long time it takes for the intercellular spaces to fill with the water coming from the melted ice. The longer it takes for the cells to absorb the water from the intercellular spaces, the greater the injury they suffer.

The external signs of winterkilling vary with the parts of the cells and the particular tissues most severely injured. For example, injury to the plastids causes a reduction in photosynthesis; if unusually severe it causes yellowing and dying of the leaves (Vetukhova, 1933). Partial injury to the cytoplasm impairs the osmotic properties of the cells and restricts their capacity to absorb and hold water. Injury to the epidermal cells results in loss of the integument by the leaves and rapid withering if the conditions promote fairly strong evaporation (Saltykovskiy, 1929).

Although frost-damaged plants may look normal, the protoplasm is likely to be substantially changed while remaining viable. This was shown by S.M. Ivanov (1931). He kept in water bits of plants first exposed to frost and then determined the electrical conductivity of the water extracts thus obtained. Even before there were any visible signs of injury, the protoplasm began to release fairly readily electrolytes that it normally held firmly, thereby resulting in increased conductivity.

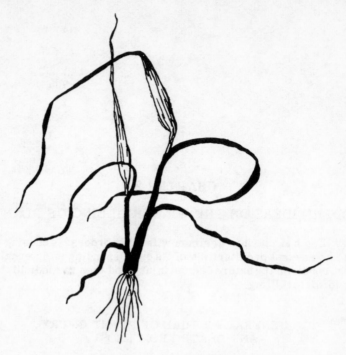

Fig. 1. Frost injury of herbaceous plants. Winter wheat,
variety Moskovskaya 2411
(Blackened leaves and parts of leaves, killed by frost)

The extent of frost injury depends both on the action itself and on the subsequent weather conditions. If the latter are favorable in the fall, the damage may be largely overcome during the wintering period.

2. FREEZING

A major cause of plant injury and death from frost is the freezing of their water. There is never any doubt when plants are frozen. Externally the leaves become stiff and brittle. It took some time before the nature of the freezing process was fully understood.

Many investigators showed that ice generally forms in the intercellular spaces of plants rather than within the cells. Slowly falling temperature results in the formation of large ice crystals which sometimes become large enough to be visible to the naked eye. When the leaves of such plants are held to the light immediately after thawing, the places of ice accumulation now injected with water look darker. When plants are chilled more quickly, ice forms everywhere in the intercellular spaces, covering the cells with a thin unbroken crust. If the plants have no intercellular spaces, e.g., algae, ice forms on the surface of the plant body.

Ice forms inside the cells only when the temperature drops abruptly. This

Fig. 2. Typical picture of frost injury of
a tree: an oak with dried branch tips
after the severe frosts of 1939

is observed in nature in unhardened and generally nonfrost-resistant plants. The phenomenon can be reproduced in the laboratory by rapid freezing of thin sections of tissue.

Let me describe a case of intracellular ice formation. Unhardened winter rape was chilled one July day at a time when the plant was growing rapidly. Bits of epidermis were promptly peeled off a freshly cut leaf, placed on a slide in paraffin oil and frozen right under the microscope by chilling the stage with dry ice. Observation of the cells revealed the presence of 15-20 ice crystals in each as soon as the temperature of the slide dropped to -3 or -4°. There was only intercellular formation of ice in winter rape leaves taken from hardened plants.

It is easy to understand why water in naturally wintering plants freezes chiefly in the intercellular spaces. Water on the surface of the cell walls is most prone to freezing. It contains almost no soluble substances and is feebly held here by surface tension. Since water is held less strongly in some cells than in others, ice does not form in all the cells; it forms only in those cells possessing the weakest water-holding capacity. The resultant ice particles later become centers of crystallization and, so to speak, suck water from the surrounding cells. This causes dehydration of even remote cells and lowering of the freezing point on their surface so that despite the fall in temperature

15

there are no new formations of ice and it grows only on the site of the initial crystals.

This process takes place only when the fall in temperature is relatively slow. If rapid, lowering of the freezing point on the surface of many cells distant from the initial centers of crystallization lags behind the fall in temperature. Water from these cells is unable to flow out at the necessary speed and meets resistance in the form of other cells, freezing before it reaches the initial centers of crystallization. The quicker the fall in temperature and the slower the flow of water, naturally the greater the number of cells in which ice forms.

The above-described freezing of water is not typical of living plants alone. Water freezes the same way in inert media as well. For example, Moran (1926) observed that in freezing gelatin gel at -11° ice crystals were strewn over the colloid in fairly large sizes if the colloid was chilled comparatively slowly. If chilled very rapidly at -190°, ice appeared throughout the mass of gelatin in the form of microscopically small crystals approximately equidistant from one another.

Supercooling, deep and stable, prevents water from freezing inside the cells. Supercooling also takes place in the intercellular spaces, but it is easily disturbed here due to the penetration of ice crystals from the surface of the plant through the stoma and to various kinds of injury to the surface tissue. Shaking supercooled water will cause it to freeze.

Supercooling of water is aided by the ectoplasm which constitutes an insuperable barrier to ice crystals. The tonoplast about the vacuole has the same properties, and even if ice forms in the vacuole it does not pass into the protoplasm. This was demonstrated by the experiments of Chambers and Hale (1932). Directly observing the freezing of red onion epidermal cells and cells of other living tissues, the authors discovered that ice crystals originating on the surface of protoplasm did not get inside even when its structure was partially disrupted. However, if ice was artifically introduced into protoplasm by means of a micromanipulator, it stayed there and did not penetrate the vacuole.

Water is also prevented from freezing in cells by the high water permeability of protoplasm in frozen plants. For example, Levitt and Scarth (1936a) demonstrated experimentally that water permeability of protoplasm in plants taken indoors in January was triple the permeability in the same plants after 35 days in a warm greenhouse. The increased permeability of protoplasm to water at low temperatures apparently prevents intracellular freezing automatically because the rapid outflow of water from the cell intensifies the concentration of cell sap and the water-holding capacity of the cell as a whole, thus decreasing the possibility of freezing.

3. MECHANICAL INJURY BY ICE

Important evidence in favor of the theory of mechanical injury by ice is the cracks in the tissues of frozen plants familiar since antiquity. Sometimes enough ice freezes in the intercellular spaces so as to become visible to the naked eye. There are also data on the wholly unexpected freezing of plants when vast solid masses of ice appear. For example, according to Caspary (1854), in November 1853 many grasses and shrubs in the Schöneberg

Botanical Garden were completely coated with ice after the first night of an autumnal frost. The ice came through the torn bark and covered the plants so that they looked like icicles. This kind of freezing is observed in plants exposed to frost while they are in a viable, active condition. Water freezes on the chilled aerial parts when it reaches them from the unfrozen soil.

Severe ruptures in tissues occur even under normal freezing conditions. Prillieux (1869) cited many examples of this kind of mechanical injury to frozen plants. He observed how ice causes the bark as a whole to separate from the xylem while large cavities form in the center of the stem and individual portions of tissue become shredded.

Fig. 3. Overgrown frost cleft in an oak

Fig. 4. Open frost cleft in an oak

Tissue ruptures aren't always caused by ice. The cracks appearing on trees during hard frosts, the so-called frost clefts, are the result of uneven chilling of the xylem. The rapidly cooling outer layers contract and squeeze the inner layers as though with a band. When the pressure exceeds the elastic limit, the tissues burst (Figs. 3, 4). Frost clefts can be compared with the splitting of felled trees. Strong pressures build up in the xylem as the trunks dry out (Caspary, 1855).

The rupture of tissue due to uneven contraction upon cooling also occurs in herbaceous plants (Sorauer, 1906).

Let us now examine more closely the mechanical pressure of ice on cells.

17

In extracellular freezing of water this pressure is naturally exerted only if the ice completely fills the corresponding portions of the intercellular spaces and is wedged between the cells like a solid foreign body. However, this is comparatively rare. More commonly, the ice remains within the intercellular spaces and does not break the tissues; with quicker freezing and, accordingly, more uniform distribution of ice in the intercellular spaces, the latter do not even fill up. This is partly due to the fact that after the water flows out of the cells into the intercellular spaces the cells shrink while the intercellular spaces expand. The approximately 10% increase in volume of water as it turns into ice is somewhat compensated for by the frequently substantial increase in size of the cells over that of the intercellular spaces. Whenever there are large frozen masses in the intercellular spaces, the ice presses on the adjacent cells and they separate from one another, thus weakening the pressure of the ice.

Ice pressure on cells does not always result in visible injury. The cell wall between the protoplasm and extracellular ice absorbs the pressure and acting like a buffer transmits it to the protoplasm considerably reduced. The protoplasm of cells not touching the ice is even better protected owing to the tremendous elasticity of the cells next to the ice. Ice pressure scarcely goes beyond a single layer of cells where it is completely contained. This partly explains why it is difficult to obtain juice from living leaves even under very strong pressure. In experiments with winter plants one fall I subjected their leaves to a pressure of 300 atm and over under a hydraulic press. A 100 g batch of well hardened plants yielded only 1-2 cm^3 of juice. Despite the pressure, most of the leaf cells remained alive. Only the very delicate cells of watermelon or peach pulp are crushed even if the pressure is comparatively slight.

Thus, in the light of current knowledge the injury caused by the mechanical pressure of extracellular ice is mainly the rupture of tissue, a fairly common phenomenon under natural wintering conditions. There is virtually no damage to protoplasm from ice forming in the intercellular spaces. The investigations of W.W. Lepeschkin (1910, 1910a), which constitute the basis of the mechanical theory of ice injury to protoplasm in its modern form, show that pressure causes damage only when it is severe and repeated. Lepeschkin's experiments involved friction as well as pressure since he pressed down on spirogyra cells with a needle through a cover glass. When pressure was applied without friction, protoplasm appeared to be much more resistant and thus less susceptible to injury.

When ice forms inside of cells, the effect of its mechanical action increases sharply. Intracellular freezing, with but few exceptions, is fatal. I spent a good deal of time trying to discover the direct causes of death of unhardened plants from light frost. I experimented on a dozen or so different plants: winter and spring grain, winter rape, cabbage, beet, kohlrabi, buckwheat, etc. When frozen in the summer during the period of intense growth, all the plants died as a result of ice forming in them, usually at temperatures between -3 and -4°. If the plants or parts of them were supercooled in any way, they safely endured somewhat lower temperatures. Direct microscopic examination of tissue sections from these plants invariably showed that the winterkilling temperature equalled the temperature of intracellular freezing. Freezing in all the plants, if unhardened, was intracellular.

However, even after intracellular freezing, protoplasm under certain conditions may survive unharmed. In Schaffnit's experiments (1910), for example, ice formed between the cell wall and protoplasm after rapid freezing and yet the cells survived. In Chambers and Hale's experiments isolated frog muscle fibers remained alive after intracellular freezing if it didn't last too long and the temperature wasn't too low. L.K. Lozino-Lozinskiy (1948) showed that intracellular ice formation was not the cause of death of chilled paramecia. The results of these experiments account for the resistance of protoplasm to mechanical injury. Cytological research involving the use of a micromanipulator has revealed that protoplasm can in many cases be removed from the cell wall, stretched, and even torn without destroying it.

4. CELL DEHYDRATION AS A CAUSE OF PLANT DEATH IN FREEZING

The freezing of plants is always associated with severe cell dehydration. Most of the water turns into ice right away, sometimes when the temperature is only a little below zero. As the temperature falls, the amount of ice increases while the amount of water in the cells decreases. The leaves, stems, buds, and other parts of plants in hard frosts often contain no more moisture than air-dried seeds. The experiments of T.S. Sulukadze (1939) showed that when winter wheat was chilled in September at -15°, some 90-91% of the water content of the cells froze, only 9-10% remaining liquid. Such loss of water naturally has to affect cell viability. Only a few of the higher plants can tolerate severe dehydration in the growing season, e.g., sea sedge — Carex physodes MB (I.M. Vasil'yev, 1930) — commonly found in the deserts of Central Asia. For most plants, however, an undue loss of water is always injurious and, if excessive, fatal.

The nature of the damage done to cells by dehydration following the formation of ice has been the object of extensive research. Molisch (1897) explained it thus: as water is withdrawn from the protoplasm, the colloidal particles come close together and when the force of mutual attraction becomes stronger than the force of repulsion, they flocculate and precipitate. This explanation was confirmed by experiments on inert colloids. Bobertag, Feist, and Fischer (1908) froze organic colloids — gelatin, isinglass, agar-agar, etc. — and observed that completely pure water remained after they were thawed. The colloids came out quite flat, which the authors naturally assumed was the cause of irreversible changes in colloids when chilled.

Nevertheless, facts were noted that did not fit in with this explanation. For example, albumin can be made air-dry without losing its colloidal properties; the addition of water turns it back into a colloid. This led to a search for a new explanation. The following was deemed satisfactory: a substance remains colloidal as long as it is electrically charged; reaching the isoelectric point, the colloid loses its charge and precipitates. The precipitation of albumins by salts used in colloid chemistry is based on this view. It was assumed that something comparable occurs to protoplasm when the cell is dehydrated and its salt concentration increases substantially.

Numerous investigations have demonstrated that there is a denser concentration of substances dissolved in the cell sap when plants are frozen. Some idea of the intensity of the process can be obtained from the data of Akerman (1927) who computed the changes in a sugar solution concentration when the water was frozen out of it. For example, if the initial concentration of a sugar solution is 1/4 normal, after the water turns into ice the concentration doubles at -0.98°, increases fourfold at -1.86°, twelvefold at -7.44°, sixteen-fold at -14.88°. This process is even more rapid in living cells because along with a decrease of water in the cell and resultant increase in the amount of soluble substances in the cell sap there is also an absolute increase in these substances due to intensification of the hydrolytic processes and dissolution of previously insoluble compounds.

The explanation of protoplasm coagulation by increased concentration of salts in cell dehydration was confirmed by the experiments of Lidforss (1907) with freezing egg white in Knop's solution and ensuing precipitation of the albumin. However, it also met with some objections, chiefly on the grounds that cell sap always contains protective substances, e.g., sugar, which prevent salting out, as noted by Lidforss after he added sugar and glycerin to a salt solution.

The theory of poisoning was also popular. According to this theory, proto-plasm is poisoned by certain substances in the cell which are either newly formed during cell dehydration or accumulate to the point where they become toxic. This possibility was once mentioned by Gorke (1907) who ascribed the toxic effect to phosphoric acid, the denaturing power of which increases as the temperature falls. In later investigations, however, attention was focused on changes in the acidity of cell sap whose reaction to freezing always shifts toward the acid side. Such increase in acidity and subsequent death of cells was observed, for example, on sections of red cabbage leaves by T.M. Zacharowa (1925). Sections kept even in very weak acid died sooner than those kept in weak solutions of caustic potash after exposure to frost.

However, experiments similar to Zacharowa's failed to explain why the cell sap in living plants is acid, whereas the protoplasm has an alkaline re-action. In some normal plants sap acidity is quite pronounced, yet the proto-plasm remains uninjured and the acid elements appear to be completely isolated in vacuoles with no access to the protoplasm. An analysis of Zacharowa's data and similar findings by other investigators left unanswered the question of whether increased sap acidity affects the protoplasm during chilling or remains only within the vacuoles and in living intact cells has no direct effect on the protoplasm. The problem is complicated even more by the fact that in experiments to determine sap acidity during chilling of plants the sap was not that of pure protoplasm but was a mixture of vacuole and proto-plasm sap obtained from the destroyed cells.

According to another theory, protoplasm is destroyed after dehydration due to the disintegration of its constituent chemical compounds. This view was first put forward by Vogel (1820) who believed that cell water is chemi-cally bound with organic substances and thereby forms hydrates. Freezing destroys this bond, and just as frozen starch paste after thawing can no longer absorb water from melting ice, so too the cell constituents of frozen plants cannot be restored after losing water.

Vogel's explanation now seems naive, but the underlying idea of chemical destruction of protoplasm is generally accepted. There are fairly adequate data available to confirm the fact that in cell dehydration complex compounds break down into simpler compounds usually soluble in water. Mothes (1931) discovered that loss of water by leaves resulted in transformation of the protein constituents of protoplasm into amino acids.

This, of course, is a highly simplified account. Actually the process is much more complex. Studying the natural regulation of proteins in plants, Mothes (1933) found that dehydration by itself does not determine the hydrolytic direction in the activity of enzymes, which comes directly from a lowering of the oxidation-reduction potential followed by all the other changes. When cells are dehydrated, their oxidation-reduction potential is decreased and the synthetic activity of the enzymes inhibited. The result is that the processes of hydrolysis prevail over those of synthesis with disintegration first of the reserve organic compounds, then of the protoplasm itself.

We have far from exhausted the various modern theories regarding the injurious effect of dehydration on the cells of chilled plants. Despite the diversity of views, two main ideas can be discerned. Some investigators believe that dehydration alone creates the conditions for coagulation of protoplasm while others maintain that the destruction of protoplasm in winterkilling is due to impaired metabolism, which results from dehydration and sometimes has a decisive influence on this process.

5. SPECIFIC EFFECT OF LOW TEMPERATURES ON PLANTS

Under certain conditions low temperatures have a specifically destructive effect on protoplasm. Although disputed by many investigators at one time or another, this conclusion has a factual foundation.

Data on the death of plants in a supercooled state constitute direct proof of the specifically harmful effect of low temperatures on protoplasm. A co-worker of Pfeffer (Bartetzko, 1909) ran a series of experiments on mold fungi. Carefully chilling the mycelium of Aspergillus niger to -13° in a nutrient medium, Bartetzko prevented ice from forming in the mycelium and kept the fungus in a supercooled state for several days. It turned out that the fungus suffered frost injury in proportion to the length of time it was kept supercooled. For example, after five days of temperatures ranging from -6.2 to -11.4° 15% of the mycelium died; after eight days of the same temperatures 75% died. Another example is the aforementioned experiments of Chambers and Hale who observed that supercooling had its aftereffects. Particularly convincing is the aforementioned research of L.K. Lozino-Lozinskiy who kept paramecia at 0° for varying periods of time and in a supercooled state at temperatures below 0°. In all cases the low temperatures proved to be injurious, sometimes fatal. For example, when the temperature was between -3.8 and -4°, supercooled paramecia remained alive 3-4 hours, about 2 hours at -6°, 20-30 minutes at -7.5°, and about 15 minutes at -10°. The paramecia died with no indications of internal ice formation.

Further proof of the specific effect of low temperatures is provided by Möbius' experiments with greenhouse plants. Möbius found it necessary to shift plants from one place to another during the winter. He conducted a special experiment to determine whether the plants would be frost killed in the process. Begonia metallica was taken from a warm room and kept at -5° for one or two minutes. The plant did not freeze during this brief period of time, but later that day its lower leaves became covered with the characteristic spots of winterkilling and eventually died. Similar results were obtained from other species of plants.

Ewart's experiments on spirogyra (S. crassa and S. nitida) are another example of plant death from low temperatures without freezing (1898). The algae were taken from a place where the temperature was +20° and put in a room with the temperature a little below 0° where they were left overnight. All the plants were dead by morning, although there was no ice on the water in which they were kept. The same thing happened to Vaucheria, Nitella flexilis, and other algae. All the vegetative parts died over night when the temperature was dropped to -2 or -3°, but there was no ice on the plants or inside the cells.

6. ABRUPT INFLUENCES OF INDIVIDUAL FACTORS DURING FREEZING OF PLANTS

Any factor abruptly applied may be injurious. A century ago Karsten (1861) wrote: "Abrupt changes in temperature are harmful to plants and make them sickly or even kill them" (p. 8). In his well known study Teachings on the Plant Cell, Hofmeister (1867) cites illustrations of the way abrupt changes in temperature within a range of normally safe values inhibit the movement of plant protoplasm. Here is one of his examples. The root hairs of Ecballium agreste were gradually warmed from a temperature of +16.5 to +40°. An hour later, when the protoplasm had begun to move about rapidly, the hairs were immersed in +16° water and re-examined under the microscope after a minute. The protoplasm was completely motionless in all the cells. A check seven minutes later revealed a resumption of motion, but at a very slow rate. Normalcy was restored after 18 minutes, i.e., the situation was the same as before the experiment when the temperature was at +16.5°. A similar inhibitory effect on the vital functions of the cells was also noted after abrupt changes in light, conduction of an electrical current, etc.

The literature carries descriptions of many cases showing that quick chilling is more destructive than slow, gradual chilling. In Winkler's experiments (1913) apple buds in the winter endured slow chilling at -30 and -35°, but rapid chilling only at -17 to -18°. Freezing of plant tissues after intense supercooling is ordinarily fatal, whereas freezing after gradual chilling to the same temperature is likely to be quite safe.

Just as harmful as quick freezing is quick elevation of temperature. The abundance of long familiar facts on the injurious effect of abrupt temperature changes led Sachs to link winterkilling of plants to quick thawing. Sachs' "theory of thawing" in its original form is no longer accepted, but all agree on the significance of a rapid transition from frost to heat in harming or killing plants. According to Janssen (1929), winter wheat plants exposed in January to a temperature of -20° and left out doors until spring survived. On the other hand, the same plants brought into a heated greenhouse (+22°) after 4-8 hours of exposure to the same subzero temperature died.

Repetition of abrupt temperature changes, as often happens in early spring when night frosts are followed by thawing in direct sunlight, is particularly dangerous. This is the reason for the so-called "sunburn" of plants, which is so familiar to gardeners.

The injurious effect of rapid chilling and thawing is naturally due not only to abrupt temperature changes, as Hofmeister observed, but also to extensive changes in water content of the cells and the intracellular formation of ice.

7. WINTERKILLING OF PLANTS IN THE LIGHT OF MODERN DATA

An analysis of all the currently available data on winterkilling leads to this general conclusion: the death of plants exposed to frost is brought about by a variety of factors, the most important being freezing, i.e., the internal formation of ice. Freezing is accompanied by cell dehydration, impaired metabolism, mechanical injury and destruction of protoplasm by ice forming inside the cells, and rupture of tissue by large bits of ice present in the intercellular spaces. However, winterkilling may occur even without freezing, but only as a result of the injurious action of abrupt drops in temperature and consequent impaired metabolism.

Any of the factors involved may be primary or secondary depending on the circumstances. Intracellular ice formation as a rule almost always kills plants, but very rapid chilling at extremely low temperatures may not harm the protoplasm because ice forms everywhere in the cells and in such small crystals that the protoplasm is not affected. Severe ruptures of tissue are possible when large masses of ice form between the cells, but no harm results when these spaces are filled with small ice particles. The specific effect of low temperatures may be decisive, as in Möbius' experiments, or be completely latent, as happens in most instances of winterkilling.

Abrupt changes in connection with frost merit particular attention. Protoplasm can tolerate severe pressure if applied gradually, but is destroyed if applied rapidly even though the pressure is less intense. Protoplasm is thus like gunpowder which can be reduced to fine particles if carefully ground but explodes on concussion.

The freezing process always features abrupt changes. Even in the case of simple freezing without supercooling, about half or more of the entire water content of the cells turns into ice so that they become quickly dehydrated. When supercooling precedes freezing, changes in the water content occur still more rapidly. The reason is that the temperature of supercooled water rises swiftly when it is frozen. Therefore, supercooling is always highly dangerous, although in itself it serves to protect plants from frost. The deeper the supercooling, the more severe the aftereffects are in the case of subsequent freezing. This is due to the abruptness of changes in the cells when water is frozen after supercooling.

Winterkilling characteristically takes place at low temperatures when most of the vital processes have slowed down markedly and growth has completely ceased, thereby attenuating the effect on protoplasm of many harmful factors, notably dehydration and impaired metabolism. Chilled plants can tolerate incomparably more intense dehydration than when they are in an active state. Nevertheless, as the temperature drops, the protoplasm becomes increasingly susceptible to mechanical injury by ice (Lepeschkin, 1937).

Low temperatures are perhaps the least significant factor under ordinary wintering conditions for the usual wintering plants. Low temperatures are dangerous only for potentially unhardy tender plants in the active growth stage, particularly if the temperature changes are abrupt. Winterkilling often occurs after ice forms within the cells. Unhardened plants are generally winterkilled if chilled rapidly. Intracellular freezing is a result of the intense activity of the protoplasm and very low water permeability. When plants are chilled rapidly, the water in the cells does not reach the ice crystals forming in the intercellular spaces. Weakly retained in the cells by osmotically active substances and hydrophilic colloids, the water freezes right in the cells. M.F. Bugayevskiy observed intracellular freezing in hardened plants following a quick drop in temperature. Intracellular freezing is generally fatal except when the freezing is done at very low temperatures, as in the cases described above. However, this does not happen in nature so we needn't discuss it any further.

A special kind of winterkilling is the death of plants due to severe ruptures of their tissue caused by large masses of ice forming in the intercellular spaces or by uneven cooling. The ruptures in themselves do not cause the plants to die. This only happens when the causative agents of various kinds of diseases penetrate the injured areas.

The commonest form of winterkilling, according to published reports, is cell dehydration caused by the freezing of water necessary to protoplasmic activity, which is essentially death from desiccation intensified by deformations in the protoplasm that are inevitable after substantial losses of cell water.

There are various degrees of winterkilling due to dehydration ranging from initially slight injury to protoplasm, resulting in diseases of one kind or another when the plants thaw, to total destruction while the plants are still chilled.

Regardless of the injury caused by frost, the effect will be eventually manifested in impaired metabolism even if the plants do not die immediately. This factor is insignificant when the plants are frozen since metabolism is extremely slow at low temperatures. The symptoms of impaired metabolism show up in the spring when the temperature is fairly high, especially during the so-called "vivification" of winter plants, i.e., when allowed to grow in the winter in a warm place in order to determine their viability. And if the plants are kept under conditions favoring photosynthesis and regeneration, they eventually die as a reslt of impaired metabolism.

CONCLUSION

Winterkilling of plants may occur in various ways depending on the nature of the plants, degree of hardening, and conditions under which they are exposed to frost. All the aforementioned theories of winterkilling may be evaluated accordingly. In so far as a given theory was based on facts and accorded with materialistic conceptions, it made a contribution to science. Each had the shortcoming of attempting to provide a single explanation for the great variety of phenomena that occur under winterkilling.

CHAPTER 3

COLD DEATH OF HEAT-LOVING PLANTS
("CHILLING INJURY IN PLANTS")

The death of plants when the temperature is low is not always caused by frost. Many plants are injured and die when the temperature is above 0°. Thermophilic blue-green algae from warm waters and bacteria living at 70 and 80° are particularly sensitive to low temperatures. Normal room temperature is too low for these organisms. All tropical plants and crops from the south, e.g., cucumber, tobacco, beans, cotton, rice, etc. are also sensitive to cold. They begin to suffer at the onset of cold weather and die if it continues for any length of time. The injury done to thermophilic plants by temperatures slightly above 0° is called chilling injury by analogy to the condition in man and animals.

1. SKETCH OF THE DEVELOPMENT OF IDEAS
ON COLD DEATH OF PLANTS

The facts of injury to and death of heat-loving plants from cold even before freezing have been known for a long time. Gardeners and amateur flower growers have had to become familiar with the phenomenon. Chilling injury in a heat-loving plant is as common an occurrence as winterkilling in a wintering plant, and is so noted in old botanical texts. For example, Link (1807) wrote in his Principles of Plant Anatomy and Physiology: "Cold damages plants not because fluids freeze but because it impairs their viability. Many plants die even when the thermometer registers several degrees above the freezing point" (p. 292). We find pertinent experimental data in Göppert's work (1830). According to Göppert, tropical plants with soft, tender leaves are particularly sensitive to cold. When such plants were exposed for several days to a temperature of about +3°, their leaves became covered with black spots, rolled up, and fell off.

The first investigations specifically aimed at determining the causes of cold death of plants are associated with the name of Sachs (1860b). Sachs observed that potted tobacco, squash, and beans kept at +2 and +4° invariably wilted and then died, but when placed under glass jars to restrict transpiration they remained turgescent and apparently suffered no ill effects from the cold. Sachs concluded that heat-loving plants exposed to low temperatures lose their ability to absorb water from the soil to replace that evaporated from the leaves, with the result that they become dehydrated and die.

However, this explanation did not account for all the peculiarities of chilling injury in plants, and it wasn't long before Kunisch (1880), a pupil of Göppert, showed that the death of heat-loving plants exposed to cold did not necessarily result from cell dehydration. In his experiments varieties of Coleus died at about 0° in air saturated with water vapor. Molisch (1896, 1897) later demonstrated the same thing in a great variety of plants. Molisch did more than establish the phenomenon. Generalizing all the available data, he worked out a new theory of "winterkilling" of heat-loving plants that became the bais of many theoretical ideas on the problem.

Molisch thought that cold death of plants occurred even before freezing, which he incorrectly defined as "winterkilling" in contradistinction to plant death upon freezing. The cause of death after formation of ice ("freezing"), according to Molisch, is the "physical" process of cell dehydration, whereas the death of plants at temperatures above 0° is a complex physiological process caused by disturbed metabolism. When plants are exposed to cold, the different physiological processes are not inhibited at the same time so that uncharacteristic products are formed. Molisch mentioned the well known fact that potato tubers acquire a sweet taste when kept at a low temperature. This is due to impairment of the normal relationship existing between the formation of sugar and its consumption for respiration because under the influence of low temperature tuber respiration is more severely inhibited than the activity of the diastase saccharifying the starch; part of the starch is not utilized so that it steadily accumulates. In the same way, Molisch thought, harmful substances build up until they poison and kill the plants.

The idea of poisoning by incompletely oxidized metabolic products wasn't really new. It was advanced several years before and experimentally proved by the Russian scientists V.I. Palladin (1891) and K.A. Puriyevich (1893, 1897, 1899) but, as in many other cases, it was ascribed to foreign investigators.* Schander and Schaffnit (1919) and Nelson (1926) thought it was Molisch's. According to Schander and Schaffnit, toxic metabolic products, if they form, may kill plants exposed to cold. The main cause, however, is general disturbance of metabolism. The disturbance of nitrogen metabolism involving the destruction of complex protoplasmic proteins and their conversion into simpler and more stable forms is especially important.

Nelson, on the other hand, believed that the formation of toxic metabolic products was the basic if not sole cause of death of tender plants exposed to cold. He reached this conclusion on the basis of the following experiments and reasoning. His objective was to find the reasons for non-parasitic diseases in cabbage, lettuce, and potatoes during storage and transport. Besides inadequate ventilation and other factors, he studied the effect of temperatures around 0°. Nelson demonstrated experimentally that diseases are likely to develop both when there is a deficiency of oxygen in the air and when

---

*It is worth recalling that K.A. Puriyevich, for example, noted in his Obrazovaniye i raspadeniye organicheskikh kislot u vysshikh rasteniy [Formation and Breakdown of Organic Acids in Higher Plants] that respiration is a succession of processes of oxidizing organic matter ending in the formation of carbon dioxide and water and that the intermediate products are various organic acids capable of injuring the plants.

the temperature is low. Oxygen deficiency is particularly significant for potatoes, whereas both factors are equal as far as cabbage and lettuce are concerned. Low temperatures slow up the rate of the oxidation processes so that toxic substances form and accumulate until they destroy the cells. These products, Nelson believed, are chiefly the liberated components of certain glucosides, e.g., sinigrin in the mustard family. Under ordinary circumstances they are quickly converted into nontoxic compounds, but at low temperatures the decontamination process slows down and the poisons accumulate.

Sachs' theory of plant death from dehydration during exposure to cold continued to find adherents. Of highest value is the research of Pantanelli (1919) who discovered the progressive increase in protoplasmic permeability while studying the effect of cold on endocarp cells of mandarins. These cells quickly lose water even when the air is saturated with water vapor. He maintained that the loss of impermeability is attributable to the dehydration of heat-loving plants subjected to cold. This is not the sole cause of chilling injury in plants. More important, Pantanelli felt, is the fact that heat-loving plants when chilled normally use the proteins in protoplasm as sources of energy after the sugar stored in the cells is consumed.

Wilhelm (1935a) conducted extensive research to discover the causes of death of plants exposed to cold. This work was a partial continuation of the aforementioned studies emanating from Schaffnit's laboratory. A specific objective was to verify Sach's statements on dehydration of heat-loving plants exposed to cold and Molisch's theory regarding the accumulation of protoplasm-poisoning substances as a result of disturbed metabolism. Tomatoes, tobacco, and beans were the objects investigated.

Wilhelm found in confirmation of Sachs' data that chilling these plants results in their dehydration and death. Preventing water loss by restricting transpiration tends to delay the process. The cause of death here is not the poisons. Wilhelm believed Molisch's view to be incorrect because in his experiments no harm was suffered by healthy plants from an extract obtained from cold-killed plants. Plants die under those circumstances from protein exhaustion. Under the influence of low temperature the synthetic processes in the cells, including protein synthesis, are suppressed while the hydrolytic processes proceed quite intensively. As a result the destroyed proteins are not restored and amino acids accumulate in their place. The process of protein disintegration induced by low temperature is accelerated by cell dehydration which is harmful per se. The plants become sick and eventually die. If transpiration is not checked by external conditions, cold death is caused by a combination of dehydration and protein exhaustion.

In recent large-scale study (1955) of injury to heat-loving plants by low temperatures (+5, +7°) V. N. Zholkevich critizes the prevalent theories of plant injury and death due to cold. He believes that the main cause of the phenomena is partial destruction of protoplasm and ensuing suppression of growth and all synthetic processes, intensification of hydrolytic processes, decreased viscosity and increased permeability of protoplasm, accumulation of toxic products of disintegration, etc.

These, in brief, are the main landmarks in the history of our ideas regarding the death of heat-loving plants from cold.

2. THE MODERN CONCEPT OF CHILLING INJURY
IN HEAT-LOVING PLANTS

Adherents of the above-mentioned theories agree on one thing, namely, that the death of plants from cold is preceded by a varying period of sickness measured in days or weeks. The fact is, however, that there are cases where plants die very quickly as shown, for example, by the experiments of Biebl (1939) with seaweed in which individual species died within 10 minutes of being cooled to +2° or +3°. Even more striking results were obtained by Gehenio and Luyet (1939) with the plasmodium Physarum polycephalum which died five seconds after the temperature was rapidly dropped to 0°.

These experiments show that chilling injury is not necessarily due to impaired water balance and metabolism in the cells. The modern view of chilling injury is much broader. The major factor in the death of plants exposed to cold is considered to be the specific effect of low temperature together with dehydration and impaired metabolism.

In ordinary chilling injury, heat-loving plants suffer long before there are visible injuries. The first indication is suppression of certain physiological processes and slowing up of the vital activity of the plants as a whole. The effect of cold is particularly marked on the sprouting of seeds and on photosynthesis. For example, squash seeds are not likely to sprout at +8° (Polishchuk, 1950). According to Ewart (1896), photosynthesis ceases in tropical plants when the temperature ranges between +4 and +8°. The synthetic processes are suppressed because the synthesizing action of all the enzymes when the plants are cold become subordinate to the hydrolyzing action. Meanwhile harmful metabolites accumulate in the cells.

The movement of protoplasm is significantly changed by cold. According to Sachs (1864), Protoplasm moves in the hairs of squash leaves quite vigorously at +18°, but virtually comes to a halt when the temperature falls to 11 or 12°. The movement of protoplasm plays a major role in the translocation of substances, which is directly slowed down by cold. In Curtis' experiments (1929) the outflow of carbohydrates from the leaf blades of garden beans almost ceased when the petioles were cooled to +6°.

Cold completely inhibits photosynthesis and associated accumulation and translocation of plastic substances although respiration continues. Thus, the plastic substances are consumed slowly but steadily. Interruption of the process of forming and consuming plastic substances leads to progressive depletion of the cell reserves, which, by the way, are stored in large amounts in heat-loving plants only in the reproductive organs. As soon as the reserves are used up the plants begin to expend cell constituents for respiration and die shortly thereafter.

Cold results in the gradual loss of protoplasmic impermeability. Selective impermeability is a typical indicator of cell viability. Cells invariably die when they become completely impermeable. This process is usually gradual so that the cells become increasingly incapable of absorbing and holding water and are easily dehydrated. In addition, the contents of the vacuoles and protoplasm, previously kept wholly apart, now tend to mingle as the protoplasm steadily loses its normal vital functions. The main cause of cold injury in heat-loving plants is the increased viscosity of the protoplasm and consequent slackening of the metabolic processes (Genkel' and Margolin, 1949).

The rate at which the pathological processes develops varies with the temperature, duration of its action, and nature of the plant. According to

Sellschop and Salmon (1928), velvet beans subjected to +5° and +10° for 48 hours exhibited no signs of injury the next day, but 24 hours later more than 60% of the plants appeared injured.

The dying off of plants exposed to low temperatures always starts with the oldest and weakest organs and tissues, gradually spreading to the more vital parts. The lower leaves and within the blades the apex and extremities die first. Organs stricken with fungus diseases or injured by pests are affected by cold sooner and more severely than healthy organs. The external signs of dying off are yellow, brown, or black spots, which then dry up. However, spots are not caused by cold alone; they may be due to other unfavorable factors, e.g., drought.

3. CHILLING INJURY AND WINTERKILLING OF PLANTS

Chilling injury in heat-loving plants at first glance would seem to have no direct connection with the problem of wintering that is of interest to us here, for all the above-mentioned warm-weather crops like cucumbers, tomatoes, squash, etc. are typical annuals in our climate. However, many of these have now become wintering plants because they are grown in the winter under glass. Moreover, while growing outdoors they are often exposed to prolonged cold and even frost during the growing season. The protection of these plants from low temperatures has been a constant concern of growers. A study of the effect of cold on heat-loving plants helps us to gain a deeper understanding of the effect of frost on ordinary wintering plants.

Let us compare the injury and death caused by cold and frost. Cold does not cause water to freeze in the cells or intercellular spaces so that with chilling injury in heat-loving plants there is absolutely no question of mechanical pressure of ice on the cell walls, as happens when there is extracellular freezing and resultant rupture of tissue. This also precludes the possibility of direct pressure of ice on protoplasm, which almost invariably destroys it.

Increased protoplasmic permeability is associated with both phenomena. When heat-loving plants are exposed to cold and wintering plants to frost, the protoplasm readily admits water and the substances dissolved in the cell sap of the vacuoles. The result is that the cells of the aerial parts transpire more vigorously while the cells of the underground parts have difficulty in absorbing water, and the plants become dehydrated. If this continues beyond a certain point, it becomes injurious and even fatal.

When heat-loving plants are exposed to cold and wintering plants to frost, the processes of autolysis prevail over the processes of synthesis. The only difference is that in heat-loving plants the disruption of metabolism becomes more pronounced and, as a rule, is the main factor in death of the plants, whereas in wintering plants it shows up after thawing. The reason is that at lower temperatures all the injurious effects of abnormal metabolism are less marked.

We are fully entitled to speak of the similarity of changes in all the other physiological processes and preceding physicochemical changes in cells (growth and respiration, movement and viscosity of protoplasm, acidity of cell sap) in heat-loving plants exposed to cold and in wintering plants exposed to frost. Accordingly, chilling injury in the former does not differ in principle from winterkilling in the latter. The cause of injury and death in both is unfavorable temperatures. Low temperatures alone may partially or totally kill plants, but more often they constitute one of the factors responsible for a variety of physiological disturbances in the cells that eventually become the main cause of death (dehydration, abnormal metabolism, etc.). The ice that forms within chilled cells may well play a decisive role in the fate of the plants.

CONCLUSION

Excessively low temperature is a basic cause of plant injury. The freezing of water when the temperature drops below 0° is just one manifestation of the effect of low temperature.

CHAPTER 4

PLANT DEATH BY WATERLOGGING

Death by waterlogging is not characteristic of wintering plants alone. It is also observed in spring crops, frequently during very rainy summers in gardens and potato fields situated in low-lying places. Waterlogging of wintering plants is particularly common when the soil is heavy and poorly drained. The reason is that the plants are in the soil during the fall, the period of heaviest rain, and during the spring, when the soil is supersaturated with thaw water.

1. SKETCH OF RESEARCH OF PLANT DEATH BY WATERLOGGING

Wet "cold" soils have been regarded from ancient times as unfavorable for the wintering of plants. "Gardens in lowlands or in wet places are frequently injured by frosts....Frosts during the winter of 1835 killed gardens in lowlands, whereas they scarcely touched gardens in elevated places and open plains," N. Dubenskiy (1853, p. 136) wrote of gardens in former Vladimir province. The older literature also carries similar comments on herbaceous plants, particularly grains.

The nature of waterlogging has long been correctly understood. For example, Professor M.G. Pavlov of Moscow University wrote in an article entitled "Spring Check of Winter Cereals" published in the 1830's in Russkiy zemledelets [The Russian Farmer]: "Water soaking the green grain breaks its free communication with the air; the plants cease to breathe, die off, the lovely green color turning yellow. The places in the fields thus deprived of their green are termed waterlogged." An interesting note on Pavlov's article appeared in the Zhurnal sadovodstva [Journal of Horticulture], 1838, no. 3. The anonymous author discussed waterlogging in detail and made the significant observation that the phenomenon is not invariably harmful. Flooding of plants in frozen soil, as happens when the snow melts, does not kill them. The thing that is dangerous is the flooding of plants in thawing soil, particularly when the water remains stagnant for a long time. This is the way the problem was handled in our older literature. Later research, summed up by V.P. Mosolov (1934-1938, 1953), is purely the amassing of factual data with insufficient theorizing.

The first attempt to analyze waterlogging was made by I.I. Tumanov (1940) who generalized the extensive work done by himself and co-workers, notably M.T. Timofeyeva and S.M. Ivanov, in the Laboratory of Plant Physiology of the All-Union Research Institute of Plant Growth at Leningrad. These investigators showed that stagnant water on the ground is extremely dangerous for germinated seeds. Stagnant water is very dangerous for green plants when they are entirely submerged; partly submerged, they are fairly resistant. The amount of light is quite important, for plants die more quickly in shade.

Frost injury decreases the resistance of plants to flooding, and that is why spring stagnation is highly dangerous. It was also shown that plants have a limited capacity to adapt to waterlogging. After prolonged partial flooding new "water" rootlets form in place of the dead roots provided that oxygen is available.

These data enable Tumanov to elaborate the following working hypothesis. The main cause of death by waterlogging is a deficiency of oxygen in supersaturated soil. If extremely tender germinated seeds are submerged in water and air is introduced, there is no waterlogging. Inadequate oxygen and light causes inundated green plants to become exhausted and eventually die. Plants weakened by excessive moisture harden off poorly and therefore do not become frost resistant. Plants inundated in the spring after winter frost injury have little capacity for regeneration and die more quickly as a result.

2. EXCESSIVE SOIL MOISTURE IN THE FALL AND ITS EFFECT ON PLANTS

Let us describe some of our own experiments with winter grains by way of illustrating the effect of excessive soil moisture in the fall.

Experiment 1. The experiment involved two dozen different strains of winter wheat and rice in enameled pots. The seeds were planted early in September. By the end of the month all the plants had the same amount of soil moisture (about 70% of the total moisture capacity), after which they were divided into two groups — experimental (in pots) and control (not in pots) — and placed in a seedbed. Water was added to the potted plants in amounts barely sufficient to cover the soil and kept at this level throughout the fall. In the control plants the moisture generally did not exceed 70% of the total moisture capacity. The plants overwintered under about 10 cm of snow. The lowest temperature in the tillering node zone, according to readings of the Savinov thermometers, was -14.1° in mid-February. The pots were taken away early in the spring and thereafter the experimental and control plants had the same soil moisture regime.

Water stagnation in the fall had no immediate effect on the plants. No external signs of injury were noted for about three weeks until the middle of October. The appearance of the plants then changed abruptly, at first in a few strains of wheat and rye, a little later in the lower leaves of the rest of the plants which the day before seemed perfectly healthy. They wilted, became ashen, and soon died. The process then spread to the leaves of the second node. Growth continued, however, and new leaves and shoots appeared on all the experimental and control plants.

Marked deterioration in the condition of the experimental plants as compared with the controls became evident in the spring. Most of the former died; the survivors grew more slowly than the controls. A graphic idea of the differences is provided by Figs. 5 and 6 showing photographs of winter wheat and rye plants taken June 10.

Fig. 5. Typical picture of waterlogged winter wheat. The markers are standing in the rows of the control plants; on the right — rows of experimental plants

Fig. 6. Typical picture of waterlogged winter rye. Two varieties of winter rye. The markers are standing in the rows of the control plants; on the right — rows of experimental plants

Experiment 2. A comparison was made between the effect of flooding only the subsurface parts of the plants and of allowing water to stand on the ground and partially cover the green leaves. The experiment was conducted simultaneously with the above on the Moskovskaya 2411 variety of winter wheat. About 70% of the plants whose subsurface leaves and roots were flooded survived. Plants in which about two-thirds of the leaves were submerged did not survive. They had rotted away by the time the photograph (Fig. 7) was taken.

Fig. 7. Winter wheat, variety Moskovskaya 2411
(1) only the underground parts of the plants were flooded in the fall;
(2) water covered most of the leaves

Experiment 3. The experiments involved plants in the active growth stage. Thirteen days after the seeds were planted and two to three leaves had appeared, four pots of each variety were covered with 2 cm of water. The first signs of injury appeared 10 days later in the most vigorously growing and greenest winter rye plants. The lower leaves drooped and the tips had turned gray. On the 11th day all the lower leaves were yellowish-gray and they seemed lifeless. The same injury was also observed at the ends of the leaves of the second node. On the 13th day the injury spread to the leaves of the third node where it halted. In winter wheat, the varieties Saratovskaya 329, and Moskovskaya 2411, wheat-wheat grass hybrid 599, perennial wheat 34085, and perennial wheat 4190, whose growth was slower and green mass smaller than the rye, the signs of injury from excessive moisture appeared much later; the slowest growing of all, the perennial wheat variety 34085, was the last to show the effects. Fig. 8 shows how the experimental winter rye plants looked 33 days after the soil of the experimental plants was overwatered.

Experiment 4. The purpose of the experiment was to determine the effect of excessive moisture on the root system of the winter rye plants used in experiment 3. On October 7, 47 days after planting, some of the specimens were carefully removed with soil from the pots. After the soil was washed

Fig. 8. Winter rye, variety Vyatka
(1) control plant with soil moisture kept at 70-75% of total moisture capacity;
(2) plants kept 33 days in waterlogged soil

off, they were replanted in the same pots, now filled with water and a little well fertilized fresh soil. The plants remained in the water 9 days. Fig. 9 shows the results. The roots were much shorter than those of the controls, the difference increasing with the length of time kept in the waterlogged soil. In addition, they looked paler and thicker and had few root hairs. In the plants kept in water 9 days the old roots formed in the soil died and in their place appeared new, thick, and poorly branched roots typical of hydroponic crops.

Fig. 9. Winter rye, variety Vyatka
(1) roots of the control plant kept continuously in soil with 70-75% of total
moisture capacity; (2) roots of a plant kept 23 days in waterlogged soil;
(3) the same, 33 days; (4) the same in water culture, 9 days

Experiment 5. This concluding experiment was designed to determine the frost resistance of the plants described above when grown in waterlogged soil. Fig. 10 shows the experimental and control plants of winter wheat, variety Moskovskaya 2411, and rye, variety Vyatka, kept outdoors from October 31 to November 20. The lowest temperature during this time was -12°. The photograph was taken three months after the plants were brought into the greenhouse.

Fig. 10. Frost injury of winter wheat, variety Moskovskaya 2411 (1, 2)
and winter rye, variety Vyatka (3, 4)
1, 3 — control plants; 2, 4 — plants grown in waterlogged soil

Both varieties of experimental plants were much more frost injured than the controls. Most of the leaves were dead and by the time the photograph was taken only a few of the shoots had survived. The same thing happened to the other varieties.

We conclude from all these experiments that excessive soil moisture in the fall inhibits plant growth and causes the oldest lower leaves to drop. The process is largely dependent on the temperature: as the temperature rises, growth becomes more inhibited and the lower leaves begin to die sooner. Plants with a greater mass of leaves and roots and growing more rapidly by the time of water stagnation start to show signs of excessive moisture before plants with a smaller mass and less marked growth. The reason is that oxygen, the deficiency of which is felt by plants when the soil is waterlogged, is used up in greater amounts by the more rapidly growing plants with their larger mass of leaves and roots.

Some waterlogged plants put out new, shorter, thick, and poorly branched roots typical of hydroponic crops. These roots are known to have more air cavities and are therefore better supplied with atmospheric air. This explains why the leaves stop dropping some time after the plants are shifted to a regime of excessive moisture. This adaptation, however, does not guarantee the conditions required for normal growth, and they suffer much more from frost than do plants with the usual root system. The decrease in hardiness is particularly pronounced in plants whose subsurface parts and leaves (in large numbers) are submerged during the fall.

3. EXCESSIVE SOIL MOISTURE IN THE SPRING AND ITS EFFECT ON PLANTS

The stagnation of thaw water in the spring on impermeable clay soils, especially in lowlands and so-called "saucers", is a common phenomenon. This is associated with "spring plant death by waterlogging", which has been known since antiquity. Research to date (Brokert, 1932; Tumanov, 1933; Timofeyeva, 1933, 1935, 1948, 1949; others) shows that spring stagnation kills a substantial number of plants injured by frost during the winter. Let us add here some of our own experiments and practical observations.

Experiment 1. Two varieties of winter wheat – Saratovskaya 329 and Moskovskaya 2411 – were planted in mid-September in enameled pots. The soil was kept throughout the fall at the level of 70-75% of the total moisture capacity. The plants that wintered under snow in pots sunk in beds suffered little frost injury. Early in the spring half the plants of each variety (the controls) were removed from the pots and then kept on the same moisture regime as in the fall, i.e., 70-75% of the total moisture capacity. The experimental plants were left in the pots and subsequently exposed to excessive moisture.

No visible differences were noted between the experimental and control plants during the first two weeks when the air temperature was still fairly low. As the weather warmed up, the experimental plants began to look worse, turning brown. It was only after the surviving portions began to grow that green stripes appeared on the leaves. A count in mid-May showed that 59% of the waterlogged Lutescens 329 wheat plants died as against 11% of the controls; 83% of the waterlogged Moskovskaya 2411 variety and 20% of the controls, respectively, died.

Thus, stagnant water in the soil and over plants caused a four- to fivefold increase in the number of plants that died in the spring following frost injury during the winter. Judging by the leaves' loss of their green color, deterioration in their condition set in after growth had started.

Experiment 2. Sifted and fertilized soil was packed 40 cm deep in furrows of two parallel beds, as is done when pots are used. At the end of August both beds were sown with Vyatka winter rye, Moskovskaya 2411 winter wheat, winter wheat-wheat grass hybrid 499, and perennial wheat 34085. Before leaving for the winter, we built an embankment around one bed to contain the spring thaw water. When the snow melted, the water flooded the embanked bed, but did not remain on the other. The water stagnated for 18 days throughout the cold period of spring before the plants began to grow. The water was released as soon as growth started on the experimental bed. An inspection two weeks later revealed no signs of injury. Indeed the plants looked even better than the controls because the water tended to reduce the amount of damage from late frosts.

We have frequently noted the absence of injury to winter crops from stagnant water in the cold period before the plants began to put on growth. The following two instances are particularly instructive. The winter of 1947-1948 in Kuban was unusually warm and rainy, and the winter crops in the flood plain were inundated over a vast area. In mid-February 1948 when I examined the crops, they had been under water for several weeks. All the plants were alive and thriving with a fresh green appearance and no external signs of injury caused by the abnormal water regime. I learned later that they came through the winter safely and yielded heavily. Also in 1948, winter crops in the Western Dvina flood plain in Latvia remained for several weeks under water during the winter without suffering any harm.

The results are quite different when plants are flooded in warmer weather while growing. This phenomenon has been thoroughly investigated by V.P. Mosolov (1934) on winter crops inundated by the Volga during the spring floods. Artificial flooding of plants produced signs of injury within 24 hours. At +20° flooded plants die within 10 days.

CONCLUSION

It follows from the above that so-called "death by waterlogging" of wintering plants has two components: direct injury by stagnant water and the greater injury by frost to the waterlogged plants. Such plants die as a result of an oxygen deficiency. Excessive water in itself is not harmful. Wholly normal plants with a large green mass can be grown in water if air is systematically bubbled in through the nutrient solution. Under such conditions even the germination of seeds is possible.

The research of Grünberg (1932), who kept tissues and whole plants in an oxygen-free medium, helps to explain why waterlogged plants die. Grünberg discovered that an oxygen deficiency affects plants in two ways: first, toxic incompletely oxidized products are formed, particularly alcohol, and, secondly, plants are exhausted due to the rapid consumption of plastic substances in respiration since with incomplete disintegration in an oxygen-free medium they are used up much more quickly than under the conditions of normal oxidation.* However, Grünberg's findings do not apply to ordinary waterlogging of plants when the water covers the roots and only a few of the leaves. In any case the metabolic changes that he describes are not the main cause of the plants' death. It is a sounder assumption that soaked plants are partially injured and their growth is inhibited by the exhaustion resulting from worsening of the nutrient regime due to an oxygen deficiency in the soil. Exhaustion is especially rapid in plants in the growing stage. When the nutrient regime is unfavorable, growth slows down but does not halt. Since there are not enough plastic substances to form new leaves and shoots, they come from the old leaves. This is apparently the reason why the lower leaves die off during the first few weeks of waterlogging before making an adequate adjustment to these new conditions. The dropping of old leaves during the growth stage is very common, invariably so in plants suffering from a nutrient deficiency.**

However, if plants are completely inundated, they have no organs to obtain oxygen from the air. This may lead to poisoning of the plants by toxins and their exhaustion due to incomplete combustion of plastic substances, as noted by Nabokikh (1905). It is obvious that the higher the temperature, the more pronounced the process of poisoning and exhaustion. Herein lies the explanation for the rapid death of completely inundated winter crops during heavy spring floods. On the other hand, when the temperature is low — in the event of flooding during winter or early spring thaws before growth starts and respiration is comparatively weak — plants may remain a long time under water without any visible harmful aftereffects because their oxygen requirement is small and can be completely covered by the oxygen from the water surrounding the plants, especially if it is flowing.

---

*This problem was studied long before Grünberg by the Russian scientist A.I. Nabokikh (1905) who wrote: "The products of anaerobic exchange poison plants as they accumulate in the plasma" (p. 113).

**We should like to call attention to I.P. Borodin's book (1876) Fiziologicheskiye issledovaniya nad dykhaniyem listonosnykh pobegov [Physiological Research on Respiration of Leafy Shoots]. The author refuted Pfeffer's contention that growth of the higher plants comes to an instant and complete halt in an oxygen-free medium.

Frost does great damage to plants in excessively moist soils because the plants go into the winter exhausted and insufficiently hardened. Frost-injured plants that start to grow when the ground is completely soaked have no powers of recuperation and thus die quickly.

CHAPTER 5

ICE CRUSTS AND THEIR EFFECT ON PLANTS

Ice crusts are a normal winter phenomenon. Stagnant water in and on the soil late in the fall eventually freezes. The same thing happens after winter thaws followed by frosts and early in the spring when melting snow freezes at night.

There are numerous references in scientific and popular agricultural literature to the harmful effect of ice crusts on plants. This is usually explained by the above-described theory of N.A. Maksimov (1913) regarding the mechanical action of ice on cells. It is believed that frozen plants come under double pressure: ice presses on the cells from within, from the intercellular spaces (formed from cell water), and from without (the crust). Thus, ice-encased plants are readily injured and die (Saltykovskiy, 1936, 1940).

According to another view, the ice crust suffocates the plant. This view, long popular among agronomists, was reinforced by the studies of A.A. Rikhter and A.I. Grechushnikov (1932) who advanced the hypothesis that plants die under an ice crust because of alcoholic autointoxication. However, the authors presented no experimental data in support.

Let us now consider the effect of ice crusts in the light of factual data.

1. MECHANICAL EFFECT OF ICE CRUSTS
AND PLANT SUFFOCATION

I ran some experiments on winter grains, clover, alfalfa, and several cereal grasses, each variety sown in pots two or three times. An ice crust formed owing to excessive watering in mid-November. Figs. 11 and 12 show the ice crust.

In the spring it was found that the plants under ice and the controls suffered equally from frost. The ice did not intensify the injury nor was it a factor in the death of the plants. This is clearly shown in the case of Vyatka

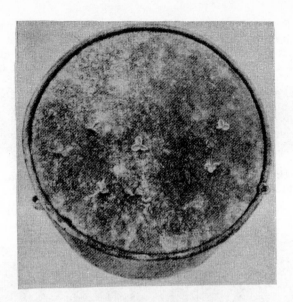

Fig. 11. Effect of ice crust on herbaceous plants:
clover completely frozen in ice

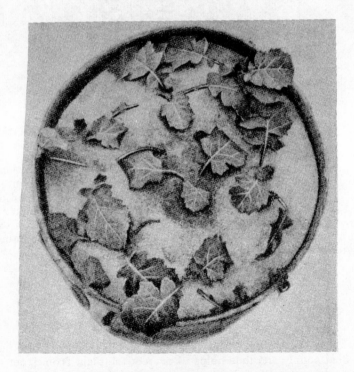

Fig. 12. Effect of ice crust on herbaceous plants: winter rape
partially frozen in ice, partially left above ice

winter rye (Fig. 13) which was kept in crushed ice for three months and suffered frost injury in the region of the tillering nodes at -19.5°, i.e., a temperature that is harmful even to this strain. Even though a good many leaves died, all the plants survived despite the fact that the tillering nodes as well as the leaves remained under ice throughout the winter. The photograph was taken April 20 after the plants had completely recuperated.

Similarly, plants do not suffocate under ice, as indicated by I.I. Tumanov's findings (1940) on air permeability of ice. Hollowed out cylinders of ice with sides of varying thickness, were filled with air and the oxygen content reduced to 8%. After remaining in ordinary air at -5° for 10 days, the oxygen in the cylinder with 2 cm thick sides was found to have risen to 21%, in the cylinder with 4 cm thick sides to 18.8%, and in the cylinder with 6 cm thick sides to 17.5%. The ice, therefore, proved to be quite permeable to air.

Fig. 13. Winter rye, variety Vyatka, after wintering in crushed ice

This is our conclusion even without special experimentation. It is a matter of common observation that water from fall rains accumulates in all kinds of pools, depressions, ditches, etc. and freezes solidly in the winter. Yet the perennial grasses wintering on the bottom do not die no matter how long they are under ice and commence their growth in the spring like plants wintering under snow. Cultivated plants react the same way on fields covered with ice a long time.

2. BENEFICIAL AND HARMFUL EFFECT OF ICE CRUSTS

Ice is often beneficial. This is a logical consequence of the fact that it conducts heat poorly and thus helps to protect the plant from frost.

Vyatka winter rye and Moskovskaya 2411 winter wheat were planted in pots early in September. In February, 20 plants of each variety were placed in enameled containers and flooded with water. Other plants in similar containers served as controls. The plants were exposed to freezing temperatures for 24 hours — the rye at -34°, the wheat at -20°. A week and a half later, when the effects of the frost had become completely manifest, the plants were sketched (Fig. 14). Those chilled in ice suffered much less that the controls.

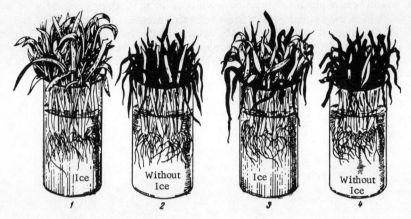

Fig. 14. Protective effect of ice crust on winter plants
1, 2 — Vyatka rye; 3, 4 — Moskovskaya 2411 wheat

The protective action of ice is weaker than that of snow because ice is a better heat conductor. That is why plants wintering under ice are more prone to injury than plants wintering under snow. They are more likely to be frozen solid in a prolonged frost. Moreover, snow falling on ice is readily blown away by the wind. Herein lies the source of the injurous effect of ice crusts.

3. PREVALENCE AND FORMS OF ICE CRUSTS

Ice crusts are to be found everywhere during the cold part of the year. They may occur in the form of individual frozen pools, mainly in the spring, and in the form of solid fields of ice in the south after winter thaws. They often look like snow adhering to the ground and turning into grainy ice in the spring, etc. It is certainly incorrect to say that in the Soviet Union plants are found under ice only in the south. The fact is plants are found under ice throughout the country wherever the soil and surface have excessive moisture in the winter and the temperature drops below 0°.

Besides "crushed ice", mentioned above, we sometimes come across "hanging crusts" usually in the spring, when water from melting snow in furrows is partly frozen by a light frost, i.e., the water is not frozen solid to the bottom. If the frost lingers for several days while the ground softens, the water under the ice is drawn into the soil and the ice remains suspended over any plants growing in the furrow. There are references in the literature to the fact that plants may start to grow under this hanging ice, as under glass, but are destroyed by any subsequent frost, however light. This is based on a misunderstanding, for it is quite obvious that the ice melts before the plants under it start to grow.

41

CONCLUSION

The fact that ice crusts are found everywhere indicates that they cannot be as harmful as is generally supposed. If they really crushed plants and prevented them from obtaining the oxygen required for respiration, herbaceous plants would scarcely be able to overwinter. In fact, they generally do well under ice which may encase them for weeks and months at a time. Ice may be beneficial in that it protects plants from frost. Nevertheless, in regions where ice forms in open treeless places after winter thaws, it is desirable to contain any snow that may fall because snow and ice together are better protection against frost than ice alone.

CHAPTER 6

WINTER DROUGHT AND ITS EFFECT ON PLANTS

When the temperature drops to 0°, plant roots have difficulty in absorbing water, and if the soil freezes, the process sometimes ceases altogether. Meanwhile water evaporates from the aerial parts even during severe frosts. Thus, plants in frozen soil become dehydrated, especially if exposed to direct sunlight and wind and not shielded against evaporation. When dehydration exceeds given limits, they die partially or even wholly.

There are conflicting opinions regarding the effect of winter drought. Let us now examine the main views.

1. BRIEF SURVEY OF RESEARCH ON THE EFFECT OF WINTER DROUGHT

It has long been known that winter drought has an adverse effect on plants. Winter drought is a major factor in determining the limit of occurrence of plants to the north and in the mountains. Geobotanical research, notably by A. Middendorf (1860), who traveled in Northern Siberia, and A. Kihlman (1890), who investigated Kola Peninsula, was very important in supporting this view. Kihlman's main conclusion was the following: "The limit of the forest is determined not by the mechanical action of the wind or the moisture or salt in the atmosphere, but primarily by the months of continuous desiccation of young shoots at a time of the year when replacement of the water evaporated is impossible" (p. 79).

This view was later bolstered by physiological data. Many investigations undertaken to study winter transpiration revealed that the parts of plants not covered by snow lost a good deal of water. Prominent contributors to our understanding of the problem were L.A. Ivanov (1925, 1936) in Leningrad, A.Ya. Gordyagin (1925, 1930) in Kazan, and A.V. Ryazantsev (1934, 1937, 1950) in Molotov.

However, the question arose as to whether the loss of water reaches fatal proportions and is not replaced by water coming into the dehydrated parts from elsewhere in the plants. These doubts, long entertained, became increasingly insistent as the findings of experimental investigations of plant water balance in the winter were published. According to P.B. Raskatov (1939), the fatal minimum of water is about 60-75% of the normal amount lost. Yet the actual water content during the winter in Voronezh dropped a little over 10%, e.g., 10% in horse chestnut, 12% in birch. Similar data were obtained even earlier by Meyer in conifers (1928, 1932).

This led L.A. Ivanov (1946) to reexamine the entire problem and reject the earlier conclusions. Ivanov now believes that mature trees are not affected by drought in the winter due to the vigorous growth of cover tissues, tight closing of the stomata and lenticels, and, above all, to the increased water-holding capacity of protoplasm. He maintains that frost is the only cause of severe injury and death of trees in the winter. This also determines the northern limit of trees (D.V. Girnik, 1953).

2. DESICCATION OF HERBACEOUS PLANTS DURING THE WINTERING PERIOD

Partial desiccation of herbaceous plants during the wintering period is familiar to everyone living in our steppes and steppe-like regions, e.g., the Maritime Territory. The grass here is yellowish brown in the winter, just as it is in the summer after severe drought. The leaves of even the most drought-resistant wild flora die. Grain crops too, even on fallow land with a better supply of water than is available to nearby uncultivated plants, suffer severely from desiccation.

The principal reason why herbaceous plants dry out in the winter is intense evaporation in the sun and wind when the soil is frozen. The following observation, made near Moscow on a field belonging to the Institute of Grain Culture in the Nonchernozem Belt, struck me as being quite instructive. Several varieties of winter rye and wheat were planted at the usual time. Dry, sunny weather followed a long, damp, cloudy spell after which came the first night frost. The temperature dropped to -6° by morning. The soils and plants froze. When the sun warmed up the ground by midday and the plants thawed, the leaves in the sun lost turgor. The same thing happened on succeeding days and the amount of wilting kept increasing until almost half the leaves dried up.

Herbaceous plants suffer greater desiccation during prolonged absence of snow, as is shown by the following experiment that I performed. Clover was sown in pots which were kept outdoors until early November and then brought into a glassed-in room with the temperature generally maintained at a few degrees below zero (innocuous for the plants). Yet by the end of winter almost all the leaves had dried up, only the youngest surviving (Fig. 15).

Fig. 15. Winter desiccation of herbaceous
plants: clover, after wintering without snow

Transpiration is an especially important factor after plants are exposed to frost. This is demonstrated by the following experiment. Table beet, sugar beet, fodder beet, cabbage, white and red kohlrabi, and carrot plants in pots were left outdoors until the end of November where they experienced cold as low as -7.5°. This temperature injured but did not kill them, as shown by the fact that after the ice melted in the intercellular spaces, the water was not absorbed by the cells for a long time. Some of the pots were transferred to a cool greenhouse with a temperature of about 0° while the others were kept in a warm room at +15-20°.

The experiment was concluded a week later. In the plants kept at the low temperature there was little evaporation and, although injured, they lost only the oldest leaves. The plants kept in the warm room transpired profusely and all the leaves shriveled, just the undeveloped young leaflets in the rosettes surviving (Fig. 16).

However, even plants that overwinter successfully frequently suffer from intense evaporation, especially if water intake from the soil is inhibited. Figs. 17 and 18 show individual winter wheat and alfalfa plants exposed in mid-April to dry winds after night temperature of -3°. Although they had come through the winter in good condition and had already begun to put on growth, they lost most of their leaves and became unrecognizable after a few days of exposure to a dry wind.

Such is the effect of evaporation on wintering herbaceous plants.

3. DESICCATION OF WOODY PLANTS DURING
THE WINTERING PERIOD

A large part of every tree and shrub goes through the winter without being covered by snow. They are more exposed to winds, at least when in an open

Fig. 16. Red kohlrabi
(1) a plant kept after frost in a cool greenhouse; (2) a plant kept in
a warm laboratory

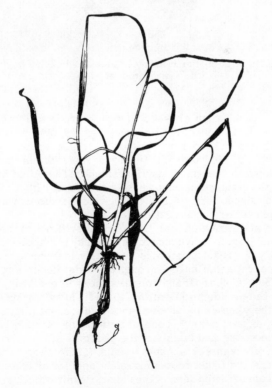

Fig. 17. Winter wheat, variety Lutescens 329, after
two days of exposure to a dry wind with
a night frost of -3°

Fig. 18. Alfalfa after two days of exposure to a dry wind
with a night frost of -3°

place or in a thin stand, than grasses, but they are better protected against evaporation by well developed cover tissues (Figs. 19, 20). The value of cover tissues in the safe wintering of woody plants is vividly shown by the research of L.A. Ivanov (1925, 1936). One fall Ivanov scraped the stems of one to two year old shoots down to the green cortical tissue. They died during the winter. If, however, the places thus exposed were covered with a thin sheet of tin foil, the shoots survived. The tin foil didn't shield them against frost, but it was effective in preventing evaporation.

Tree branches still growing and "immature" with poorly developed cover tissues suffered most from dehydration. In one year old apple shoots, according to P.I. Vasil'yev (1930), water is generally lost through the periderm, then through the scars, and, finally, through the buds, depending on their size. In the oak, it is the leaf scars that transpire most intensively, then the buds, and, least of all, the periderm (Danilov, 1947). These differences in rate of transpiration of the various parts of shoots in different plants vary with the nature of the "ripening" period, time of defoliation, size of buds, etc. As a rule, however, the scars and buds are the portions of the surface that transpire most. A.V. Ryazantsev's experiments (1950) showed that at subzero temperatures scars and buds, depending on the species of tree, suffered 32 to 66% of the total transpiration loss of the shoot, despite their relatively small surface.

The water lost through evaporation in the winter is frequently replenished during warm spells by water coming from the roots, trunk, and thick branches

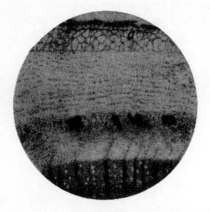

Fig. 19. Cross section of part
of a "ripened" shoot of an Amur cork
with multilayered loose cork tissue
already formed (a)

Fig. 20. Cross section of part
of a "ripened" shoot of a Siberian
apple with multilayered dense cork
tissue already formed (a)

and by drops of water absorbed by shoots during thaws in damp weather.
This is the main reason for the comparatively favorable water balance of one
year old shoots during the winter. That part of the water which is left liquid
in the cells and vessels of a frozen tree is still able to move. When a tree
has no protection from the sun or parts of it are exposed to direct sunshine,
the water evaporates rapidly and is drawn to these parts. Under certain conditions this is an important source from which the plant can replenish its
water reserve lost through evaporation (Ryazantsev, 1950).

The water balance in the winter frequently changes drastically so that the
satisfactory situation noted, for example, in Voronezh by Raskatov is neither
constant nor universal. In the Pamirs, as L. F. Ostapovich (1948) showed, the
water deficit in the young shoots of many species of trees was 70% or more,
the crown drying out every winter. Winter drought here is the major adverse
factor for herbaceous as well as woody plants.

In the Maritime Territory too the sunny winter and warming of parts of
plants not covered with snow is highly unfavorable for their normal water
balance so that winter desiccation of the vegetation is a common phenomenon.
Fall irrigation of the local fruit trees helps to protect them from winter
drought. Intense evaporation in the bright winter sun is chiefly responsible
for winter injury to trees in the mountains. Pirschle (1934, 1934a) thinks that
this determines the timber line in the Alps.

Accordingly, there is no reason to deny, as L. A. Ivanov now does, the
marked effect of winter drought on trees. Sometimes it constitutes the controlling factor in the life of woody plants.

CONCLUSION

It follows from the above that desiccation of wintering plants may injure or
kill them. The degree of evaporation largely determines the fate of annual
grasses in our virtually snowless steppes and steppe-like regions and of

trees high in the mountains. The combination of frost injury and subsequent winter drought, common early in the spring in sunny weather, is particularly dangerous.

CHAPTER 7

HEAVING, DEFLATION, AND WASHING OUT OF PLANTS

Heaving, deflation, and washing out refer to the exposure of subsurface parts of plants and resultant injury and death. Herbaceous plants are particularly subjected to these processes: in winter cereals the tillering nodes and sometimes the bases of the roots are exposed while in clover and alfalfa the collars are exposed. Lying unprotected on the surface of the soil, they are easily injured by frost, sun, and wind, leading to their death and eventually to the death of the entire plant. Heaving, deflation, and washing out occur both in winter and in summer, but they are more frequent in the former and cause greater damage.

1. HEAVING

By heaving is meant the exposure of the subsurface parts of plants due to alternating freezing and thawing of the soil. The plants are pulled out of the ground frequently suffering torn roots in the process. Heaving is directly caused by swelling of the soil during freezing when it is saturated with water. The top layer expands and lifts up the frozen plants. After the ice melts and the soil settles, the plants resting on their "heaved" roots stand higher than their previous level. Following repeated swelling and settling of the soil the plants are raised well above the ground, frequently with exposed tillering nodes or collars and with partially exposed and torn roots.

The above is a description of what might be called active heaving. There is also passive heaving which occurs when seeds are sown in soil that has not settled after cultivation. The seeds germinate and sprout, but the tillering nodes and collars soon become established, usually at a depth of 1-2 cm, more rarely at greater depths. When the soil settles after rain, the tillering nodes and collars come to the surface or close to it and not being warmed by the soil they are readily killed by frost. Heaved plants sometimes live through the winter, but die in the spring from desiccation or remain poorly developed and unproductive.

We shall begin with a discussion of passive heaving of winter cereals which is a major economic problem. It is the most frequent cause of poor wintering of cereals in many parts of Europe and Asiatic U.S.S.R. There are few references to it in the literature.

I first encountered passive heaving in the spring of 1932 in state grain farm No. 2 "Verblyud" in the Northern Caucasus. Large areas of wheat had overwintered very poorly and about 1500 hectares had to be sown over again. An inspection revealed that all the dead plants had exposed tillering nodes. The reason was to be found in the farming practices, time of cultivating the soil or sowing the seeds. It turned out that sowing took place soon after unsettled soil was plowed (I.M. Vasil'yev, 1932).

I observed a similar case in 1946 in Mordovian ASSR where there was mass death of winter rye. Passive heaving in almost all the regions was the main cause. The plants lay on the soil with exposed tillering nodes. Occasional survivors had the first roots with exposed bases; there was no secondary rooting. Here too sowing took place soon after plowing unsettled soil. The interval between plowing and planting was measured in days rather than the usual two or three weeks (I.M. Vasil'yev, 1946).

An analogous picture of dead winter wheat was observed almost all over the Ukraine in 1946-1947. The situation was particularly depressing in Kiev oblast which I inspected from south to north. The cause was somewhat different from that in the two areas mentioned above. Here are a few typical examples.

At Mironov Experimental Station, noted for its generally high level of technology, most of the winter wheat, variety Ukrainka, zoned for Kiev oblast, died or seemed very sparse. The crop overwintered well on the sides of the breeding nursery where the sowing machines turned around and the soil before planting was packed down hard. The wheat sown on bare fallow with additional loosening just before planting died; the wheat sown without this loosening all survived.

In Petrovskiy Obukhovskiy Rayon collective farm the soil under winter wheat was prepared in the most approved fashion. The fallow was cultivated four times, the last time just before planting. The wheat here looked good in the fall, but all died during the winter. In the neighboring collective farm where the last cultivation took place some time before planting and the soil was cultivated fewer times in the summer, the plants survived. The wheat in a field on "12-Letiye Oktyabr'" collective farm, Borispol'skiy rayon, was very sparse after the winter, but on strips where the tractor wheels passed over the plants came through in good condition. There were many such cases.

The summer of 1946, the second half in particular, was unusually dry. The soil prior to sowing the winter crops was parched and became looser with each tilling. It remained in this condition throughout the sowing period because there was scarcely any rain, which normally settles the soil. However, well prepared fallow had enough moisture for the seedlings and subsequent growth of the plants. The soil settled late in the fall when it began to rain and in the spring as soon as the snow melted. As a result the tillering nodes were either on the surface or close to it and thus more exposed to the winter or early spring frosts. In those places where it had rained at the end of the summer, before or during the sowing period and where the soil had settled somewhat by the time the tillering nodes became established, the crops thrived. However, in those places where there was no rain, the crops died or were sparse with all the signs of typical passive heaving. This could be clearly seen in Korsun'-Shevchenkovskiy rayon from the pattern of the rain (I.M. Vasil'yev, 1947).

Passive heaving of winter crops is very common. It is sometimes caused by obvious violation of sound agricultural practices with unwarranted reduction of the necessary two to three week interval between final cultivation and sowing. At other times, when this interval is observed, passive heaving may be due to the lack of rain during the latter part of the summer because the soil settles in the fall after the tillering nodes become established.

A.F. Lebedev and Ye. V. Talalayev (1928) present data on active heaving. According to Lebedev, active heaving is caused by the formation of ice in the top layer of soil through condensation of water vapor. As the soil rises, it pulls up the plants. G.M. Klunnyy (1935) observed active heaving in Azerbaijan where the collars of guayule were 5-6 cm above the ground and the roots were torn 15-17 cm from the base. Soviet and foreign literature contain other reports on manifestations of active heaving (Kokkonen, 1926; McCool and Bouyoucos, 1929). However, the term active heaving is very frequently applied to what is actually passive heaving due to subsidence of the soil.

2. DEFLATION

Deflation is a common phenomenon. It normally occurs on plowed, structureless soils, especially in open treeless places during a dry fall. Deflation is a major cause of the poor wintering of crops in the steppe part of the Ukraine, Northeren Caucasus, and steppes of Siberia. The so-called "dust-storms" just before the soil freezes are well known. During these storms 2-3 cm of the top pulverized layer of soil is sometimes blown away and the tillering nodes and collars become exposed. There were severe dust storms in the Ukraine during 1927-1928, which was memorable for the mass destruction of winter crops. Extensive areas in the northern regions of Krasnodar kray were devastated by these storms during the winter of 1946-1947. The wind exposed the subsurface parts of the plants so that they toppled and, as the saying goes, "they hung on the roots". The dust settling on the edges of shelter belts was half a meter thick and it almost filled the ditches on the side of the road.

The physiological aftereffects of deflation are the same as those of passive heaving. An additional factor is the mechanical injury to leaves and exposed subsurface parts by rapidly moving particles of sand and the drying effect of the wind, which is intensified by exposure of the roots and fissures in the cover tissues caused by the sand. In the absence of snow, exposed and mechanically injured plants are readily damaged by frost.

3. WASHING OUT

Washing out usually occurs on slopes, on loose, plowed soils. Streams of rain water or melting snow erode the top layer of the soil and thus expose the subsurface parts of the plants.

In an experiment on a plot with structureless soil I made a bed in such a way that part of it was on a level place while the rest of it came over a slight slope. The bed was sown at the end of August with winter wheat. Late in the fall, just before the soil froze, I built an embankment so that the spring thaw water could flow from one end to the other. In the spring the nodes in most of the plants on the slope were exposed along with the base of the roots. These plants proved to be stunted and by earing time most of them died.

In 1946 soils in the Mordovian ASSR were extremely powdery and thaw water and rain caused large washouts on slopes. The winter rye, which overwintered comparatively well on level ground, was very sparse on slopes, and the tillering nodes and base of the roots in all the dead plants were exposed.

A typical picture of washing out of plants along with passive heaving was observed on a swampy, low-lying field belonging to the Tiraynenskaya Experimental Station near Riga, Latvia. Winter rye planted very late went into the winter in the two-leaf phase. Early in the spring all the plants without exception were lying on the ground with bare tillering nodes and 2-3 cm and more of the roots exposed, particularly on the slopes. In some plants the roots were exposed to a distance of 5-6 cm from their base. These plants were easily pulled from the soil even though the roots were not torn. The roots were not exposed by active heaving.

CONCLUSION

All the instances of heaving, deflation, and washing out of plants with which we are familiar are due essentially to the failure to observe the rules of proper cultivation of the soil. Seeds are sown on pulverized, structureless soils and the plants go into the winter poorly rooted and weakly developed. On structured, firm, properly tilled soil, planted at the right time, the tillering nodes and collars do not ordinarily become exposed. Heaving, etc. is always local in character and caused purely by the nature of the particular field. Strong winds or streams of water are only a contributing factor in exposure of the subsurface parts of the plants. All these factors are at work on properly cultivated fields too, but they have no injurious aftereffects.

The best way of preventing heaving on unsettled soil is to use a heavy roller right after the seeder. It settles the soil and the seeds rest in well packed rather than loose soil. The harm done by the roller in disturbing the structure is more than compensated for by its usefulness in preventing heaving. The roller should also be used in the spring to press down the subsurface parts of plants that may have become exposed.

An effective way to combat heaving, etc., as suggested by T.D. Lysenko, is to sow winter crops on stubble, i.e., on compact soil, using a disc seeder on weedless fields. The stubble holds the snow, keeps it uniform, and moderates the flow of thaw water in the spring.

CHAPTER 8

THE ROLE OF PESTS AND DISEASES
IN THE DEATH OF WINTERING PLANTS

Pests and diseases frequently determine whether plants will survive the winter. Plants injured by pests or diseases do not harden well and are prone to frost damage. Frost damage, in turn, predisposes plants to ultimate destruction by pests and diseases.

1. INJURIES CAUSED BY CATTLE AND RODENTS

Wintering plants are frequently hurt by cattle and rodents. Cattle were once permitted to graze on winter grains in order to thin out excessively bushy plants. Mice, rabbits, etc. chew the green parts of herbaceous plants and gnaw the bark of trees and shrubs. The harm they do is sometimes irreparable. It is conducive to winterkilling and makes the plants more vulnerable to insects and diseases of one kind or another.

A good example of crop damage by fall grazing of cattle took place in 1947 on "Komintern" collective farm in Mogilev oblast, Byelorussia. A large field of winter rye was sown in mid-August, an unusually early time for this region. There was vigorous growth and to prevent damping off prior to the onset of frosts — about two weeks hence — cows, horses, and sheep were allowed to graze in the field. Bare spots showed up all over the pasture in the spring, the low plants having been eaten up. If some of the leaves on an occasional plant remained intact, the plant survived although in weakened condition. Those plants untouched by the animals survived and looked healthy. The field which promised a high yield, judging by the individual plants and small flocks of birds, had to be written off as a loss in the fall.

Similar cases of partial or even total plant mortality due to fall pasturing of cattle were fairly frequent until recently. Yet as far back as 1857 S. Lavrent'yev, author of an article entitled "Raising of Winter Rye in the Yelisavetgrad Area" published in the Trudy Vol'nogo ekonomicheskogo obshchestva [Transaction of the Vol'niy Economics Society], wrote: "Mowing or allowing cattle to graze on thriving winter crops is more harmful than beneficial....Pasturing cattle in this locality is always a measure of desperation" (pp. 182 and 184).

Plants are injured even more by rodents. During the winter of 1945 mice

52

te up the leaves of clover growing on the experimental field of the Institute of Grain culture in the Nonchernozem Belt at Moscow. All the clover died, except for a few isolated plants. I also found the same thing had happened here and there in Mordovian ASSR. The few plants that escaped the mice came through the winter in good condition.

These observations of low frost resistance in plants eaten during the fall and winter by cattle and mice naturally led to a search for an explanation of the reasons for the damage caused plants by leaf loss. The Institute of Grain Culture in the Nonchernozem Belt ran the following experiments from 1945 to 1947.

Experiment 1. Winter wheat No. D-31 was sown August 31 in Mitscherlich pots in a tenfold replication. The pots were kept outdoors and on October 16 all the plants but two (to serve as a control) were cut to 1.5 cm above the surface. By the time of the first frost the tubules of the young leaves had grown about 1 cm above the cut stems. The plants wintered under a natural snow cover. Only the uncut plants survived, all the cut plants dying. Half rotted stems were the only thing left when the photograph was taken (Fig. 21).

Fig. 21. Winter wheat, variety Sibirskaya.
Only the uncut control plants survived
the winter

Experiment 2. A study was made of different times of cropping plants. Winter wheat 599 (wheat-wheat grass hybrid) was sown July 16 on a well prepared bed. Every 15 days from August 30 to October 15 part of the plants were cut down to 1 cm from the ground. The results are shown in Table 1.

It is quite evident that the cropping at the end of September and middle of October was much more harmful than the two earlier croppings. The reason is that early cropping enables the young leaves to store some plastic substances by winter.

53

Table 1

Effect of time of cutting aerial parts of winter wheat
on overwintering

Day of cutting	Number of plants in the fall	Number of plants that overwintered	Plants surviving %
30.VIII	161	97	60
15.IX	149	63	42
30.IX	169	0	0
15.X	256	9	3

No less destructive is the injury to trees. Cattle eat around and break the branches, while rodents and goats gnaw the bark. The site of the injury dries out more quickly and becomes winter killed. Intact bark, as we have seen, protects the trees from desiccation and drought. However, incomparably greater damage is done by pathogenic organisms penetrating the internal tissues.

2. INJURY CAUSED BY INSECTS

Midges, wire worms, and other pests are frequently a decisive factor in the successful wintering of plants. Sometimes early planting results in such severe injury by frit and Hessian flies that the plants die even when the wintering conditions are extremely favorable. Winter wheat suffers the most because the sowing period is briefer than, for example, that of winter rye.

The Institute of Grain Culture in the Nonchernozem Belt compared different times of sowing winter wheat, variety Moskovskaya 2411, on its experimental field. After the snow was gone in the spring, it was noted that a considerable number of plants, especially those sown early (in mid-August), were dead. An investigation revealed signs of injury inflicted by destructive insects in the fall. The greater bushiness of the dead plants was often accompanied by weak development of the individual shoots. The flies evidently stimulated growth, thus weakening the plants. They were weakened further by the wound and sucking of the plastic substances by the larvae so that they were eventually killed more easily by frost.

Wire worms inflict equally severe injury, sometimes devastating entire fields. They often mix up the results of strain testing on experimental beds. Early in the spring of 1932 almost all the fields belonging to state grain farm No. 2 "Verblyud" in the Northern Caucasus were destroyed. This was ascribed to unfavorable winter conditions when in fact it was the work of wire worms. They also caused heavy damage on the fields of the seed-growing state farm at Saratov and elsewhere.

Destructive insects injure plants both before and after winter. Many of them attack only winter weakened and injured plants, e.g., the deadly enemy of fruit trees, the borer, which is found all over the Far East. A variety of bark beetles likewise prefer to attack plants weakened by various unfavorable conditions, including wintering conditions. Desiccation of the Sayan spruce, a frequent problem for foresters in the Far East, is usually caused by beetles which attack already weakened trees. This further enfeebles the trees and they eventually die of conditions which they previously tolerated. Beetles are also active in the pine forests of the Ukraine (Golovyanko, 1949).

Insects greatly weaken the frost resistance of woody plants by eating the leaves at the end of summer and in the fall. New leaves grow from the buds, naturally consuming plastic substances. If the plants do not succeed with the help of new leaves in replenishing the reserves used up or in accumulating what they need for the winter, they do poorly and even die.

Late in the summer of 1949 my former co-worker in the Far Eastern branch of the Academy of Sciences USSR at Vladivostok, G.D. Novopashennaya, performed the following experiment. She removed the leaves of several three year old apple trees and all subsequently developing buds to reproduce the phenomenon observed after a mass attack by caterpillars. These trees were all winterkilled. However, trees standing together and allowed to keep their leaves came through the winter safely.

3. DISEASES OF WINTERING PLANTS

Fungus or bacterial diseases may not necessarily be due to wintering. However, wintering and associated injuries greatly increase the possibility of infectious diseases among plants. Winter "sunburn" is a major precondition of injury to woody plants. Until recently it was the major cause of death of large-fruited apple and other trees in the Maritime Territory (Fig. 22). I examined many gardens there from 1948 to 1950 and invariably found this to be the case (I.M. Vasil'yev, 1950, 1951). This is also true of other parts of the Soviet Union (I.M. Vasil'yev, 1953).

The "burn" develops this way. Dark brown bark forms during the winter on the sunny side of branches not yet fully suberized. Microscopy shows dead cortical cells clearly demarcated from living cells that were not exposed to direct sunlight (Fig. 23). During the summer the resultant wound becomes partly cicatrized, but another wound forms in the same place the next winter. This continues year after year. The wound weakens the branch and decreases its hardiness. Infection kills the branch and eventually the entire tree. (Fig. 24.)

The same thing happens after various kinds of mechanical injury, e.g., breaking of branches by cattle or gnawing of bark by goats and rodents, because an injury promotes the penetration of pathogenic organisms through the dead portions. Under favorable conditions the infection spreads and gradually destroys the tree.

A former colleague, V.A. Tyrina, planted a small plot with fruit trees in 1949 in the Botanical Gardens of the Far Eastern branch of the Academy of Sciences USSR at Vladivostok. The bark on one side of the stem of apple seedlings was slightly damaged in transit. The wounds were not covered and within a year they became infected causing total or partial necrosis.

The commonest disease of fruit trees is popularly called "gangrene", long familiar to gardeners. Here is a description of it by an anonymous author in Sad i ogorod [Garden and Orchard], 1898, no. 24: "Gangrene is particularly common in apple trees....It can be detected by the sap flowing on the bark of the branches. The affected spots soon become black from the multitude of tiny, powdery fungi and the bark, like the underlying tissue, dies....This disease is usually the result of poor, premature pruning, severe injury, etc." In no. 11 of the same journal we read in an article entitled

"Gangrene of Fruit Trees": "The cause is generally a wound....a frost cleft. Small gangrenous spots are not especially dangerous. Gangrene is dangerous only when the infection encircles the branch. In this event the part of the branch above the gangrenous area dies." This description, written over 50 years ago, is equally applicable today.

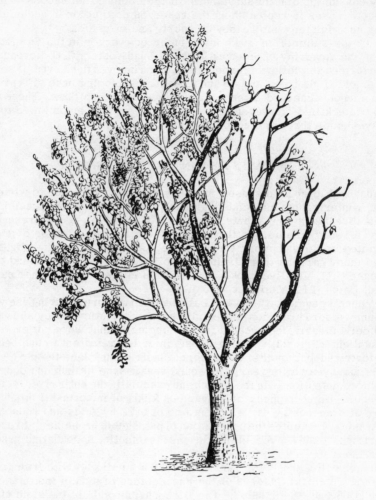

Fig. 22. Typical picture of dying off of an apple tree with
"sunburns": branches dried out on the southern side

The usual causative agent of "gangrene" is <u>Nectria galligena</u> Brls. There are also others (Bondartsev, 1931; Vanin, 1931, 1932, 1933).

Cancer is another serious disease of fruit trees (Fig. 25). In <u>Sad i ogorod</u>, 1898, no. 24 we read: "Cancer is a disease that strikes young trees in particular and shows up as a coffee-brown fungoid formation between the upper

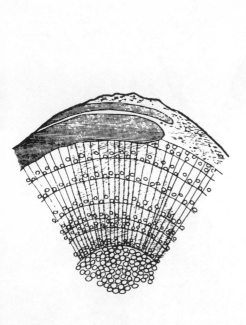

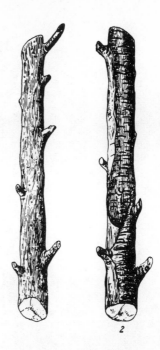

Fig. 24. Typical picture of "sunburn" of an apple branch 1 — northern side of branch completely normal; 2 — southern "burned" side

Fig. 23. Cross section of an Amur cork branch with "sunburn" (place of "burn" crosshatched)

pellicle and the suberized layer. The former falls off while the latter swells like a sponge and then dies. The cambium layer is brown and the site of the lesion is surrounded by a swollen border. The disease continues to spread and the swollen borders grow larger'' (p. 373). According to recent data, certain bacteria and fungi are the causative agents of cancer in fruit trees. The fungus <u>Sphaeropsis</u> malorum does a great deal of damage to the trunk and branches of apple trees (Kazenas, 1948).

Malsecco, a common disease of lemon trees in Italy and Turkey, has recently been brought into the Black Sea coastal area. It is caused by the fungus <u>Deuterophoma tracheiphila</u> Patri which enters through cracks on the top of branches damaged by frost and then spreads through the entire tree. Malsecco is best prevented by increasing winter hardiness and avoiding bark injury.

Rupture of cover tissues during the wintering period causes a variety of diseases in herbaceous plants. An example of this is the mass destruction of alfalfa in the United States by bacterial wilt (Aplanobacter <u>insidiosum</u> L. McC.) described by Jones (1928). The causative organisms penetrate the plant (after the snow melts) through breaks in the tissues occurring in the winter.

CONCLUSION

Cattle and rodents eat the leaves of herbaceous plants, sometimes the subsurface parts, and thereby weaken the plants. If the injury is inflicted in the

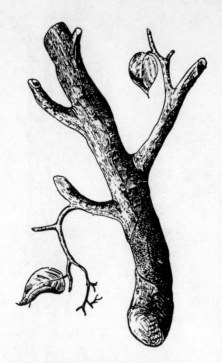

Fig. 25. "Cancer" ring on an apple
branch; the wound became infected
as a result of a "burn"

fall, it inhibits growth and prevents the plants from hardening properly. If the injury is inflicted in the winter or early spring, it weakens their regenerative capacity. In either case the plants may not come through the winter in good condition even though the soil and climatic factors may be quite favorable. Wounds in trees caused by cattle and rodents may serve as the point of entry for insects and pathogenic bacteria. Moreover, the wounds are harmful in themselves for the sites are particularly susceptible to frost and drought.

Destructive insects attack plants in the fall, suck their juices, and inflict wounds that weaken their winter hardiness. In the spring the insects attack plants weakened during the wintering period and eventually kill them.

Open wounds caused by rupture of cover tissues due to frost, pests, etc. promote the development of diseases in plants. Plants weakened or damaged by frost or other unfavorable factors are likewise susceptible to infection. An example of this is the so-called "damping off" of winter cereals.

CHAPTER 9

DAMPING OFF OF PLANTS

Damping off is a disease affecting plants under snow or soon after it melts and is caused by an invasion of parasitic fungi at the end of winter. There are two stages of the process: plant injury and exhaustion as a result of unfavorable winter conditions, then attack by fungi under the snow. Let us consider each stage in turn.

1. PHYSIOLOGICAL PRECONDITIONS FOR DAMPING OFF

It was generally believed not too long ago that the physiological precondition of damping off is plant "suffocation" under snow due to oxygen deficiency. This explanation is found in many textbooks on horticulture and plant diseases, e.g., the well known Bolezni kul'turnykh rasteniy [Diseases of Cultivated Plants] by A.S. Bondartsev (1931). The explanation is clearly based on a misunderstanding because snow is porous and does not prevent gas exchange, as proved, for example, by the experiments of I.I. Tumanov, I.N. Borodina, and T.V. Oleynikova (1935). Investigating the composition of air over winter crops under a meter of snow, the authors showed that even at the beginning of April air in the leaf zone of crops under snow contained 19.7-20% oxygen, i.e., only .5% less than over snow. The untenability of ascribing the death of plants under snow to suffocation is further indicated by the well known fact that wild plants winter successfully on the edges of forests or along snow fences near railroad tracks where the snow remains several weeks longer than in fields. Moreover, in mountains where heavy snow lasts until the beginning of summer, biennials and perennials promptly start to grow as soon as it melts. I frequently observed this phenomenon at passes in the Caucasus, Western Tyan'-Shan', and Southern Sakhalin where the snow lay in drifts several meters high. Revealing too is the successful wintering of winter grains on Kamchatka, where the snow may be two meters high and remain on the fields throughout the spring (Titlyakov and Lebedeva, 1940; Titlyakov, 1941).

Let us now examine the physiological preconditions of damping off on the basis of available data.

Experiment 1. The objective of the experiment was to determine the effect of prolonged near-zero temperatures on the viability of winter crops. The conditions of the experiment duplicated those in the field when snow falls on unfrozen ground and lies all winter in a thick layer. A dozen different varieties of rye and wheat were used. They were sown on Mitscherlich pots at four times: July 11 and 19, August 28, and September 16. The plants remained outdoors until the end of October when they were placed in an empty coldframe about a meter deep without manure and covered with glass and straw. The temperature in this unusual thermostat ranged between 0 and -2° throughout the winter.

The coldframe was opened on a warm sunny day early in March and the condition of the plants immediately appraised. They were snow covered but unfrozen, alive, and green. Both the winter and spring varieties, including those placed in the coldframe in the heading stage, survived. Only the old leaves of the two or three lower nodes had died. They were black and thickly covered with the saprophytic fungus Cladosporium herbarum Link. There were no signs of "snow mold" fungi or sclerotinia.

The experiment clearly showed that prolonged zero temperatures do not destroy plants. They remained as though preserved for the four and one half months they were exposed to these temperatures and externally, at least, seemed healthy. They were not injured by parasitic fungi under the snow although conditions that winter were exceptionally favorable for the fungi: high humidity, near-zero temperatures, and dense foliage, particularly of the varieties sown early and noted for low winter hardiness. It was a natural assumption that the plants escaped the snow fungi because they had not been infected in the fall. However, I later observed repeatedly that even when infectious agents are present snow fungi do not always attack plants.

In 1947–1948 the wintering conditions for crops in Leningrad oblast were extremely unfavorable. Snow fell in November on unfrozen ground, the temperature was comparatively high, and in the spring some plants were dug out of the melting snow. On March 28 at the Leningrad Experimental Station it was possible to find plots with soil frozen under a thin snow cover and plots in which the snow was tens of centimeters thick. Plants were inspected on a plot under 70 cm of snow near a forest. There were three distinct layers of ice indicating thaws followed by frosts and snowfalls. The soil underneath was soft and a spade could easily be pressed in up to the shaft, yet all the plants nearby were alive and healthy, with only the old, lower leaves dead. At the same time snow mold was found alongside and on the plants in the form of a thin gray cobwebby film.

Experiment 2. This experiment was designed to determine the hardiness of plants after prolonged exposure in unfrozen condition to temperatures around 0°. Rye and wheat sown September 16 were the plants used. The conditions of growth and wintering were the same as in experiment 1, the only difference being that the plants were in another, parallel coldframe and were set out in the air toward the end of March, 20 days later than the plants in experiment 1. In other words, they remained unfrozen between 0 and -2° for five months, from the end of October to the end of March. Nevertheless, they remained alive and green, as in experiment 1, with no signs of fungus growth. Only the dead leaves were more numerous, especially on the spring varieties.

As soon as the coldframe was opened the plants were set in the ground alongside plants that had wintered in the place and emerged from under the snow the day before. Both were later subjected to late frosts lasting about three weeks when the temperature on some days dropped to -10° and below. The number of live plants were tallied in mid-May. It turned out that 80% of Vyatka winter rye survived in the coldframe, 99% in the ground; 80% of winter wheat, variety 329, survived in the coldframe, 89% in the ground; 36% of winter wheat, variety 2411, survived in the coldframe, 60% in the ground.

The plants that had wintered in the coldframe in unfrozen condition at temperatures from 0 to -2° proved to be less hardy than those which had wintered normally under snow. However, even five months in the unfrozen condition did not completely overcome the hardiness of certain plants and the sturdiest specimens like Vyatka rye and wheat 329 endured temperatures of -10° and below with comparatively minor damage (20% dead plants).

Experiment 3. Artificial "damping off" was induced by delaying the melting of snow in the spring. Snow was heaped at the end of February on several varieties of winter crops, sown in beds at the regular time. More than a meter of snow was kept on the plants for about two weeks. Similar beds a little distance away remained under the natural snow cover which was 50 cm high when it began to melt, ending April 6. The artificial snow cover lasted until April 22. There was no observable heaving of the plants underneath. On the contrary, they all looked much better than the plants under the natural snow cover because they were protected from the severe frosts of early April. Upon emerging from under the natural snow on April 6 all the frost-resistant varieties of rye and wheat were fresh and green, only the lowest leaves having died. The comparatively unhardy varieties, like perennial wheat 34085, had many more dead leaves, although they retained their green color. When the frosts ended sometime after the middle of April, the plants of all varieties lost every one of their developed leaves. Even in Vyatka rye only the two upper nodes survived a bitter frost when the temperature fell to about -18°. In the unhardy varieties all the fall leaves died, except the youngest which had not yet unfolded and were protected from the frost by the sheaths of the older leaves. The plants appearing on April 22 after the snow melted suffered no frost injury and were completely healthy.

There was one unusual feature marking this experiment. During the additional period the plants were under snow the weather was generally cloudy and cool so that the ground warmed up very slowly. The plants obtained no warmth through the soil from the neighboring, snowfree plots and they did not grow under the snow, as confirmed by close inspection. The question arose as to what would happen to plants that started to grow under snow. The answer was obtained on fields belonging to the Leningrad Experimental Station during the investigation mentioned above.

I came across a field of winter wheat sown earlier than usual for this region. I dug up plants from under deep snow; they were not frozen and clear signs of growth were evident. Young leaves, which had not finished growing in the fall and had the etiolated tissues characteristic of growth under snow, were wrinkled at the base. Next to the wheat plants were the webs of the snow mold. Nevertheless, there was no damping off, for they were fresh and green.

Thus, the aforementioned experiments and observations led to the conclusion that neither a long stay under snow in the unfrozen condition nor the start of growth before the snow melts predisposes plants to invasion by snow fungi, which evidently requires some other condition. This was discovered in Latvia where winter crops more or less suffer every year from damping off largely due, it is believed, to injury and death during the wintering period. Riding over the roads of Latvia from March 22 to 26, 1928, I saw snow mold in fields everywhere. They had the pale look invariably noted after the snow melts, but a closer inspection showed the rosy color associated with the mycelium of fungi. But this was the way the plants looked when they emerged from under the snow before the March frosts. On the other hand, the plants left under snow at the edges of forests, in lowlands, and on the ice side of northern slopes and emerging from under the snow only at the end of March were in excellent condition even though snow mold webs were next to and on the plants themselves. This clearly suggests that fungi invade only plants injured by frost.

2. BIOLOGY AND ROLE OF PARASITIC FUNGI IN DAMPING OFF OF PLANTS

In 1825 the Swedish scientist Fries described a fungus whose mycelium in early spring covered the ground and plants under snow in the form of a cobwebby deposit resembling a thin layer of wool. He therefore called it "snow wool" (Lanosa nivalis Fries). It was soon discovered, however, that "snow wool" is not a pure species but a mixture of several species of the genus Fusarium, which includes parasites and saprophytes. The most harmful fungus, found early in the spring in the conidial stage on wintering plants, is called Fusarium nivale Sacc., "snow mold". F. nivale is ordinarily accompanied by F. culmorum Sacc., F. avenaceum Sacc., and others. The entire group is also called "snow mold" (Yachevskiy, 1922).

The biology of the snow mold has been thoroughly studied by Sorauer (1901), Schaffnit (1912), S.M. Tupenevich (1936, 1940), and others.

It has been established that F. nivale is a parasite, but an unusual type in that it grows on dead as well as on living plants. Moreover, it is not purely cold-loving organism. It develops optimally when the temperature is around +20° (somewhat lower according to Tupenevich), but is capable of readily adapting to low temperatures, starting growth even at 0°, which explains its activity when snow is melting. The fungus requires above all air moisture close to saturation so that it is usually found in warm weather in low-lying places under dead leaves and in thick grass stands, but under snow during the winter.

In 1919 the Russian mycologist P.F. Yelenev identified a second parasitic snow fungus, sclerotinia (Sclerotinia graminearum Elen.). This fungus was later studied by Tupenevich (1939), A.G. Yakovlev (1941), and others on the staff of the State Falenkov Plant Breeding Station in Kirov oblast.

Sclerotinia resembles the snow mold in biological features. It grows chiefly in years with a humid summer and humid, cloudy fall. It multiplies in the fall with the help of ascopores carried by wind and water. Spores start to grow as soon as they alight on leaves if the requisite humidity prevails and penetrate the tissues through the stomata. If the leaves are healthy and active, the spores do not develop any further or enter the cells. Plants weakened and exhausted by a variety of unfavorable factors are attacked by the fungus toward spring and used as a nutritional substrate. Particularly vulnerable are plants on unfertile, largely water-impermeable, acid, and unfertilized soils. Very early or late sowings also promote the development of the fungus. Even if the fungus is present, plants overwinter well on fertile soil sown at the right time.

This is the main published information on the biology of parasitic snow fungi. The list of these organisms will very likely continue to grow. Typhula Itoana Imai, which resembles Sclerotinia graminearum, was discovered comparatively recently. They differ in the nature of the injury they inflict on plants and the size, form, and locus of formation of sclerotia in tissues (Kozhevnikova, 1947).

However, we are not so much concerned with describing all the snow fungi as we are with setting forth the conditions under which they invade and injure plants. I performed several experiments to determine: (1) the interrelation of fungus parasite and plant host, (2) the frost resistance of the fungi, and (3) the circumstances under which snow fungi attack plants.

Experiment 1. Winter rye, several varieties of winter wheat, two varieties of winter rape, sugar, table, and fodder beet, green and red kohlrabi, carrots, cabbage, and several different grasses were sown in the spring or summer while winter cereals were sown at the end of the year. They grew in pots outdoors during the warm weather, but late in the fall, with the onset of frosts, they were brought into a cool greenhouse and left there for the winter. The temperature was always higher than in the air, although it dropped below zero on very cold days. The plants were not attacked by mold fungi although the conditions were favorable in the greenhouse — low temperature and air almost saturated with water vapor. The experiments with the beets graphically illustrated the relations between plant host and parasitic fungus.

The beets were brought into the greenhouse November 5. From the end of November and all through December the temperature was generally several degrees below zero, but the plants did not suffer from the slight frost and only the old, lower leaves tended to die off. The tops of the roots emerging from the soil were completely uninjured and during thaws looked fresh and turgescent. There were no signs of mold on the plants.

In mid-January the temperature in the greenhouse fell to -7 to -8°, which was harmful to the plants. The roots in particular suffered because they are the least frost-resistant parts. From that time on I observed snow mold on the plants. The tops of the roots were generally girdled with the mycelium of fungi, including Fusarium betae Sacc., Fusarium sp., Verticillium lateritium Berk., Alternaria tenues Nus., Sclerotinia graminearum Elen., and others.*
The ring of mycelium then spread over other parts of the roots, most of the plants dying before the winter ended (Figs. 26, 27). The older frost-injured part of the root was thickly covered with mycelium. Then came a transitional zone and a little further on a completely healthy, fungus-free part. There was no mycelium on the root in the transitional zone, but microscopic analysis showed that the cells had been invaded. In the course of time the transitional zone was thoroughly covered with mycelium. The adjacent and previously healthy cells became infected and formed a new transitional zone.

On days when the air and soil temperature fell to -7 or -8° and when the soil and leaves were frozen, the roots injured by the fungi as well as the healthy and uninjured parts of roots above the annulus of the mold remained unfrozen. It was easy to cut them and the surface of the cuts appeared to be moist just as when the temperature was above 0°. While in the active stage the fungi produced so much heat that the water in the portions of the plants they invaded as well as in the directly adjacent areas remained liquid. Thus,

---

*Identification by Ye. Z. Oknina.

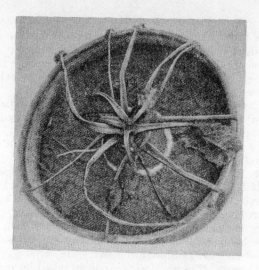

Fig. 26. First stage of mold growth on the
root and leaves of a beet: root top and young
leaves in the rosette are still alive

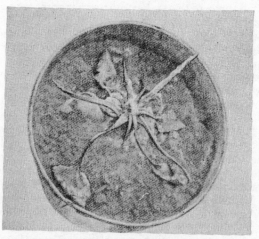

Fig. 27. Final stage of mold growth on a beet:
all parts of the plant are covered with the
mycelium of the fungi

the fungi continued active even in frost. Once on the roots, the mycelium
after one or two weeks of steady frost spread all over.

The above–described picture of mold injury was observed in the other
experimental plants too after they were injured by frost. However, the hardy
wheat varieties and rye remained completely resistant to mold fungi.

Experiment 2. To study the frost resistance of mold fungi, bits of beet
root with well developed mycelium clinging to them were frozen in Petri
dishes at -19° on moist filter paper and placed in a refrigerator for two days.

After thawing the mycelium was colorless and the cells lacked turgor. However, the fungi completely revived after they were kept for a few days at +4 to +6° in a place saturated with water vapor.

Experiment 3. A study was made of the effect of snow mold on plants in late autumn. Shortly before the soil froze, several varieties of winter wheat and rye were sown on beds infected with F. culmorum and F. avenaceum. The fungi under snow were exposed during the winter to -9.6°, the lowest reading on the Savinov thermometer, the bulb of which was buried in the soil as far down as the fungus cultures. Mycologist Ye. D. Yakimovich did the actual inoculating of the plants with the fungi.

Despite the deep snow, there were no signs of plant injury by the snow mold in the spring. Yet among the varieties that came through the winter there were some comparatively unhardy plants which emerged from under the snow with extensive frost injury. Inoculating plants with snow mold late in the fall, therefore, proved to be ineffectual. The fungi did not spread from the soil to the leaves of the plants.

3. THE MODERN VIEW OF DAMPING OFF

We must first clarify the term "damping off". It is frequently applied to plants just emerging from under snow with a "cooked look", i.e., colorless and lacking in turgor. But this is incorrect, for the "cooked look" is characteristic of plants that have died under snow or been weakened by something and remained for a long time in water or in an atmosphere saturated with water vapor while snow is melting. Damping off, strictly speaking, is always caused by parasitic snow fungi. Widespread invasion occurs when there is a long, overcast, and wet fall and the plants develop a thick green mass. This weather is typical of the Baltic region, Leningrad oblast, and some northeastern oblasts, where damping off is prevalent. The Volga region, Northern Caucasus, and the Ukraine generally have a sunny dry fall so that damping off never occurs, at least on a wide scale. The conditions mentioned above are largely responsible for the damping off of winter crops in individual years in the central oblasts of European U.S.S.R.

The circumstances under which snow fungi invade plants are quite well known. Spores germinating on the leaves penetrate the tissues only when the stomata are open. This occurs during warm weather in the daytime. Cold weather keeps the stomata closed and that is why plants are not infected under snow or in cold weather generally, even if fungi are present. Low temperatures inhibit their growth and the lack of thaw water and snow prevent the infection from spreading. Even the most active fungi use for nutrition only weakened and damaged cells, particularly if frost is responsible. The protoplasm loses some of its selective permeability. The water and part of the organic and inorganic matter is discharged from the cells into the intercellular spaces where they serve as food for the fungi. This is the basis of their growth.

The entire group of snow molds start out as saprophytes, but gradually turn into parasites secreting metabolic products toxic to the cells of the plant host. First settling on injured cells, particularly by frost, the fungi soon invade neighboring healthy cells until the entire plant is involved. Damping off in this respect resembles the rot of fruits and vegetables stored in cellars for the winter. Rot originates in places where cover tissues are torn and cells crushed and then spreads to healthy parts.

An important factor in the infection of plants by snow fungi is that the latter release a great deal of heat which enables them to warm themselves as well as the cells they occupy and the adjacent cells in the plant host and to thrive even at subzero temperatures. Hence, temperatures above zero are not a precondition of damping off. It may also occur when plants not injured by fungi are frozen.

A cloudy spring with occasional rain makes it possible for snow fungi to grow even in the absence of snow. Recurrent frosts and ensuring injury to plants not protected by snow are especially favorable for the fungi. They attack plants even more severely and kill them while tolerating very low temperatures.

It is clear from the above that snow falling on thawed ground does not prevent damping off, prevailing opinion to the contrary. Plants may remain unfrozen under snow throughout a long winter and yet not be exhausted to the point where they are prey to parasitic snow fungi. The danger arises when the plants start to put on growth, and then only after frost injury. This happens, however, only when the seeds are sown too early, which results in relatively rapid growth at low temperatures. A temperature of 0° on the surface of the soil, when snow falls on unfrozen ground (the temperature at which snow melts), does not cause visible growth in crops planted at the normal time.

CONCLUSION

Parasitic snow fungi are the causative agents of damping off. They grow rapidly during a long, cloudy, and rainy fall and invade the plants. They are favored by early snow on unfrozen ground and delayed thaws in the spring. The basis of damping off, however, is poor hardening, growth under snow and resultant exhaustion. Strong, healthy plants are immune to damping off in these conditions despite the presence of fungi and factors favoring their growth. These plants are never affected by damping off even if infected by fungi.

Damping off, A.S. Bondartsev maintains, is often due to excessively wet soil. On such soil plants do not harden properly and go into the winter lacking the necessary reserve of plastic substances. They become exhausted and prone to frost injury. This predisposes them to invasion by parasitic snow fungi.

It has been known for a long time that premature planting is dangerous, especially for grains. This view is wholly justified. Sown too early, the plants become tall and thick by fall. Their frost resistance is low and if covered with snow when unfrozen, they continue to grow under the snow and eventually become totally exhausted.

Crops planted very late and going into the winter in the two-leaf stage are also subject to damping off. Low frost resistance, limited reserve of plastic substances, and delicate, weakly developed epidermal tissues are conducive to this disease. Grain sprouts and shoots even in warm weather, if there is a good deal of rain and the soil is poorly aerated, are easily infected by fungi, especially fusarium wilt, and die. Many more plants are invaded by parasitic fungi after a long winter and frost injury.

CHAPTER 10

PROTECTION OF PLANTS FROM UNFAVORABLE WINTERING CONDITIONS

Modern agronomy has at its disposal numerous methods of protecting cultivated plants from the injurious effect of frost and other unfavorable conditions obtaining during the winter. Many of them have been developed empirically. For example, the peasants of former Yaroslav province during the first half of the nineteenth century made extensive use of snow fences to prevent the winterkilling of unhardy varieties of clover imported from Western Europe into Russia (Sovetov, 1859). The Penzenskiy school of horticulture, one of the first of its kind in Russia, was at the same time successfully using ground culture of unhardy European varieties of apple and pear trees. The school had a large "earthen barn" in which such heat-loving plants as peaches and apricots were raised (Rego, 1853). Many more such historical examples could be cited. Perhaps most of the methods of protecting plants from frost now known to us were worked out before our ideas on winterkilling were developed. Quite often science has merely explained the methods evolved by trial and error and thus increased their efficacy.

Let us now consider the principles underlying the methods of protecting the following three groups of plants from frost and other unfavorable wintering conditions: (1) winter grains, grasses, and other herbaceous plants, (2) fruit trees and bushes, and (3) subtropical crops, chiefly citrus.

1. PROTECTION OF HERBACEOUS PLANTS

The principal means of protecting herbaceous plants from frost is snow. If it comes early enough, the plants remain through the winter as though under a "fur coat". In Moscow oblast 20-30 cm of snow is sufficient to prevent the winterkilling of not particularly hardy varieties of winter wheat adapted to the region. Some winters when the snow fell early and was 40-50 cm thick, even spring wheat on the experimental fields of the Institute of Grain Culture in the Nonchernozem Belt at Moscow came through the winter in good condition. On the fields of the Institute of Grain Culture in the Southeast located in Saratov oblast where the frosts are more severe than around Moscow, Kooperatorka — one of the least resistant varieties of winter wheat — winters safely when snow fences are used. In the taiga regions of Siberia with their frosts of

-50° and more and normally heavy snow cover, winter rye never suffers as long as it remains under snow. Any injury or death occurs only after the snow melts.

The warming action of snow is due to its extremely low heat conductivity, which is 6-10 times less than that of soil. For a number of years I made observations of soil temperature near the tillering nodes of winter crops on the fields of the Institute of Grain Culture in the Nonchernozem Belt. Even when the snow was only 10-15 cm thick, the soil temperature never fell below -14.5° during the coldest frosts of February, whereas it fell to -30° and lower above the snow. In the vicinity of Moscow the soil temperature under natural snow generally does not fall below -4°.

The heat conductivity of snow rises as it becomes more compact. By spring its protective properties diminish but, as though by way of compensation, another property — penetrability by radiant energy — becomes intensified. Thus, in late winter and early spring, when sunny weather sets in, the snow promotes warming of the plants on the ground by solar radiation (Voyeykov, 1872, 1889; Kalitin, 1938).

In almost every place in the U.S.S.R. where winter crops are grown, 20-30 cm of snow guarantees that the plants will winter safely. The snow, however, is not distributed evenly. In open treeless expanses the winds blow it off the fields so that it accumulates in gullies, etc. From ancient times farmers have sought ways of keeping snow on fields. Effective methods are now available and widely used on our collective and state farms.

Windbreaks, as conceived by such outstanding Russian agronomists and silviculturists as P.A. Kostychev, V.V. Dokuchayev, and G.N. Vysotskiy, are best of all. The trees planted in Veliko-Anadola and Kamennaya Steppe are today veritable oases where crops from year to year come through the winter safely regardless of conditions. Arranged in strips, the trees blunt the force of the winds and thus tend to keep the snow where it falls. The snow is almost twice as high on the fields between the trees at the end of the winter as it is on the open steppe. In 1946-1947, for example, the average height of the snow on the open Astrakhan Steppe was 12 cm, whereas it was 21.2 cm on the wooded tracts of the experimental station. The height of the snow on the open steppe in the northern Volga region is usually about 20 cm, but double that amount between windbreaks. The Stalin collective farm in Sal'sk rayon, Rostov oblast, had 194 hectares of protective plantings on its fields in 1948. The yield of winter grains has invariably amounted to hundreds of poods and more.

I saw an excellent example of the usefulness of windbreaks in 1947 in Korsun'-Shevchenkov rayon, Kiev oblast. In that year winter wheat in Kiev oblast and elsewhere in the Ukraine suffered greatly in open treeless areas. The crops near the small forest stands were particularly outstanding. On one field about 200 m wide the winter wheat between two such stands was waist-high, thick with no bald patches by the heading period. The superb condition of wheat was wholly due to the snow that was contained by the trees. The snow not only protected the plants from frost, but also provided them with additional moisture during the growth stage.

A major method of assuring natural retention of snow is the so-called coulisse fallow. Corn or sunflower stalks left on the field after harvest serve as coulisses. Corn or sunflower is planted in rows with enough space left in between to permit seasonal plants by machine of the winter crops. This long-forgotten method has recently regained its popularity. The usual objection raised in the past was that the coulisse plants partially dried out the fallow. However, this does not diminish the value of the method as a means of retaining snow and thus virtually guaranteeing the successful wintering of plants. In 1947 winter wheat on most of the fields of the Mironov Plant Breeding Station died or was very sparse, whereas wheat on a coulisse fallow came through the winter in good condition. In Rostov oblast the coulisse fallow is regarded as the "surest and safest way of keeping snow on winter crops" (Khoroshilov, 1947, p. 73). This is also the belief of agronomists in many other oblasts as well where winter crops in a crop rotation go on fallow (Kuperman, 1946).

A special method of snow retention is mixed sowing of winter crops with rapidly growing high-stalk plants, generally mustard or sunflower, which grow around the shoots of the wheat or rye before the cold sets in. They die during the winter, their stalks serving as a snow fence.

T.D. Lysenko has proposed a practical method of controlling winterkilling of crops in the open steppe of Western Siberia. It involves planting crops not on fallow but among the stubble of spring wheat or oats sown in the spring on well tilled and fertilized fallow. The field under winter crops is thus supplied with adequate nutrients and is weed-free. The sowing is done by the cross-row method using a tractor-drawn seeder. The stubble protects the young plants from mechanical injury by sand during strong winds and serves as an excellent snow fence. Stubble sowing has the incomparable advantage (for the steppe regions of Siberia) of being done on compact, firm soil, which cannot be blown away by the wind and which is not settled by fall and early spring rains, invariably leading to dangerous exposure of the tillering nodes.

The value of sowing winter crops among the stubble of spring crops can be judged from the results of experiments conducted by the Siberian Institute of Grain Culture. Winter wheat yielded some 32 centners per hectare, winter rice 27 centners. Both winter and spring wheat wintered well under the cover of stubble.

Another method of some value is to dig furrows across the prevailing direction of the winter winds and plant the seeds at the bottom. The ridges prevent the snow lying in the furrows from blowing away and it remains there until spring protecting the plants from frost.

Snow can also be kept on fields by sticking cornflower or corn stalks into mounds of snow, spreading bundles of straw or branches, or erecting special screens like those used near railroad tracks, etc. Rolling the snow to minimize the effect of the wind, snow plowing to create uneven spots, etc. are other techniques.

Sometimes the wind serves a useful purpose in blowing snow onto otherwise bare fields in areas enjoying little snow. The accumulation of snow on winter crops and perennial grasses from neighboring fields is common in the southern regions of the U.S.S.R. where the snow is not over 10-15 cm high. Wet straw, scattered by special machines over the fields, is also used in regions with little snow. Strawy manure is even better since it is not as easily blown away.

Protective measures are needed not only in the winter but also during fall frosts. Winter grains and grasses are often injured, sometimes fatally, by frost after the snow melts, as happened, for example, in the spring of 1945 on many experimental plots of the Institute of Grain Culture in the Nonchernozem Belt. The direct cause of death was intense frost with a drop in soil temperature to $-18°$. Plants that hitherto looked excellent faded, many of them dying.

Those sown very late and which went into the winter in the one- or two-leaf stage were most vulnerable. The plants under snow all survived. A similar situation has been observed from time to time on the fields of collective farms. The use of snow fences, straw, and strawy manure is very helpful in protecting plants from fall frosts.

Snow also protects plants from drying out. There is always an abundance of moisture under snow which prevents transpiration. Prolonged lack of snow tends to dry out plants since transpiration takes place even when the temperature is below zero. Winter evaporation is a serious problem in our open steppes. To combat winter drought in irrigated regions, it is recommended that the crops be watered shortly before the soil freezes.

Reclamation measures must be resorted to in the case of excessively wet soils if waterlogging of plants is to be avoided. The value of closed drainage, for example, is well illustrated by the situation in Latvia. In 1948 crops on reclaimed tracts generally came through the winter in good condition. Elsewhere, even when sound farming practices were followed (cultivation, fertilization, sowing time, etc.), as much as half the crops were covered with snow mold. High yields of winter crops in Latvia, from 20 to 30 centners per acre, are obtained only on reclaimed lands, to be sure, when reclamation is combined with other worthwhile measures.

The simplest and oldest method of draining excessively wet land is to use ditches or, in depressions with no outlet (so-called saucers), wells. The latter are dug in the center of the saucers to the water-permeable layer and filled with brushwood. The result is a vertical fascine through which the water flowing into the center of the saucer is carried into the water-impermeable layers of the soil. Hill sowing along slopes is one of the measures employed on soils subject to waterlogging. Plants on ridges suffer less from excess of water and the soil dries out more quickly (Vorob'yev, 1932; Timofeyeva, 1935).

In cases where circumstances make it impossible to prevent the soil from becoming soaked in the fall so that the plants go into the winter with low frost resistance, special steps must be taken to protect the plants from frost, especially in the spring. Snow retention here is undoubtedly very helpful. Plants may remain unharmed in saturated soil for some time while the snow is melting. The greatest danger comes from frost. Waterlogging can be completely eliminated on reclaimed soil if grass is used in a crop rotation, thereby ensuring good structure, water permeability, and aeration, and sound agricultural principles are observed. Plants become injured and die after active or passive heaving in the winter only on structureless, impermeable, and poorly aerated soils.

To prevent subsidence after planting — the main cause of heaving — crops are usually sown at least three weeks after plowing. However, it often happens that for a variety of reasons the farmers don't wait that long. Moreover, in a very dry summer it may not be sufficient. In such cases it is a good idea to go over the soil with a heavy roller, or simply to include a roller in the sowing unit.

Wind and water erosion also exposes roots only on structureless soils. Sound agricultural practices are effective in combatting erosion, which causes great damage on poorly run state and collective farms. Snow fences may be used to protect exposed roots from frost; soil packing is helpful in the spring. The roller presses the plants into the soil, thereby promoting rooting if the soil is still moist.

Herbaceous plants can be protected from pests by destroying the weeds on which they multiply. It is also important to sow winter crops early enough to permit fall growth and hardening and at the same time to "take them away" from the period of maximum spreading of the pests. In practice sowing is done very early, e.g., in mid-August and before in the central belt of the U.S.S.R. Such crops are invariably threatened with extensive infestation by midges, which weakens their winter hardiness. They are also more likely than not to be attacked by wire worms.

General measures to control the damping off of herbaceous plants in the wintering period include drainage of waterlogged soils and improvement of fertility. Among the specific steps that can be taken is treatment of the seeds with mercury preparations. The yield of winter crops after presowing treatment increases 26% on the average. Used for many years in Latvia, it has recently been made mandatory elsewhere, its efficacy against snow mold having been fully demonstrated. However, seed treatment alone does not prevent damping off because the infection is present in the soil as well as on the seeds. This condition can be overcome by general improvement of fertility, melioration, etc.

To prevent the damping off of "overgrown" crops planted too early, they should be mowed at the beginning of fall so as to decrease the amount of foliage and improve the circulation of air both for the plants themselves and for the soil. This hinders the growth of snow mold.

2. PROTECTION OF FRUIT TREES AND BERRY PATCHES FROM UNFAVORABLE WINTERING CONDITIONS

Although snow is not as effective in protecting trees and bushes as it is in protecting wintering grains or perennial grasses, it is nevertheless a significant factor. It covers and warms the bases of tree trunks and roots, which are even less frost resistant. That is why from ancient times, especially in the northern regions, the trunks have been hilled up with snow, sometimes as far as the branches. In Sverdlovsk oblast, for example, snow is abundant, but is blown away by the wind, leaving the trunks exposed sometimes down to the ground. An important procedure, therefore, is to keep tree trunks covered with snow throughout the winter.

The same goal is achieved by mounding trees with manure, as is done in Latvian orchards in the fall. When the weather warms up in the spring, the manure is strewn about and used as fertilizer.

The warming of berry patches with snow is a common practice in all the northern regions and even in the central belt of the U.S.S.R. It is very frequently used for raspberry bushes. The thin stems are easily forced to the ground and in snowy areas become completely covered with snow. Grapevines are mounded with earth shortly before the ground freezes and after the shoots "mature", i.e., they stop growing, more or less lignify and lose their leaves. Mounding of grapevines is universal in the U.S.S.R., except in the subtropical regions with relatively warm winter.

The protection of trees and bushes from frost by means of snow is helped by their shape. A so-called "hinge" is formed by cutting the roots on one side. The tree can thus be forced to the ground and, if necessary, covered with earth. It is restored to upright position in the spring. The "hinge" is rarely used at present because root cutting tends to mutilate the tree. Carelessness in mounding or digging up the tree is also harmful.

The decumbent form, long used in Siberia, is now more common in the Soviet Union, especially in the northern regions. It was successfully employed by the famous Krasnoyar amateur horticulturist Krutovskiy. The aerial parts of the tree are pulled to a horizontal position close to the ground and covered with earth or pine boughs, then with snow.

The scientific development and perfection of the decumbent form is associated with the name of A.D. Kizyurin (1937). Kizyurin does not use any artificial covering for the decumbent trees, which are protected by snow. The trees themselves are grown like melons, i.e., with branches very close to the ground, the height of the trees ordinarily not exceeding 30 cm. The method protects them from frost and the drying action of winter winds. Moreover, the fruits ripen better and more quickly in the summer because of the warmth coming from the soil.

Northern fruit growers also make extensive use of low-trunk methods. P.S. Gel'fand, a former member of the staff of the Sverdlovsk Fruit and Berry Station, is particularly noted for his work in this field.

An old technique for preventing winter and spring burning of trees by the sun is the application of whitewash. Sometimes spruce or pine needles are used for the same purpose and as protection from rodents. In serious cases burlap may be wrapped around the trunks. This is the method employed in Moscow to protect the trees in the main squares and streets during the winter.

However, these measures are not completely effective. Sunburn always starts with young branches on the sunny side and the area enlarges as the tree grows. That is why trees should be whitewashed from the beginning and the process repeated every fall, concentrating on the new growth. In other words, the trees have to be covered with the lime from top to bottom. This can be done very easily with the help of ordinary garden sprayers equipped with the nozzles used for whitewashing the fronts of houses (Fig. 28).

I suggested thorough whitewashing of fruit trees in October 1949. The method has been incorporated in the agricultural regulations for the Maritime Territory where the problem of sunscald is unusually severe (I.M. Vasil'yev, 1950, 1951). About the same time K.G. Nikitin (1949) of the Krasnodar Fruit and Berry Station proposed that apricot trees be coated with whitewash to protect winterkilling of the fruit buds. The whitewashed trees retained more buds and produced higher yields than untreated trees (Shumkov, 1904; Goncharov, 1907; Kizyurin, 1950; Bluvshteyn, 1950).

Horticulturists have long been concerned with combatting the effects of fall frosts. Among the methods employed is the placing of tubs of water under trees and watering of gardens in irrigated regions. The underlying principle is that freezing water generates heat which helps to warm trees. Sometimes trees are sprayed with water before and during frosts. The water freezes and the warmth spreads to all parts of the trees. The resultant ice crusts, moreover, decrease the amount of heat radiated by the trees. The value of this at first sight ineffectual measure becomes clear when we recall that during the period of spring frosts the fate of buds and flowers sometimes is decided by just a few tenths of a degree. Open flowers have little frost resistance and they may die, depending on the vigor of their growth and preceding weather, when the temperature drops to -2 to -4°. Thus, warming plants by as little as one or two degrees may save them.

Warming trees by lighting bonfires between them has some value. Special

Fig. 28. Fall spraying of fruit trees with lime as a protection from "sunburn"

heaters are even more efficacious. These heaters are commonly used in the Soviet Union for citrus trees, and we shall discuss the subject in more detail below. However, regardless of the method used, good results are attained only if the weather service is adequate. Timely, accurate forecasts of imminent frosts are the first prerequisite for successfully combatting them. Forecasts are important because frosts are usually unexpected with a very rapid drop in temperature.

Delaying the opening of flower buds is even better protection from spring frosts. An ancient method of accomplishing this is to cover snow under trees with manure early in the spring, thus holding up melting and warming up of the soil and growth of the trees by as much as 5-7 days or more. The same results are obtained by whitewashing trees in regions with a sunny spring. Deflecting the rays of the sun, the whitewashed branches do not warm up too rapidly and start their growth later. According to the experiments of V.A. Tyrina, a former colleague of mine in the Far Eastern branch of the Academy of Sciences USSR, apple trees whitewashed in the fall of 1949 were 3-7 days late, depending on the variety, in blossoming the following spring.

3. PROTECTION OF HEAT-LOVING, SUBTROPICAL, AND TROPICAL PLANTS FROM UNFAVORABLE WINTERING CONDITIONS

Our damp and dry subtropics are the coldest subtropics in the world so that the problem of combatting winterkilling of subtropical plants is more acute here than in any other country. Measures must also be taken to protect heat-loving plants from cold. The first prerequisite of the safe wintering of subtropical crops grown for commercial purposes is proper selection of the site. Slope of the land, closeness to the sea, flow of masses of cold air, etc. determine the suitability of a site for cultivating subtropical plants. Subtropical crops are raised in commercial quantities in some, but not all, regions of the Black Sea littoral (Gutiyev, 1939).

Oil heaters placed between the trees are considered to be the most effective method of combatting frost. There are a number of different types. The heaters are lit during a frost and kept going until it ends. They are not very effective in windy weather. In calm weather the heaters may raise the temperature in the crowns of the trees 2-4° (Safoterov, 1937). However, the method is very expensive because each heater consumes more than 3.5 kg of fuel an hour. Efforts to find cheaper and no less effective means of protecting unhardy subtropical plants from frost are therefore continuing.

The Soviet scientist G.B. Nadaraya (1939a, b) has suggested covering each tree with three layers of gauze. His research showed that lemon trees so protected came safely through an ordinary winter, whereas uncovered trees died. According to Nadaraya's data, in 1939 in Anaseul -9° temperature killed lemon trees down to the root collar while trees under the gauze tents didn't suffer at all.

The purpose of the gauze is not to conserve any soil heat remaining from the summer, for the temperature under the tent is actually lower than outside because the gauze radiates more heat than the soil. The value of the gauze is that if frost is preceded by snow, as often happens on the Black Sea littoral, the snow clings to the gauze and thus serves to protect the trees from the ensuing cold. In addition, the trees are shielded throughout the winter from the direct rays of the sun and are not prematurely stimulated to start growth. This is particularly important for subtropical plants which have a slight winter dormancy period, e.g., the lemon, and become active as soon as the temperature permits.

Intense night frosts are very common in our subtropics. In the spring of 1948, for example, they caused tremendous damage to citrus groves and ornamental plants on the Black Sea littoral. On the morning of March 16 the temperature around Sukhumi dropped to -9° in a few hours. Almost all the lemon trees were winterkilled and the orange trees and even mandarins suffered severely. Palm trees on the streets and in the parks of Sukhumi, which normally come through the winter safely without any protection, looked in the spring of 1948 as though they had been scorched by fire, their leaves blackened and dead. The reason for the severity of the frost was that the winter had been warm and that it had been preceded by sunny weather, thus stimulating early growth and loss of normal hardiness. Plants which emerged from dormancy earlier suffered the most. Those dormant at the onset of the frost were unscathed, e.g., the unhardy avocado trees, which were slow in emerging from dormancy the spring of 1948 and thus suffered comparatively little from the frost. Gauze coverings may not completely save plants like the lemon from injury, but they do blunt the effect of frost.

Gauze is expensive, although once put on it lasts several years if carefully handled. Therefore, still widely used is the cheaper and more durable, although less effective, covering provided by reeds, ferns, plywood, etc. Plywood protects palm trees all along the coast from Sukhumi to Tuapse. It does not winterproof the trees because an opening is always left at the bottom, nor would it do so even if there were no openings; in fact, it may intensify the cold during a frost. Moreover, if the leaves come in contact with the plywood, they are "burned" by frost due to strong heat radiation of wood.

Therefore, a free space of a few centimeters must always be left between the plywood and the leaves, which are gathered together and tied. Nevertheless, plywood is of value in that it protects plants from the direct rays of the sun on bright days and from the injurious effect of winter winds and snow, which breaks off leaves and branches.

A very simple and effective way of shielding subtropical plants from the direct rays of the sun in winter is to sprinkle them with lime water so that they remain white during the cold months. The leaves are not harmed by the lime. I sprayed some trees in the summer of 1949 in the botanical gardens of Vladivostok. The lime remained on the leaves over a month before it was washed off by rain and did no harm. In the fall of the same year a former colleague, A. F. Lakhtionov, sprayed lime on scores of potted tea plants, which he left outdoors all winter. The experiment was repeated in 1950. Late in the fall they were sprayed and placed in a sunny trench for the winter where they were exposed to temperatures as low as -12°. By spring the unsprayed plants were dead, but all the others survived.

Of some value in protecting subtropical plants from frost is the so-called wall culture, i.e., planting near buildings or on slopes where walls are created by terracing. Walls shield the plants from wind and warm them at night with heat absorbed during the day. In addition, they make it comparatively easy to cover the plants during frosts with burlap or some other cheap material. The defect of wall culture is that it tends to stimulate plants to start growth earilier, thus increasing the danger of injury by spring frosts (A.D. Aleksandrov, 1947).

Decumbent culture of subtropical plants, especially lemon trees (Lavriychuk, 1939), has gained considerable popularity in recent years. In the northern damp subtropics, e.g., the Sochi region, decumbent lemon trees are covered with various kinds of mats for the winter. In Sukhumi snow, which generally precedes frost, serves as the warming agent. Decumbent culture of lemon trees in Sukhumi completely justified itself during the spring of 1948, for they incurred much less frost injury than did the other trees and bushes. The "hinge" method described above has been used since antiquity in the Samarkand region in Central Asia. Fig and pomegranate trees are pressed as close to the ground as possible with reed or some other kind of mats. They are raised and staked in the spring (Dylevskiy, 1939).

Keeping subtropical plants in warm places is another way of enabling them to survive the winter. For example, trees may be dug out with a ball of earth and brought into a warm shed and set out again in the spring in their old places. Then there is tub culture, i.e., the trees are kept in tubs all the time and brought indoors for the winter, etc. (A.D. Aleksandrov, 1947).

Another method worth noting is trench culture now widely used in the southern part of the Ukraine, Crimea, Northern Caucasus, and in regions where citrus was not cultivated before. This method utilizes the heat of the soil to keep plants warm in the winter. The trenches are covered with light, nonporous mats, serving as a kind of coldframe in which the temperature remains a little below zero. The plants do not grow at this temperature; at the same time they suffer no injury (Vlasenko, 1938).

There is after all just one truly effective method of protecting tropical plants from cold and that is to set them out only after the advent of warm weather. That is how such imports from the tropics as cucumbers, tomatoes, etc. have been grown for centuries in Russia. Seedlings from coldframes rather than seeds are used to obtain mature plants sooner, especially in the northern regions. This method is now very popular and almost every truck garden has its own coldframes.

Widely used too in all our northern regions and in the central belt is continuous culture of warm-season plants in greenhouses so that fresh vegetables can be obtained even in the winter. Light is artificially provided. Fluorescent bulbs are now used for this purpose because their spectral composition is more favorable to the growth and development of plants than that of ordinary incandescent bulbs. Moreover, they are five times more economical. The Marfino State Farm near Moscow is noted for its extensive use of hothouse culture, luminescent lighting, etc.

Cacao and coffee trees can also be cultivated in hothouses. Experiments in the garden of the V.L. Komarov Botanical Institute, Academy of Sciences USSR have shown that even in Leningrad these typical hothouse-grown plants are sufficiently productive to meet the needs of the confectionery industry (Kozlov, 1933; Ginsburg and Yurashevskiy, 1934). Hothouse culture of pineapples on the Black Sea littoral has also justified itself (Valyumar, 1939).

CONCLUSION

We examined the principal methods currently used to protect plants from frost and other unfavorable wintering conditions. Many of them have been derived from practical experience. Thus, everyone concerned with the problem of winter protection of plants should study the techniques in actual use.

PART II

PHYSIOLOGY OF WINTER RESISTANCE IN PLANTS

INTRODUCTION

The adaptation of plants to wintering is determined by the various characteristics of form, structure, and physiological processes. These characteristics may be divided into two groups: one group helps the plants directly to withstand unfavorable conditions, the other helps them more or less to avoid the unfavorable effects of winter.

The overall ability of plants to come through winter successfully is called winter hardiness. There are also frost hardiness, i.e., the ability to withstand frost; cold hardiness, i.e., the ability of heat-loving plants to withstand cold (temperatures somewhat below 0°); ability to withstand heaving; resistance to damping off; ability to withstand waterlogging; resistance to winter drought.

For ordinary wintering plants in the temperate zone the main element in winter hardiness is frost resistance and it is appropriate, therefore, that we examine it in detail.

CHAPTER 1

HISTORICAL SKETCH OF THE DEVELOPMENT OF IDEAS ON FROST RESISTANCE

1. PRINCIPAL INVESTIGATIONS OF FROST RESISTANCE BEFORE MODERN TIMES

According to the earliest views, frost resistance depended on plants, like warm-blooded animals, having their own temperature, which they retained thanks to the low heat conductivity of tissue. Many years passed before this notion was abandoned, although there were many other theories. For example, Hales (1748) wrote in his well known Statics of Plants: "Evergreen trees transpire much less than grapevines and apple trees, which lose their leaves by winter. The consequence of the slight transpiration of these trees is that they tolerate winter better....I studied 12 species of plants that remain green all year long, and all of them exhibited a low rate of transpiration" (p. 12).

The frost resistance of deciduous trees was explained by Strömer's theories (1749). Starting with Hales' data on the substantial decrease in the water content of trees after shedding their leaves, Strömer came to the conclusion that early defoliation increases their frost resistance. As the amount of water diminishes in plants, Strömer reasoned, there is less danger of vascular rupture by the sap set in motion after thawing and, consequently, of frost injury or death.

Senebier's theory attributing frost resistance to the great elasticity of the plants' cell walls was very popular at the beginning of the 19th century. This theory was the logical outcome of the prevalent ideas on the rupture of cells after freezing and was discarded only after Göppert's (1830) microscopic studies conclusively showed that neither freezing nor thawing of plants causes the cells to rupture.

Besides revolutionizing ideas on winterkilling, Göppert's work laid the foundation for a new and more accurate understanding of frost resistance. After combining his own observations and experimental data with earlier published material, Göppert concluded that frost resistance in plants was largely a function of their condition and external factors. He also confirmed the earlier finding of Schübler and his co-workers (Schübler and Halder, 1827; Schübler and Neuffer, 1829) that plants have no specific temperature of their own. The heat emitted in the course of their metabolic activity is slight and has no perceptible effect on their body temperature. The latter depends almost entirely on the external temperature while the role of the tissues, which conduct heat poorly, is merely to smooth out sharp fluctuations in the external temperature.

Water content, Göppert held, was the decisive factor in the frost resistance of plants. He observed that plants with the most water were always the least hardy. The amount of water present varies with the moisture of the soil and atmosphere as well as with the nature of the plants themselves and stage of development. Herbaceous plants are winterkilled earlier than woody plants because of their greater water content. For the same reason shrubs and trees, many of which can tolerate the most severe frosts, are readily injured with the return of even light frosts in spring and summer. Göppert also noted the relationship between the frost resistance of individual plant organs and their age: "We may state as a law and general rule that young leaves and shoots are more resistant to the prolonged and gradually intensifying cold than old leaves and shoots on the same plant" (p. 19).

Among the external factors influencing frost resistance, Göppert stressed the harm done by repeated freezing and thawing. In experiments with Euphorbia lathyris he found that plants chilled once at -10 or -12° lived, whereas they died when frozen six times at -4°.

"Acclimatization" was another major factor in frost resistance, Göppert believed.

We find very important ideas on frost resistance and practical methods of intensifying it in 19th century Russian publications. For example, Vyust (1850) wrote: "Very little attention is paid to the characteristics of soil, its cultivation in particular, or it is not examined the way it should. Yet it is only through cultivation that we can resist the climate. Plant health depends more on cultivation than on climate" (p. 134). N. Yarnek (1856) wrote in the same vein: "It has now been definitely shown that it is not temperature alone in a given locality that influences acclimatization of plants and that the soil, location, and other factors play no small part in the process" (p. 132).

N. Dubenskiy's survey (1853) is of great value in appraising the ideas on frost resistance of fruit trees in the middle of the 19th century. He wrote, as if it were a solidly established fact, that fruit trees are endangered chiefly by winter and spring frosts, particularly after thaws in February and March. He noted the variability of frost resistance in the same plants in relation to such external factors as rate of fruit bearing during the summer before, length of time the fruit is on the tree, time the leaves are shed, etc. Excessive fruiting and resultant exhaustion is always harmful. "In 1826 all the gardens in Vyaznik following an extremely productive summer died of the thaws, ice crusts, and bitter frosts that ensued." Slow ripening of fruit has an adverse effect on trees. "They are not only not fertile the next summer, but they do not always withstand the severity of our winters." On the shedding of leaves Dubenskiy wrote: "There is a superstition among gardeners and farmers that the year in which winter sets in with the leaves still on the trees will be a severe one. This popular view is sound because as long as there is even a single leaf left, the tree continues to suck in moisture through its roots, which dilutes its sap, and thus naturally becomes prone to frost injury" (pp. 134–135).

Among the investigations of the 1870's and 1880's the work of Russian scientists on questions relating to growth and fall-winter dormancy is worthy of special mention. For example, N.I. Zheleznov (1869) observed that dwarf trees produce earlier and better fruits and have greater frost resistance. The article of an anonymous author published in the first issue of the journal Vestnik russkogo obshchestva sadovodstva [Herald of the Russian Horticultural Society] , 1878, is exceptionally interesting. The author wrote that plants are not fully dormant in winter and that dormancy is caused by a change in the conditions affecting the plants.

A new stage in the study of frost resistance was inaugurated at the beginning of the 20th century by the research of Apelt (1907) and Rein (1908). Apelt discovered that the lower the temperature at which potato tubers are stored, the lower the temperature at which they are winterkilled. The process of heightening frost resistance in tubers stored at low temperatures, according to Apelt, is fairly rapid, but is still measured in weeks. When the tubers were transferred from a warm room to ice, they acquired within four weeks frost resistance corresponding to the new temperature conditions. Approximately the same amount of time was required for the tubers to lose this resistance when they were returned to the warm room. This rate of increase in resistance, Apelt said, corresponds to the adaptation of plants to frosts in the fall and explains why spring frosts have a destructive effect.

According to Apelt, the green shoots are more susceptible to frost than the tubers because under the normal conditions of potato culture they are less exposed to low temperatures since they die off sooner. However, their frost resistance varies with the temperature that precedes their freezing. The younger and higher shoots on the stem are more resistant than the lower and older ones.

Rein's work published a year after Apelt's is to a certain extent a continuation of it. Rein tested the frost susceptibility of a great many plants and discovered that it varied with their taxonomic position, ecological conditions, and geographic location. Terrestrial plants are more frost resistant than aquatic plants. Temperate zone plants are more resistant than subtropical and tropical plants.

Rein's data on the relationship between winterkilling point and temperature preceding freezing are unusually interesting. Rein found that when this temperature drops, frost resistance rises perceptibly only in temperate zone plants. It changes much less in subtropical plants, not at all in tropical plants, and they die at the same temperature regardless of the temperature that prevailed before freezing. He studied the rate of changes in resistance and discovered that it ranges from 0.04 to 0.21° a day. The maximum resistance of plants kept on ice develops within 10-12 days.

A great contribution to the subject was made in Pfeffer's laboratory by his students Bartetzko (1909), Irmscher (1912), and Winkler (1913). Growing cultures of mold fungi on a variety of nutrient media, Bartetzko found that as he increased the concentration of the nutrient solution the frost resistance of the fungi invariably rose. He also elucidated the specific action of nitrogenous substances: when the content of potassium nitrate in the nutrient solution was increased, the frost resistance of Aspergillus niger decreased rather than increased. Bartetzko also learned that maintaining the temperature somewhat above the winterkilling point lowers the fungus' frost resistance and eventually kills it. The same thing occurred with the supercooled state.

Irmscher's main purpose was to compare drought resistance and frost resistance in mosses and to check Müller-Thurgau's dehydration theory on these plants. Several frost-resistant varieties exhibited considerable drought resistance, although there were sharp exceptions. For example, water moss (Fontinalis), which has the highest degree of frost resistance, was completely unable to tolerate drought. Data on the adaptability of mosses to low temperatures are very important in understanding frost resistance. Irmscher found that the increased resistance of mosses taken from a high-temperature environment occurred both at temperatures just above and below 0°. Following exposure to low above-zero temperatures the frost resistance of mosses under the influence of subsequent slight chilling at -10° rose even more. Their resistance was greater after slight chilling than after exposure to temperatures just above zero.

Winkler's research on coniferous and deciduous trees (pine, arborvitae, birch, linden, maple, etc.) yielded new and important information on changes in frost resistance over the year. In warm weather, from May to September, the resistance of all trees is very low. Growing leaves and buds are killed at this time by temperatures between -3 and -5°, wood at temperatures between -8 and -10°. Starting with September, however, resistance gradually increases, reaching the maximum in January. All the trees studied by Winkler were capable of enduring frosts of -30° in the winter. As the weather warms up, resistance again diminishes, the minimum occurring by May.

The process of adaptation by trees to frost may take place rather quickly, according to Winkler, within a few days. The trees become most resistant when the temperature drops gradually. They also lose their resistance quickly, a fact that Winkler uses to explain the injurious effect of brief winter thaws. Trees in sunny, southern exposures suffer the most.

2. IDEAS ON INTRACELLULAR CHANGES
RESPONSIBLE FOR FROST RESISTANCE

One of the earliest attempts to elucidate the nature of frost resistance was made by A.S. Famintsin and I.P. Borodin (1876). After determining microchemically the starch content of the bark and xylem of poplar and linden branches, the authors discovered that starch disappears in winter and reappears in spring or after the branches have been brought into a warm place. Several years later Russow (1882) of former Yur'yev University analyzed 92 species of woody plants and confirmed that starch accumulates before winter, disappears during winter, and reappears in spring. In winter oil forms instead of starch.

Further work on the conversion of starch in plant cells during the wintering period was done by Fischer (1888, 1891) who showed that starch stored during summer is converted during fall and winter into sugar in the bark of all trees. However, it remains unchanged in the xylem of some trees, whereas it is converted into oil in the xylem of others. Accordingly, Fischer divided trees into two groups — "starchy" and "oily". The "oily" trees have greater frost resistance and the northern limit of their occurrence is beyond that of the "starchy" trees. The former group includes all the northern zone conifers and, among the deciduous trees, birch and linden. By spring starch and oil are converted into sugar used by plants in the process of growth. The same thing happens when plants are brought into a warm room in winter. Starch may be converted into sugar very quickly — after two hours of +20° temperature.

Fall-winter conversion of starch into sugar and oil was regarded by Fischer as the determinant factor in frost resistance. According to Fischer, oil reduces the water content of protoplasm so that it becomes less susceptible to the destructive influence of frost. In evaluating the role of starch Fischer came close to Müller-Thurgau's view (1882) that sugar increases the concentration of cell sap and thus lowers its freezing point.

Lidforss' studies (1896, 1907) on 130 species of woody and herbaceous plants in Central and Southern Europe, high-altitude regions and beech forests, and on winter-green annuals and aquatic plants were of great value in clarifying the chemistry of frost resistance. Lidforss focussed on the fact that starch in stomatal guard cells of wintering plants is almost entirely gone at the beginning of winter while cell turgor is substantially increased. Microchemical analysis of the sap in these cells after the disappearnce of starch revealed the presence of glucose. If leaves are brought into a warm room in winter, starch again forms in the cells, often in greater quantities than in summer.

Lidforss discovered from his far-ranging research that all leaf cells in winter are completely lacking in starch, which remains only in aquatic plants. In plants whose leaves rest on water, e.g., Veronica beccalunga, starch disappears in the external cells of the leaves, but the lower and deeper they are in water, the more starch they retain.

Lidforss concluded that sugar storage in cells before winter is their most important means of protection from frost. This is confirmed, in his opinion, chiefly by the fact that in aquatic plants not exposed to frost, there is no conversion of starch into sugar. By way of proof the author cites some experimental findings: artificial increase in the content of various sugars (sucrose, fructose, glucose, galactose, lactose, maltose) in cut branches after immersion in the corresponding solutions intensified their frost resistance. The nature of the protective action of sugar, according to Lidforss, is determined both by heightened osmotic pressure in cells and by its specific chemical action on protoplasm which prevents coagulation caused by frost.

Although he attached considerable significance to the sugars Lidforss did not consider them the only protection of plants from frost. He also believed that oil, the storage of which in the inner layers of the xylem of "oily" trees was noted by Russow and Fischer, has a part to play in the process. So too some salts soluble in cell sap, e.g., potassium oxalate, large quantities of which are present in summer in the cells of green tissues in the form of crystals; in winter, like starch, it dissolves. Lidforss stressed the significance of protein composition and permeability of protoplasm and composition of cell sap salts in frost resistance. The high resistance of mosses and bacteria is due, Lidforss maintained, to the high degree of protoplasmic permeability to salts which reduce the danger of its coagulating. Among the anatomical and morphological features relevant to frost resistance Lidforss noted xeromorphic structure, which affords plants protection from physiological desiccation.

This research exerted great influence on all subsequent investigations of frost resistance. The finding that sugars along with other substances are significant in lowering the freezing point of cell sap and in chemically affecting protoplasm stimulated a series of special studies, notably those of Schaffnit (1910) who further elucidated the chemistry of frost resistance.

After determining the sugar content of young rye plants taken in winter from the field and greenhouse, Schaffnit discovered that the field plants had twice as much sugar as the greenhouse plants. In winter the sap of field-grown plants left no residue after freezing, whereas the sap of greenhouse plants contained coagulated albumin after freezing. Coagulation did not take place when sugar was added to the sap. The same thing happened when sugar was added to a salt solution of egg white before chilling. Schaffnit fully corroborated Lidforss' principal finding regarding the protective action of sugar, but, unlike him, he did not ascribe the decisive role in frost resistance to sugar. His analysis showed that when the temperature is low, the splitting of complex carbohydrates and storage of sugars in cells is accompanied by the disintegration of complex proteins resulting in simpler, more stable proteins and in amino acids. Schaffnit regarded the formation of stable proteins as the basis of frost resistance.

Mez (1905) recognized two types of substances as determining frost resistance: those which eliminate the possibility of supercooling and those which increase the liberation of heat in plants while they are being cooled. He considered supercooling harmful in that it increases the danger of the temperature falling to a lethal minimum. Mez regarded as defensive all the properties of plants which make supercooling either transient or impossible. Among them he included the accumulation of oil which, in emulsion with water, is an effective means of combatting supercooling. Mez attached considerable significance to freezing because the transformation of water into ice results in the liberation of heat. Heat is also liberated when sugars and salts dissolved in cell sap crystallize. Mez called those substances crystallizing in plants "thermally active" in contrast to "thermally passive" substances (starch) which do not liberate heat when the plants are cooled. However, the main factor in frost resistance, he believed, is the internal characteristics of protoplasm itself. These characteristics are mainly responsible for the difference in hardiness from plant to plant. This theory was adopted and expanded by his students (Apelt, 1907; Rein, 1908; Voigtländer, 1909). It was highly praised by Molisch (1910), but sharply criticized by Maksimov (1913).

3. MORE RECENT INVESTIGATIONS
OF FROST RESISTANCE

N.A. Maksimov (1908, 1908a, 1913) was the first Russian to make a thorough study of frost resistance and direct the attention of other scientists to the subject. His research was intimately connected with his above-mentioned work on winterkilling. Beginning with mold fungi, Maksimov discovered that increasing the concentration of the nutrient solution by adding glucose and glycerin to it markedly intensified the frost resistance of <u>Aspergillus niger</u>. The protective action of these substances was incomparably stronger than could have been anticipated from lowering the freezing point of the solution. This stimulated Maksimov, independently of Lidforss, to question the value of attempts to reduce frost resistance simply to a matter of lowering the freezing point of cell sap.

Maksimov's later experiments involved red cabbage and spiderwort. He immersed bits of leaf tissue in aqueous solutions of sugars, alcohols of different composition, and salts of mineral and organic acids and then chilled them. Every substance tested raised the frost resistance of the cells. It turned out that the more soluble the substance at low temperatures and the lower the temperature at which it reaches the so-called eutectic point (i.e., when it begins to be precipitated from a solution), the more potent its protective action. Substances whose eutectic point is very high and which, accordingly, achieve the limit of solubility and are precipitated from a solution only at temperatures slightly below zero, like mannite and potassium sulfate and sodium sulfate, have no protective action at all. It was also established that the length of time the tissue sections remained in the solutions tested had no perceptible effect on their frost resistance. When the sections were transferred from the solution into pure water, their acquired resistance disappeared.

Maksimov proposed the following theory of plant protection from winterkilling. A great variety of water-soluble, nontoxic substances with fairly low eutectic points possess protective action, which is manifested as soon as they come into contact with protoplasm. The action is not related to their entry into protoplasm and is much stronger than the lowering of the freezing point that they cause. It is dependent on the physicochemical and chemical influence of these substances on protoplasm. Maksimov's research also showed that the water-soluble substances present in cells, if they are not toxic, cannot cause protoplasm to coagulate after it is dehydrated as a result of the formation of ice. On the contrary, substances soluble in the sap of the vacuoles and in the protoplasm itself have protective properties. This led to rejection of Gorke's "chemical theory of winterkilling" (1907) whereby coagulation of protoplasm after freezing is said to take place after the concentration of soluble salts in the cells increases.

Having established the decisive significance of protective substances, Maksimov was in a position to refute the above-mentioned views of Mez, who maintained that the frost resistance of protoplasm is determined by its own specific properties.

Rosa's work (1921) on the hardening process in vegetables — cabbage, kohlrabi, tomatoes, etc. — was an important contribution to our understanding of the causes of frost resistance. He showed that frost resistance in cabbage increases with its exposure to cold, whereas tomatoes have virtually no capacity for hardening. It was subsequently discovered that the resistance of those plants capable of hardening can be heightened not only by exposing them to cold, but also by reducing soil moisture and by watering with salt solutions.

In an attempt to find the direct causes of intensified frost resistance during the hardening process, Rosa made a chemical analysis of leaves and determined the bound water not frozen when plants are chilled at -5°. It seems that during hardening sugars and amino acids are stored in the cells. However, the quantity of these osmotically active substances was not enough to explain the sharp increase in amount of bound water. The problem was solved by determining the content of pentosans, highly hydrophilic colloids. The accumulation of pentosans during hardening proceeded almost simultaneously with the rise in content of bound water and growth of frost resistance. In tender plants (tomatoes, eggplant, and sweet potatoes) the pentosan content remained unchanged when the plants were exposed to cold. Rosa concluded that osmotically active substances in the cell play only a subordinate role, the process being determined mainly by the presence of hydrophilic colloids.

These views were amplified by Newton (1922, 1924) who set out to find physiological indicators of frost resistance in different varieties of winter wheat. Newton compared changes in water content during hardening, in dry substance, carbohydrate and nitrogenous compounds, lowering of freezing point ($\Delta t°$), amount of acidity (pH), electrical conductivity of cell sap and water-holding capacity of colloids in living cells and in the sap pressed from them. Varieties known to differ in frost resistance were scarcely distinguishable in the unhardened state in terms of the indicators just listed. Clear differences appeared only in completely hardened plants at the end of fall and beginning of winter. During the hardening process sugars and water-soluble nitrogenous substances accumulated, water content decreased, dry substance increased, etc. Most characteristic of all, however, was the sharp increase in water-holding capacity of the cell colloids. These colloidal changes, according to Newton, are the most reliable indicator of frost resistance.

Investigation of the connection between frost resistance and osmotically active substances in the cell continued. Åkerman (1927), Swedish breeder and physiologist, made the most far-reaching study of the phenomenon in different varieties of cultivated plants. He set out to determine "whether it is possible to ascertain the hardiness of wheat varieties by means of laboratory methods" (p. 3). His experiments were on economically important varieties in Sweden that had undergone over a period of years tests under field conditions and by freezing in a cold chamber. At the same time he determined the sugars, osmotic pressure of cell sap, and content of dry substance in the plants. His studies revealed the existence of a close connection between sugar content and frost resistance, which showed up very clearly at the beginning of winter when the plants were completely hardened.

Åkerman's work greatly influenced all subsequent physiological research on cultivated plant varieties. The determination of sugars was an invariable procedure in virtually every laboratory engaged in comparing the hardiness of varieties. The conviction arose that sugars were of decisive importance in resistance. It came to be believed that the degree of resistance could be ascertained by the relatively simple method of chemical analysis of plants at the end of fall and beginning of winter without resorting to lengthy and laborious testing in the field and in cold chambers. This obvious exaggeration of the significance of sugars soon became apparent, as we shall see below.

The work of Dexter and his co-workers (Dexter, Tottingham, and Graber,

1930 and 1932; Dexter, 1933, 1933a, 1934, 1934a, 1935, 1941) was also important. To begin with, Dexter, Tottingham, and Graber elaborated a method of
evaluating the degree of plant injury caused by frost, thereby making it possible to determine whether plants are actually injured before the external
signs of damage appear. Using this method, which is based on changes in the
permeability and electrical conductivity of cells injured by frost, Dexter
showed that hardening of plants at low temperatures just above zero is directly related to the amount of plastic substances present. The latter process
is closely connected with photosynthesis. If during hardening plants are
placed in a warm room or the inflow of carbon dioxide is halted, their frost
resistance decreases. Plastic substances are lost during growth and respiration. The well known phenomenon of decreased resistance after thaws, when
the temperature remains fairly high for some time, is attributable to the
start of growth and intensification of respiration. However, even after the
start of growth, particularly in spring, when plants are in the stem extension
stage, they can again be hardened if kept at low temperatures in the light.

Dexter doubts that the accumulation of nitrogenous substances promotes
frost resistance. His experiments in changing the mineral nutrient regime
showed that an excess of nitrogen in soil at low temperatures leads to the
storage of large quantities of soluble nitrogenous substances in plants, but
this does not promote resistance. Nor does frost resistance depend on alkalinity of the cell sap. A major precondition of frost resistance, Dexter believes, is an increase in dry substance and decrease in water along with
increased protoplasmic permeability to salts. His comparative determinations of the salt content of 35 wheat varieties differing in frost resistance
showed that the more resistant the variety, the more dry matter and the less
salt it had when hardened.

A major contribution to the field was made by I.I. Tumanov (Tumanov and
Borodina, 1929; Tumanov, 1931, 1933, 1933a, 1935, 1938, 1940, 1945, 1947,
1951) who worked in Maksimov's laboratory in the former Institute of Applied
Botany at Leningrad, the first place in the U.S.S.R. to be equipped with cold
chambers especially designed for scientific research. Tumanov made comparative tests of frost resistance in many varieties of grains obtained from
all over the world. Relying both on his own extensive physiological research
and on published material, Tumanov constructed the following theory of
hardening and cold resistance in plants, which was the culmination, so to
speak, of all the work that had gone before.

In Tumanov's opinion, hardening is caused chiefly by the fall storage of
sugars which are the sources of plant energy and the main protection of
protoplasm from winterkilling. Sugar storage is closely related to photosynthesis and growth. The more intensive the photosynthesis and the less
sugar expended on growth, the greater the reserve that builds up. Sugar
storage is the first stage in hardening, which in winter plants takes place at
temperatures ranging from 0 to +10 and +15°. The second stage occurs when
the temperature drops to -2 to -5°. The total resistance characteristic of a
given plant is acquired during the second stage. At this time the cells become
dehydrated because a substantial amount of water turns into ice and protective
substances are scattered throughout the protoplasm. Enhanced ability to pre-
serve the external layer of protoplasm, which prevents the penetration of ice
crystals forming in the intercellular spaces, is particularly important for the
plants.

More recently, Tumanov has also ascribed considerable significance to physiologically active growth substances on the basis of well known data on the adverse effect of growth on the development of frost resistance in plants. The storage of growth substances in cells, Tumanov believes, prevents hardening. On the other hand, a decrease in these substances — outflow into other parts of the plant and inactivation — is a prerequisite of the development of frost resistance.

V.S. Iljin (1933, 1935) took a different position on frost resistance. He believes that the death of cells occurring when plants are chilled or exposed to drought is caused by mechanical injury to protoplasm due to contraction and expansion when water is frozen out of it and later restored by thawing. Shrinkage and disappearance of vacuoles following cell dehydration inevitably causes protoplasm to contract, become deformed, and frequently rupture. Deformation and rupture of protoplasm are even more pronounced when it expands as a result of the dehydrated cells' absorbing water. This danger can be averted by replacing the cell sap of the vacuoles with some nonfreezing and nondrying substance. The vacuoles of highly drought- and frost-resistant plants as well as spores and seeds actually become filled during the winter and periods of drought with oil, proteins, starch, etc., which also serve as reserve nutrients. In addition, many drought- and frost-resistant plants are likely to have small, elongated cells and a very thick protoplasmic layer so that there is relatively little displacement of protoplasm when the water regime changes. And the great thickness of the protoplasmic layer makes it more durable than usual. Of considerable significance too is the separation of salts observed in certain plants, e.g., in the myxomycete Fuligo, after cell dehydration, thereby preventing them from becoming more concentrated and injuring the protoplasm.

Iljin's work once again drew the attention of investigators to protoplasm. For example, Kessler and Ruhland (Kessler, 1935; Kessler and Ruhland, 1938) set out to determine whether frost resistance varies with osmotic pressure and acidity of cell sap and to discover the significance of changes in protoplasm as well as the nature of these changes. The objects of investigation were saxifrage (Saxifraga cordifolia), ivy (Hedera helix), houseleek (Sempervivum glaucum), opuntia (Opuntia crassa), boxwood (Buxus sempervirens), and other cultivated evergreens.

After comparing the changes in frost resistance in saxifrage, ivy, and houseleek in the course of a year, Kessler proved that resistance was closely connected with natural changes in temperature. It increases as the temperature drops in fall, decreases in winter during thaws, and steadily diminishes as spring approaches. Osmotic pressure in cells rises with increasing frost resistance in fall at the same time that acidity decreases. On the other hand, acidity rises and osmotic pressure falls with diminishing resistance in spring. However, this kind of connection between changes in frost resistance, osmotic pressure, and sap acidity is not constant so that Kessler came to doubt the causal relationship between frost resistance and these physiological indicators. After artificially raising osmotic pressure in saxifrage cells in summer by infiltrating glycerin to the winter level, the author observed only a very slight increase in frost resistance. He also discovered that young saxifrage leaves contain more acid sap and yet are more resistant. Kessler concluded that osmotic pressure and cell sap acidity, which many investigators consider the major indicators of frost resistance in plants, actually have no connection with it and merely change concurrently.

Kessler then turned to protoplasm the viscosity of which became the focal oint of his and Ruhland's research. Their experiments showed that viscosity invariably increases with the growth of frost resistance and vice versa. Even more important is protoplasmic hydration which changes at the same time as viscosity. As viscosity increases during hardening of plants, protoplasmic hydration increases. Water remains more tenaciously in the protoplasm and becomes more abundant, most of it coming from the vacuoles. This causes the vacuoles to shrink and the protoplasm to expand. The nuclei of hardened cells double in size. Increased protoplasmic viscosity and hydration of hardened cells do not change readily when external conditions change. As plants harden, their protoplasm becomes increasingly permeable both to electrolytes and to water.

Kessler and Ruhler call attention once again to the increased frost resistance of plants in fall as they start the winter dormancy period. Experiments showed that artificial interruption of dormancy inevitably causes a reduction in resistance. On the other hand, when plants are made dormant, e.g., as a result of applications of ethylene in low concentrations, their frost resistance increases. Thoroughly dormant plants remained resistant even though kept two months in a warm place.

Luyet and his co-workers (Luyet, 1937; Luyet and Gibbs, 1937; Luyet and Gehenio, 1938a, b, 1939, and 1940a, b, and others) offer an original explanation of frost resistance, especially at very low temperatures. Luyet studied matter in a "state of vitrification" when it possesses the properties of a solid, but its molecules, unlike the cystalline state, are arranged not as in a crystal lattice, but at random as in a solidified liquid. Any gaseous or liquid substance can be transformed into a vitrified state by dropping the temperature rapidly to prevent it from crystallizing. The investigations of Luyet and his co-workers revealed that both organic colloids and living cells can be transformed into a vitrified state. Individual cells sometimes remain viable despite a very sharp drop in temperature.

Although the data obtained by Luyet and his co-workers are interesting, they are not enough to explain frost resistance in all its manifestations chiefly because the vitrified state of the substances composing protoplasm is very unstable and does not appear during an ordinary frost. Moreover, a good deal of information is available which clearly suggests a connection between frost resistance and other changes in protoplasm and products of its nutrition and vital activity.

CONCLUSION

At least two centuries have passed since the phenomenon of frost resistance became the object of scientific research. There have been two main trends. Some investigators endeavored to correlate frost resistance with changes in osmotic pressure resulting from the accumulation of various products of protoplasmic vital activity — sugars, products of protein decomposition — or with changes in acidity and other properties of cell sap helping protoplasm to withstand frost. Other investigators sought the cause of frost resistance in protoplasm itself, in changes in its chemical composition and physicochemical properties. These trends were not always strictly kept apart, but they were almost always distinguished. Echoes of the struggle between the two trends have not died down even to this day.

Our historical survey of research on frost resistance is far from complete. We have merely outlined the scope of the problem. We shall now describe in some detail the nature of frost resistance in plants in the light of up-to-date data on the subject.

CHAPTER 2

RELATIONSHIP BETWEEN FROST RESISTANCE AND EXTERNAL FACTORS

1. CHANGES IN FROST RESISTANCE IN THE COURSE OF A YEAR

The relationship between frost resistance in plants and external factors is clearly shown in the changes that take place in the course of a year. Hildreth (1926) set up an experiment to determine the winterkilling temperature of two apple varieties. Branches taken from trees growing under normal conditions were frozen once or twice a month in a refrigerator at various temperatures and then allowed to root. The adverse effect of the freezing temperatures was judged from the lack of growth and presence of evident frost injury. The results of the experiment are presented in Table 2.

Table 2

Freezing point of apple branches (in °C)

Apple variety	Date branches taken for freezing									
	18.X	5.XI	4.XII	3.I	13.II	5.III	26.III	10.IV	10.V	7.VII
Jonathan	−15	−20	−30	−41 below −41	−41 below −41	−40 below −41	−36	−25	−6	−3
Duchess	−25	−30	−35				−40	−30	−6	−3

The table shows that frost resistance in both varieties gradually rose until the beginning of January. It began to drop late in March, almost vanishing in July. During this time a temperature of −3° was fatal to the branches.

A fair conclusion from a study of these changes in frost resistance is that temperature is a major external factor. This has been confirmed by specific investigations.

2. RELATIONSHIP BETWEEN FROST RESISTANCE AND TEMPERATURE

Let us examine the results of one of our own investigations in which we compared changes in frost resistance and temperature in the fall.

Winter rice, variety Vyatka, winter wheat, variety Kooperatorka, and spring wheat, varieties Lutescens 62 and Melanopus 69, were sown in Mits- cherlich pots at the regular time for winter crops — end of August — and set outdoors. A Stevenson screen with three thermometers — fixed, maximum, and minimum — were set alongside the plants on the same level. Frost resistance was determined by freezing plants in a refrigerator and then allowing them to grow in a greenhouse. The first freezing was performed September 22. The preceding weather was warm and at times hot. Through- out September until the day of freezing the mean daily temperature was +11.4°, the maximum was above +20°, while the minimum was never below +7.2°. The temperatures for the week before freezing are presented in Table 3.

Table 3

Temperature regime the week before the plants were first chilled (in °C)

Temperature	16. IX	17. IX	18. IX	19. IX	20. IX	21. IX	22. IX
Mean daily	13.5	15.8	16.0	16.0	16.5	18.5	17.9
Maximum	17.6	21.0	24.1	23.0	24.2	28.7	21.7
Minimum	7.2	12.4	11.1	9.1	10.1	11.2	14.0

The plants were frozen for 24 hours at -8°. A week later, when the effects of freezing had become manifest, we discovered that all the wheat was dead, whereas the rye was alive and thriving, only a few of the leaves having been killed. The experiment showed that frost resistance in different plants sets in at different temperatures. Only rye became adequately resistant when the mean daily temperature rose to +16° and higher. Spring and winter wheat both died.

The next freezing took place two weeks later — October 7 — when the temperature dropped considerably but remained above zero, generally a little over +6°. The temperatures for the week before freezing are presented in Table 4.

In one experiment the plants were frozen at -8 and -11.5°. The rye showed no signs of injury from -8° a week later, the winter wheat lost the tips of the leaves while the spring wheat lost about two-thirds of the leaf blades. After exposure to -11.5° the tips of the rye leaves died as did about one-third of the leaves of winter wheat, whereas both varieties of spring wheat were winter- killed.

Table 4

Temperature regime the week before the plants were chilled
the second time (in °C)

Temperature	1.X	2.X	3.X	4.X	5.X	6.X	7.X
Mean daily	5.7	6.3	7.9	8.0	8.0	7.8	6.1
Maximum	6.8	8.3	9.4	11.4	11.4	16.9	13.8
Minimum	5.0	4.5	4.4	5.6	5.1	4.4	2.8

A comparison of the two experiments shows that from September 22 to October 7 the frost resistance of all the varieties tested rose markedly after exposure to a mean daily temperature of about +6°.

The plants were tested on October 17 for the third time after the night frosts set in. The temperatures for the week preceding the test are given in Table 5.

Table 5

Temperature regime the week before the plants were chilled
the third time (in °C)

Temperature	11.X	12.X	13.X	14.X	15.X	16.X	17.X
Mean daily	8.9	4.5	1.5	1.1	0.3	0.0	-0.5
Maximum	11.0	6.8	4.6	3.2	3.8	4.2	2.4
Minimum	6.8	1.9	-1.1	-0.8	-2.6	-2.4	-2.7

The freezing was performed after a night frost of -2.7°, and the plant were placed frozen in a refrigerator. The temperature in one section of the refrigerator was kept at -7.6° for two days and in another section at -11.3° None of the plants, not even the leaf tips, suffered at all from -7.6°. All the plants survived after exposure to -11.3°, the winter varieties with no visible injury, the spring varieties losing part of their leaves.

Thus, from October 7 to 17, following a drop in temperature, there was a further rise in frost resistance.

Before freezing, frost resistance rises more or less gradually, but invariably rises sharply after freezing. By way of illustration I cite the results of an experiment involving the determination of frost resistance in sprouted seeds.

Winter wheat, variety Moskovskaya 2411, and spring wheat, variety Lutescens 62, seeds sprouting at room temperature were divided into three groups. The first group was immediately placed in a refrigerator at -7° for 24 hours. The second group was kept for 19 days in an icebox at about 0° after which they were frozen for 24 hours in the refrigerator at -11°. The third group of seeds was kept for 18 days in the icebox at about 0° after which they were frozen for 24 hours in the refrigerator at -4.6°. These seeds were tested for frost resistance at the same time as the second group of seeds at the same -11°.

All the seeds in the first group were winterkilled. In the second group 16% of the winter wheat seeds survived and 1% of the spring wheat. In the third group 80% of the winter wheat and 52% of the spring wheat seeds survived. Fig. 29 shows how the plants looked at the end of the experiment.

Fig. 29. Winter wheat, variety Moskovskaya 2411
(1, 2), and spring wheat, variety Lutescens 62 (3, 4)
1, 3 — seed sprouts of the second group (19 days at
0°, then 1 day at -11°); 2, 4 — seed sprouts of the
third group (18 days at 0°, 1 day at -4.6°, then
1 day at -11°)

Thus, a temperature of -4.6° for 24 hours sharply increased the frost resistance of sprouts kept 18 days before at about 0°. This very marked effect of brief exposure to light frost justifies our talking of a leap in the growth of frost resistance. However, the increase in resistance is more than a leap, for it continues as the temperature falls. It is evident from Table 2 (Hildreth's experiment) that the resistance of apple rose before January. The negative, injurious effect of low temperature places a limit on their positive, hardening effect. This limit varies from plant to plant depending on its nature.

The frost resistance developed in winter gradually dissipates by spring due to rising temperatures, as is shown by Table 2. The same thing happens during winter thaws, which was clearly demonstrated in the aforementioned experiments of Kessler who determined frost resistance in several evergreens in the course of a year by refrigerating them. He then compared the temperature at which the leaves were winterkilled with the mean air temperature outdoors where the plants had been kept for a week before the freezing. The curves drawn by Kessler of frost resistance and the temperature to which they were exposed prior to freezing reveal a marked decrease in resistance in January, which happened to coincide with a thaw.

Frost resistance diminishes even when plants are kept under snow. I.I. Tumanov, I.N. Borodina, and T.V. Oleynikova (1935) ran an experiment to compare the resistance of winter crops in mid-December before there was snow, when the plants were thoroughly frozen, and after they remained under a meter of snow for a month at a steady temperature of just a few degrees below zero. In both instances the plants were frozen at -23°. About half of the plants, frozen before the snow, survived. Those frozen after being under the snow for a month at a higher temperature died.

Although the evidence of dependence of frost resistance on environmental temperature is convincing, this relationship is by no means a simple one. For example, we have seen that Vyatka winter rye tolerated -8° in September after typical summer weather with a mean daily temperature of +16° and higher. On the other hand, the same Vyatka after the same temperature in June–July died at -3°. I checked this several times. Consequently, certain factors are operative in the fall that intensify frost resistance in plants even when exposed to relatively high temperatures.

Temporary elevations in temperature also have differing effects on the loss of frost resistance by plants at various times of the year. In fall they sometimes have no effect, whereas in winter, especially towards spring, they invariably reduce resistance.

3. RELATIONSHIP BETWEEN FROST RESISTANCE AND LIGHT

The value of light in the development of frost resistance by plants was first demonstrated experimentally by S. Toporkov (1899) who grew winter wheat in direct sunlight and in shade. In light the plants tillered, in shade tillering was inhibited and the shoots became elongated. With the onset of frost the shade plants were half winterkilled, all the light plants survived. Toporkov concluded from this experiment and field observations: "Intense light is one of the major factors promoting the development in plants of resistance to low temperatures" (p. 502).

The problem was studied in greater detail by I.I. Tumanov (1931) when he compared the resistance of winter wheat kept in the light and in the dark at +2 and +5° before chilling. In all cases the resistance of the light plants was higher. For example, 92% of the wheat plants, variety Lutescens 1060/10, kept in light at the above temperature survived after exposure to -11°. The same wheat, kept in darkness at the same temperature, died after exposure to -11°. One of the experiments involved a comparison of frost resistance in Lutescens 1060/10 and the wheat variety Novokrymka kept several days at +5, +6° in full daylight and under hotcaps of closely woven white cloth. The light plants of both varieties all survived freezing under the same conditions; of the plants kept in darkness 50% of Lutescens 1060/10 and 25% of Novokrymka survived.

The views of Toporkov and Tumanov on the great importance of light in the acquisition of frost resistance were later expanded by Dexter (1933). Dexter studied the effect on hardening of varying durations of natural and electric illumination and darkness and amount of carbon dioxide in the air. Winter wheat, alfalfa, cabbage, and tomatoes were the objects investigated. The degree of frost injury to protoplasm was determined by the conductivity of the electrolytes washed out of the cells.

Dexter confirmed the data of Toporkov and Tumanov on the importance of light in the development of frost resistance by plants exposed to low temperatures above zero. He also discovered that if plants have large reserves of plastic substances, e.g., alfalfa in the fall, their resistance may rise even in darkness. Dexter further learned that light is helpful in hardening only when there is carbon dioxide in the air; otherwise, the effect of hardening in light is the same as in darkness. He reached the same conclusion as Tumanov, namely, that light in the hardening process of plants acts as a factor in photosynthesis, causing them to store plastic substances needed to acquire frost resistance.

However, the role of light in raising frost resistance is not limited to its effect on photosynthesis. It also exerts an effect through changes in growth. I set up the following experiment. I planted 360 germinated seeds of winter wheat, Moskovskaya 2411, in each of several boxes containing 20 kg of soil. Each plant had a feeding area of 1.75 cm^2. As soon as the shoots appeared, all the boxes were placed on shelves outdoors. The plants clearly had insufficient feeding space and, moreover, shaded one another so that they scarcely tillered and became elongated. Only the outermost rows around the open sides of the boxes had a normal amount of light. The plants were covered with snow in November and eventually became thoroughly frozen, especially underneath and on the sides. The lowest temperature was -18°. In mid-January the plants were shifted to a hothouse and left there until spring. Out of 360 plants an average of 29 per box survived and grew normally. These were all on the southern, open side of the box. Out of 19 plants in the front row completely exposed to the direct rays of the sun 16 survived; in the second row 11 and in the third row only 2 plants survived. All the other rows consisted of dead plants.

Of great interest is the connection between frost resistance and photoperiodism. B. S. Moshkov (1929-1930, 1935) studied near Leningrad the photoperiodism of trees from different geographical areas. Small nursery-grown plants were exposed to artificially shortened or lengthened day throughout the summer and individual periods in the summer and fall. For the shortened day the plants were covered for several hours before sunset with dark sheets of plywood, which were removed several hours after sunrise. The day was lengthened by using 200 watt bulbs at night at the rate of one bulb per square meter of space.

Lengthening the day decreased frost resistance while shortening the day increased it. For example, white acacia from Belorussia, kept under natural light all summer, was winterkilled during the winter, but the same acacia, kept under the conditions of a shortened 14-hour day throughout the summer, survived. Wild growing willow did not suffer at all from frost, whereas the same willow exposed to electric light at night suffered frost injury in the tips of the shoots.

Frost resistance was intensified by brief (no more than three weeks) periods of short days, if they came in the middle or at the end of summer while the plant was actively growing. It was further discovered that each plant has its optimum period to develop frost resistance.

Increasing frost resistance by shortening the day was in all instances associated with the early cessation of growth in fall, the young shoots going into the winter in a more "ripe" condition with their surface tissues better developed. On the other hand, when the day was lengthened, the plants continued to grow until late in fall in so far as the temperature allowed and entered winter in a less "ripe" state.

Similar results in checking growth by artificially shortening the day and thus strengthening frost resistance were obtained in experiments that I conducted with A.F. Lakhtionov on a variety of woody plants.

4. RELATIONSHIP BETWEEN FROST RESISTANCE
AND AVAILABILITY OF WATER

A temporary lack of water in soil tends to wilt plants and usually helps to strengthen their resistance to frost. This is illustrated by I.I. Tumanov' experiments (1931) in comparing the resistance of pot-grown winter wheat variety Lutescens 329, in the turgid and wilted condition. Wilting was caused by stopping the watering of plants in the active growth stage. They were then hardened at 0 to +5°, and frozen in a refrigerator. In all cases the wilted plants proved to be more frost resistant, especially when the process was repeated. Such plants, even without preliminary hardening at 0 to +5°, tolerated light frost better in the wilted condition than did the control plants which remained turgid throughout. Wilting was thus a partial substitute for hardening at 0 to +5°.

A prolonged lack of water in soil leading to severe exhaustion has an adverse effect on plant frost resistance. Here is an example from my own investigations. On September 12 seeds of 12 varieties of spring and winter wheat with previously determined frost resistance were sown in wooden boxes containing 20 kg of soil, 16 germinated seeds of each variety in each box. The boxes were kept outdoors until the end of the month and then brought into an unheated greenhouse. Soil moisture was maintained at about 70% of total capacity. In mid-October, when the plants were quite bushy, the boxes were divided into two groups. Every other day for 10 days 200 ml of 6.5% potassium chloride solution was added to the soil of every box in one group (experimental) while 200 ml of distilled water was added to the soil of every body in the other group (control).

As the soil solution of the first group became more concentrated, the plants kept on losing turgor and began to lag in growth. Frost penetrated the unheated greenhouse at the end of November when all the plants were wilted. The plants remained frozen for about a month. When the temperature in the greenhouse fell to -14° after a strong frost outdoors, the boxes were taken out and kept for 24 hours in a cool room at a temperature of about +5° for slow thawing. The plants were then watered copiously and placed in a warm greenhouse. The results were checked three weeks later.

In the control group seven of the hardiest varieties survived, five varieties in the experimental group. Within each surviving variety more plants remained alive in the control group and they suffered less frost injury. In winter wheat, variety Gostianum 237, for example, 34% of the plants in the control group remained alive, but only 6% of those in the experimental group Prolonged wilting, therefore, clearly weakened frost resistance, despite the increased concentration of salt solution caused by potassium fertilizer which by itself, as we shall see below, is conducive to the development of frost resistance.

Let us consider another case of the influence of insufficient moisture on the hardiness of plants grown from the start with little moisture so that they form fewer leaves, stems, and roots. In this case, they experienced no visible loss of turgor and acquired distinct qualities of adaptation to drought, manifested physiologically, anatomically, and morphologically. Klages (1926a) studied the effect of soil moisture on the hardiness of wheat grown for this purpose in pots with moisture maintained at 20, 30, 40, and 50% of the total capacity. The plants were frozen at a temperature between -14 and -20° when they were one to four weeks old. In all cases the plants grown with less moisture acquired a xeromorphic structure and were hardier.

Thus, the effect of inadequate moisture on hardiness is determined by how long the plants are deprived of water and when this begins to influence their condition. We shall examine the nature of this phenomenon more closely in a later section.

5. SIGNIFICANCE OF SOIL NUTRITION FOR FROST RESISTANCE

We have had many examples of the favorable influence exerted on frost resistance by fertile soil. Plants always winter better on fertile soil properly cultivated and fertilized than on poor soil poorly cultivated with little or no fertilizer. Manure (including green manure) containing all the needed nutrients is especially beneficial. We shall therefore begin with data obtained from research involving the use of manure.

The data of F.F. Yukhimchuk (1935), obtained at the Uman Experimental Station during 1927-1928, a catastrophic year for winter crops in the Ukraine, are particularly instructive. In a five-field crop rotation — clean fallow, winter wheat, peas, beets, oats — the wheat came through the winter comparatively well, yielding 12.8 centners per hectare. Manure was applied to the fallow, i.e., directly under the winter wheat, at the rate of 36 tons per hectare. The beets were completely winterkilled in those places where the manure was applied under the crop, i.e., three fields before the grain. In another crop rotation — occupied pea fallow (pea on grain), winter wheat, oats, beets, millet — the wheat yield came to 10.3 centners per hectare in those cases where 36 tons of manure per acre were applied to the crop occupying the fallow. In those places where only superphosphate was added at the rate of 90 kg of P_2O_5 per hectare, the winter wheat was completely winterkilled. The results were similar on the other fields.

M.M. Gocholashvili (1940) determined the frost resistance of citrus to which a variety of fertilizers had been added. Trees with portions fertilized with manure proved to be the most resistant. For example, when frozen in a refrigerator at -10° for six hours, mandarin branches taken from manured portions lost only 25% of their leaves, 25% from portions fertilized with mineral fertilizers, and 90% of the leaves and some 28% of the shoots from unfertilized portions. The results were virtually the same in experiments with the lemon.

Thus, manure as a complete fertilizer undoubtedly strengthens hardiness. However, this is not necessarily true of certain kinds of mineral fertilizers and, consequently, of individual elements of soil nutrition. Nitrogen, phosphorus, and potassium have been very thoroughly studied in this respect.

6. ROLE OF THE PRINCIPAL ELEMENTS OF SOIL NUTRITION — NITROGEN, PHOSPHORUS, AND POTASSIUM — IN FROST RESISTANCE

Nitrogen is the most important constituent of manure which, as we have seen, promotes frost resistance. However, the addition of a nitrogenous fertilizer alone, especially in excessive amounts, reduces resistance. This phenomenon has been interpreted in various ways. For example, Arland (1932a, 1932b) thinks that too much nitrogen in the nutrient medium prevents the epidermis from developing properly so that the plants fail to gain their normal protection from evaporation. Moreover, the stomata of these plants are always open very wide. Thus, plants exposed to an excess of nitrogen suffer considerable frost damage in winter and when the snow melts in spring they lose water sooner than others and are more likely to become desiccated. They also suffer more from fungus diseases because the spores of the fungi experience little difficulty in entering the intercellular spaces through the wide open stomata. Low resistance to frost and to unfavorable wintering conditions in general is combined with low resistance to fungus diseases.

Wilhelm (1935a, 1935b) approaches the problem somewhat differently. On the basis of his research on a number of grains and vegetables, Wilhelm was able to show that nitrogen and phosphorus have the same effect on hardiness. Following prolonged chilling, especially if light, hardiness is diminished when the nitrogen and phosphorus content of the nutrient medium is increased. Only the addition of these elements to the soil in unusually large amounts has an adverse effect if the frost is of short duration. However, an insufficiency also has an adverse effect. The best results are obtained when the plants obtain nitrogen and phosphorus in normal amounts.

Wilhelm then formulated the following theory. With normal amounts of nitrogen and phosphorus protoplasm becomes more stable and at the same time more resistant to frost. On the other hand, protoplasm consumes more sugar, which plays an important part in protection from frost. That is why after a prolonged light frost, when sugar is still not too rapidly consumed for respiration, protoplasm containing a good deal of nitrogen and phosphorus may be in a state of sugar starvation and thus lose the hardiness acquired in the hardening process. If plants are exposed to frost only briefly, sugar exhaustion does not occur and the protoplasm retains its hardiness.

Wilhelm's data, especially on phosphorus, have not always been confirmed. Thus, in the experiments of I.N. Kuksa (1936, 1937, 1938, 1939) and B.I. Sablinskaya-Ivanova (1935) with winter crops, phosphates had a different effect on frost resistance from the nitrogenous fertilizers. A supplemental application of phosphorus to the soil had an effect on the wintering of plants under natural conditions, i.e., it was beneficial after prolonged frost. Hence, Wilhelm's theory explains the phenomenon only in part, but by no means in all of its manifestations.

Potassium fertilizers, as a rule, strengthen frost resistance. Opinion on this score can be considered unanimous. However, there is as yet no sound explanation why this is so. It has long been known that potassium, in contrast to nitrogen, inhibits growth and promotes differentiation of tissues. This is the view of Arland too who believes that potassium is responsible for the better development of surface tissues and thereby intensifies hardiness.

According to Wilhelm, potassium affects frost resistance by increasing the concentration of cell sap. As potassium increases in the soil, more of it is taken up by the plants so that the cells hold water better, which freezes in smaller quantities and at lower temperatures. However, Wilhelm's idea of the nature of potassium action is contradicted by the facts. For example, K.S. Semakin, Ye. S. Moroz, and V.K. Abashkin (1937) investigated the effect of various forms of potassium fertilizers combined with nitrogenous fertilizers and phosphates on the hardiness of Italian mandarins, oranges, and lemons; for comparison, they also studied the effect of sodium chloride. The plants were frozen in a refrigerator at -9° during the winter and at -5 and -7° during the spring. Changes in hardiness were compared with changes in osmotic pressure of the cell sap. Heavier concentrations of soil solution increased osmotic pressure and hardiness. However, to attribute the rise in hardiness wholly to osmotic pressure was unwarranted. Potassium chloride and sodium chloride caused the greatest rise in osmotic pressure of the cell sap, but their effect on hardiness was incomparably less than the combined effect of nitrogen, phosphorus, and potassium applied in a mixture of KH_2PO_4 and KNO_3. It follows from the authors' data that it is not the increased concentration of cell sap, but the overall nutrition regime and resultant growth factors that determine the hardiness of plants.

Let us now review the work of the well known Czech agronomist Stoklasa who studied the effect of several nutrients, chiefly potassium, and radium irradiation on hardiness. Stoklasa discovered that plants, both in pots and in the field, tolerated frost better when they were provided with all the basic nutrients — nitrogen, phosphorus, and, above all, potassium. Sodium too had a beneficial effect on hardiness. Plants (e.g., beets) taken from soil lacking available potassium, had a low rate of respiration. These plants were less hardy and were more severely injured by all kinds of fungus infections. The author interprets the nature of potassium action on plant hardiness as follows. Potassium is a radioactive element emitting beta and gamma rays. It stimulates the activity of protoplasm by intensifying the oxidation-reduction processes. The high rate of respiration resulting from available potassium is an indicator of the general vitality of the protoplasm and its even greater hardiness. The author ascribes the specific effect of potassium to its radioactivity because the plants irradiated with radium likewise became more vigorous and frost resistant.

Stoklasa's explanation of the significance of potassium for frost resistance is worthy of serious attention. The importance of potassium, for example, in intensifying carbohydrate metabolism has now been completely demonstrated (Shcherbakov, 1938, 1946, 1948; Voskresenskaya, 1948). Carbohydrate metabolism is intimately related to hardiness. Stoklasa's findings on the relationship between hardiness and overall vitality of protoplasm are very significant. However, he failed to take into account the various ways in which potassium affects plants and their resistance to frost, particularly the role of potassium in the growth process.

7. MODERN VIEW OF THE EFFECT OF EXTERNAL CONDITIONS ON HARDINESS

Frost resistance is intensified or weakened by changes in external conditions, e.g., temperature. It increases with a drop in temperature and decreases as the temperature rises. This relationship shows up both during the annual cycle of temperature and when there are changes during comparatively brief periods of time, e.g., winter thaws.

As the temperature rises, almost all processes in plants (except vernalization, etc.) accelerate to a certain point; as the temperature falls, they slow up. Respiration is very instructive in this respect. I shall cite data from the comparative studies of Newton and Anderson (1931) on the rate of respiration in four wheat varieties exposed to temperatures of +7.0 and –7° (Table 6). The determinations were made in hardened plants between November 17 and 30.

Table 6

Changes in respiratory rate of wheat at low
temperatures (in milligrams of CO_2
released per g of dry weight of leaves
in 4 hours)

Wheat variety	+7°	0°	–7°
Minhardi	2.54	1.10	0.51
Turetskaya	2.40	1.17	0.55
Fulcaster	2.52	1.25	0.61
Squarehead Meister	2.86	1.63	0.61

Disregarding the differences between individual varieties and using round numbers, we may say that the rate of respiration was half as intense at 0° as at +7° and half as intense at –7° as at 0°. At lower temperatures respiration is almost imperceptible.

A decrease in respiratory rate with falling temperature indicates reduced cell activity (but not vitality), the cells becoming dormant. This enhances their resistance to frost as well as to other unfavorable factors.

A drop in temperature also induces a number of functional and structural changes in plants. Before the start of freezing a drop in temperature checks growth. As growth slackens and photosynthesis continues, plants begin to store plastic substances. With low temperatures the processes of disintegration begin to prevail over the processes of synthesis and relatively simpler compounds accumulate in the cells. At the same time there is an increase in osmotic pressure, suction power and water-holding capacity of the cells. When the temperature falls below zero, the cells become dehydrated and their water-holding capacity increases even more as does their hardiness.

The function of light in frost resistance is chiefly due to the fact that it is the main factor in photosynthesis. As a result of intensified light plus other favorable conditions plants assimilate plastic substances more vigorously and store them in greater quantities. The presence of these substances is a prerequisite for the development of frost resistance. And this is not all, for light also has a direct influence on growth. Intense sunlight as well as a shortened day inhibits growth. Diffuse and weak sunlight, on the other hand, tends to accelerate growth. Moreover, light has a powerful effect on differentiation of cells and tissues. In intense and direct sunlight cells are smaller with thickened walls while surface tissues develop heavier cuticle and cork. Shortening the day has the same effect; a shortened fall day helps to halt growth and intensify differentiation of tissues in all plants.

During the fall light normally becomes less intense as the days grow shorter. Low intensity of light is unfavorable for the development of frost resistance, whereas a shortened day is favorable. In those areas where the fall is characterized by sunny weather, direct sunlight reinforces the beneficial effect of a shortened day.

The moisture factor under the natural wintering conditions of plants is much less variable than temperature and light. Acting directly on plants, moisture depends not only on the amount of precipitation, but also on the water properties of the soil, surface runoff, etc. Excessive moisture is always harmful, whereas too little moisture may sometimes be helpful in promoting frost resistance. Dehydration leading to exhaustion is invariably harmful; dehydration that halts growth when it is extremely vigorous and that intensifies hydrolysis may be useful. When plants are frozen, mild cell dehydration promotes frost resistance because it intensifies hydrolysis and is conducive to deeper cell dormancy.

The complex and sometimes contradictory influence of the individual elements of soil nutrition will be understood from the following. Hardening, like other processes, normally takes place only in plants well provided with food. A deficiency or excess of individual nutrients disturbs the normal course of the hardening process during the fall. Excessive nitrogen, for example, stimulates the synthesis of proteins as the main component of protoplasm. Considerable amounts of carbohydrates are also consumed in this synthesis. An excess of nitrogen and resultant extreme growth inevitably exhausts the carbohydrate reserve and the quickly growing parts of the plants become poorly differentiated. Too much nitrogen in the fall prevents plants from hardening. This may well be the effect of excessive phosphorus too because it is part of protoplasm as a necessary component of proteins and lipoids. Too much potassium, on the other hand, has a somewhat different effect on frost resistance, for it retards growth. The reserve of plastic substances remains as the cells overflowing with potassium acquire more suction power and greater water-holding capacity.

Such, in outline, is the relationship between frost resistance and external conditions. In reality it is much more complex. Any external factor affects plants in a variety of ways by itself and when combined with other factors. A good deal of work has been done on the effect of temperature, light, moisture, and the various nutrients on the physiology of plants (Sabinin, 1940; Shkol'nik, 1950). An account of this work would lead us too far afield.

CONCLUSION

This chapter is far from exhaustive. We concentrated chiefly on the obvious direct connections between frost resistance and external conditions and touched only briefly on internal, anatomical, and physiological factors. Yet the nature of the effect on plant hardiness exerted by all the external factors is manifested in various physiological, anatomical, and morphological changes which, strictly speaking, determine the changes in hardiness. The relationship between hardiness and external conditions can be more fully understood only when the internal changes preceding the changes in resistance are known. This is the task now confronting us.

CHAPTER 3

FALL GROWTH AND THE DEVELOPMENT
OF FROST RESISTANCE

It has long been known that frost resistance is closely related to the early termination of fall growth. Many investigations have demonstrated the importance of the checking of growth for the development of resistance.

1. GROWTH OF WINTER AND SPRING WHEAT
AT LOW TEMPERATURES

Comparative studies of winter and spring wheat clearly show the relationship between hardiness and arrest of growth at low temperatures during the fall (I.M. Vasil'yev, 1939a, 1939b, 1946). These studies will now be examined in greater detail.

Experiment 1. Seeds of six spring and four winter plants were sown in 10 wooden boxes containing 20 kg of soil each. Each box included 20 germinated seeds of all 10 varieties tested. Sowing all the varieties in one box made it possible to provide the most uniform conditions for the growth of each variety.

There were two sowings — April 10 and May 28. The plants were kept in the laboratory until they sprouted after which they were transferred to a plot outdoors. From about mid-April to mid-May the mean daily air temperature was no higher than +10 or +12° while the minimum night temperature was +5°. The experiment was concluded when the plants reached the four-leaf stage. The experiment with the May-sown plants was concluded June 11 when they too were in the four-leaf stage. The mean daily temperature was about +20°; the night temperature did not drop below +13°.

Fig. 30 shows the striking difference in growth between the winter and spring wheat of the April sowing. The former is smaller and decumbent in form, the latter tall with long, broad leaves. The difference between the winter and spring wheat sown in May (Fig. 31) is not apparent, and even the trained eye of the breeder could not distinguish them by external appearance alone.

The smaller size of the winter wheat as compared with the spring wheat when grown at low temperatures was naturally due to the different in rate of growth. The winter plants grew slowly and therefore formed smaller leaves. At fairly high summer temperatures the winter wheat grew as rapidly as the

Fig. 30. Plants sown April (photographed May 17) 1 - 6 — spring wheats, from left to right: Gordeiforme 10, Melanopus 69, Gordeiforme 189, Mindum, Tsezium 111, Lutescens 62; 7 - 10 — winter wheats, from left to right: Kooperatorka, Moskovskaya 2411, Gostianum 237, Lutescens 329

Fig. 31. Plants sown May 28 (photographed June 11) 1 - 6 — spring wheats, from left to right: Melanopus 69, Gordeiforme 10, Gordeiforme 189, Mindum, Tsezium 111, Lutescens 62; 7 - 9 — winter wheats, from left to right: Moskovskaya 2411, Kooperatorka, Gostianum 237, Lutescens 329

spring wheat and so no differences in habit showed up. However, the difference in size of leaves at low temperatures might have been related to the well known difference in tillering of the two varieties, although there was no sign of it here. Perhaps sowing the winter grains early in spring was responsible for the smaller leaves because at low temperatures the root system was thicker, which inhibited the growth of leaves. The following experiments were undertaken to resolve these doubts.

Experiment 2. The same 10 wheat varieties were used. The seeds were

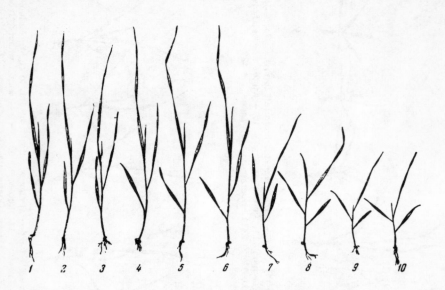

Fig. 32. Winter and spring wheat in the four-leaf stage grown at
low temperatures, just before the stem-extension stage
1 - 6 — spring wheats, from left to right: Melanopus 69,
Gordeiforme 10, Gordeiforme 189, Mindum, Tsezium 111,
Lutescens 62; 7 - 10 — winter wheats, from left to right:
Kooperatorka, Moskovskaya 2411, Costianum 237, Lutescens 329

sown February 22 in a cool greenhouse under conditions closely approximating those in the preceding experiment. The temperature was maintained at +5° through the first 10 days in March and thereafter between +5 and +10°. We concluded the experiment April 10 just before the stem-extension stage. The plants were carefully observed throughout and typical specimens were photographed and sketched from time to time. This made it possible to trace the dynamics of growth from the moment they began to sprout. Fig. 32 shows all the winter and spring wheat varieties in the four-leaf stage. The plants had a single stem at the time because the seeds had been sown thickly and the light in the greenhouse was weak. All the leaves of the winter wheat were much smaller than those of the spring wheat. This experiment showed that the smaller size of the winter wheat as compared with the spring wheat when grown under identical low temperatures could not be attributed to the differences in tillering.

Experiment 3. The purpose of this experiment was to compare the leaves and roots of winter and spring wheat grown at low temperatures. Germinated seeds were sown September 14 when the weather had grown markedly cooler. As in the preceding experiments, seeds of all 10 varieties were planted in each of 10 boxes kept outdoors. On October 4 when three leaves had formed on each, the soil was washed off the roots and the plants were collected in bunches by variety from each box separately and sketched. The plants from one of the boxes are shown in Fig. 33.

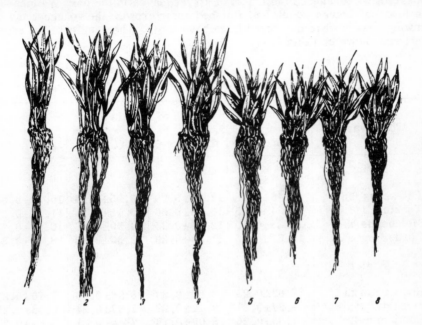

Fig. 33. Correlation of leaf mass with root mass of plants grown
at low temperatures
1 - 4 — spring wheats, from left to right: Gordeiforme 10,
Melanopus 69, Tsezium 111, Lutescens 62; 5 - 8 — winter wheats,
from left to right: Lutescens 329, Gostianum 237, Kooperatorka,
Moskovskaya 2411

Since the root mass of winter and spring wheat matches the leaf mass, it is fair to say that root growth does not check the growth of the aerial part of winter plants growing at low temperatures. The conclusion is that the smaller size of the winter plants as compared with the spring plants when grown at low temperatures is due to the general arrest of growth of the aerial part and root system of the plants.

2. GROWTH DIFFERENCES AT LOW TEMPERATURES BETWEEN INDIVIDUAL VARIETIES OF WINTER AND SPRING WHEAT

A comparison of the growth of winter and spring wheat at low temperatures discloses that the varieties in each group likewise do not grow the same way.

However, the differences are not very sharp nor are they always perceptible. We used several methods to determine them.

Experiment 1. On September 14 after a comparatively late fall sowing we measured the size of the leaves of those varieties of winter and spring wheat which served for group characterization of the growth peculiarities of winter and spring wheat. The sowing was done with already germinated seeds selected for the size of the sprouts. The growing conditions were identical for all the boxes each containing 20 plants of each variety. When the fifth leaf appeared, we measured the length of all the leaves in the box. We measured the blade of leaves which had finished their growth; the youngest and still growing leaves were measured from base to tip. The results of the experiment are shown in Table 7.

Table 7

Length of leaves in different wheat varieties sown September 14

Wheat variety	Length of leaf (in cm)			
	second node	third node	fourth node	fifth node
Spring				
Lutescens 62	10.46±0.26	12.84±0.29	13.35±0.34	10.10±0.30
Tsezium 111	10.34±0.23	13.18±0.20	15.13±0.21	11.11±0.32
Melanopus 69	10.35±0.15	12.75±0.23	14.99±0.22	10.81±0.31
Gordeiforme 10	10.61±0.35	11.80±0.29	12.85±0.23	8.49±0.34
Winter				
Kooperatorka	7.62±0.23	8.25±0.30	8.08±0.23	7.70±0.25
Moskovskaya 2411	7.94±0.21	8.12±0.22	7.87±0.24	6.48±0.25
Gostianum 237	7.33±0.26	8.09±0.19	7.44±0.17	5.84±0.22
Lutescens 329	7.50±0.17	7.62±0.10	7.00±0.16	5.01±0.09

Let us compare the size of the leaves of the winter varieties beginning with the young ones. The sharpest difference between the individual varieties was noted on the youngest leaves of the fifth node. The difference from variety to variety on the older leaves of the fourth and third nodes was less marked. The varieties changed places with respect to size of leaves of the second node, but even the greatest difference is well within the limits of experimental error.

Among the spring varieties only Gordeiforme 10 had unusually large leaves. However, the difference from the other varieties began with the leaves of the third node and was most pronounced on the youngest leaves of the fifth node.

In the fall sowing each succeeding leaf formed at a lower temperature. In this experiment the mean daily temperature during the growth period of the leaves of the second node was still fairly high, remaining at 10 to 15 . This temperature was sufficient to enable us to distinguish between the spring and winter groups by size of leaves, but was not low enough to distinguish between the individual varieties within each group, which required lower temperatures. The lower the temperature at which the leaves grew, the more pronounced were the differences in leaf size from variety to variety.

This experiment shows that to distinguish differences in growth between individual varieties it is necessary to use lower temperatures than to distinguish between the winter and spring groups as a whole. If grown in the fall when the temperature is gradually dropping, it is necessary to compare the varieties by the size of the most recently formed leaves.

Experiment 2. This experiment was performed under the same conditions and on the same plants, which were sown at the same time in another box. On November 27 the plants were transferred from the bed into the greenhouse where the temperature was maintained at +6 to +8°. The same day we measured the height from base to tip of the fifth leaf which was still growing. The plants continued to grow for the next six days at the same temperature. On December 3 we measured them again the same way. The results are shown in Table 8. The varieties are arranged by growth in length of leaves in the same order as for size of leaves.

Table 8

Length of leaves of the fifth node of different
winter wheat varieties

Wheat variety	Length of leaf, cm		Growth of leaf, cm
	27. XI	3. XII	
Kooperatorka	7.1	11.7	4.6
Moskovskaya 2411	5.7	9.4	3.7
Gostianum 239	5.3	7.9	2.6
Lutescens 329	4.8	7.0	2.2

Experiment 3. The purpose of this experiment was to find out whether the differences in growth of the individual varieties noted above show up as clearly in the spring as they do in the fall. Germinated seeds of the same four varieties of winter wheat were planted February 26 in Mitscherlich pots. They were kept until mid-April in a cool greenhouse at about +10° and then outdoors in a seed bed. The experiment was concluded May 4. Fig. 34 shows wheat specimens representing two opposite patterns of growth— Kooperatorka and Lutescens 329. The leaves of Kooperatorka both on the main shoot and on the lateral shoots are larger. The two other varieties, not shown in the figure, occupy an intermediate position. Moskovskaya 2411 is closer to Kooperatorka while Gostianum is closer to Lutescens 329.

The experiment shows that growth differences appearing between individual varieties at low temperatures show up in the spring just as they do in the fall.

The experiments described above leave no doubt that individual wheat varieties, especially in the winter group, grow at different rates at low temperatures. However, as between the winter and spring groups, the differences between the individual varieties in each group are not very pronounced, appearing only at lower temperatures.

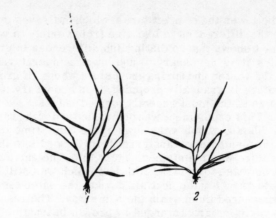

Fig. 34. Winter wheat varieties differing in
hardiness, grown at low temperatures
1 — Kooperatorka, 2 — Lutescens 329

3. HARDINESS OF WINTER AND SPRING WHEAT
VARIETIES IN RELATION TO GROWTH
DIFFERENCES AT LOW TEMPERATURES

The purpose of the investigations to be described below was to show the comparative hardiness of the winter and spring wheat varieties which we studied in other connections. The hardiness of some of these varieties was repeatedly determined before the differences in growth were established. Part of the varieties were tested for hardiness using the same plants in which growth differences were previously established. We shall review here only a few of the experiments.

Experiment 1. The comparative hardiness of spring wheat varieties Lutescens 62 and Gordeiforme 10 was determined. They were chosen because of the marked difference in growth at low temperatures. Soft Lutescens 62 showed the most rapid growth at low temperatures, hard Gordeiforme 10 the weakest. Both varieties were planted September 4 in a field using a horse-drawn seeder and with an effort made to achieve uniform conditions. The seeds were germinated before sowing, thus assuring even sprouts in both varieties.

Hardiness was tested by freezing plants dug from the ground in a refrigerator and subsequently grown in a cool greenhouse in glasses of water. In one of several experiments involving the use of different temperatures to freeze the plants, the particular choice of temperature to determine the differences in hardiness between the varieties being compared turned out to be very appropriate. The plants in this experiment were frozen for 44 hours (November 9 and 10). The temperature in the refrigerator was maintained at −10.0 to −10.8° . Figs. 35 and 36 show the plants before freezing and nine days later in the greenhouse. It is obvious that Lutescens 62 was larger than Gordeiforme 10 before freezing and, consequently, grew more rapidly under the same conditions. However, the taller Lutescens 62 suffered more from the frost; almost one-third of the leaves were winterkilled. Gordeiforme 10, on the other hand, scarcely suffered at all.

Experiment 2. The familiar Kooperatorka, Moskovskaya 2411, Gostianum 237, and Lutescens 329 were tested for hardiness. Kooperatorka showed the maximum rate of growth at low temperatures, Lutescens 329 the minimum. Seeds were planted in boxes on September 14. The plants were kept outdoors where they hardened. The night of December 14 was very cold, the temperature dropping by morning to -26°; there was virtually no snow. The plants

Fig. 35. Spring wheat before chilling
1 — Gordeiforme 10; 2 — Lutescens 62

were allowed to remain exposed to the frost for several hours and then brought into a greenhouse with a temperature of about +5°; several days later they were transferred to a warm greenhouse. When the plants were checked two weeks later, 15% of the Kooperatorkas survived, 35% of the Moskovskaya, 58% of the Gostianum 237, and 36% of the Lutescens 329. The survivors were by no means equally viable (Fig. 37). The Kooperatorkas failed to grow and eventually all died. Moskovskaya 2411 grew very slowly, some plants not at all and they too died. Gostianum 237 did well. Lutescens 329 did best of all.

The experiment shows quite clearly that the slower the fall growth of a variety, the more resistant to frost it is.

Experiment 3. Twelve wheat varieties were compared for hardiness. The plants were grown at low temperatures (in a cool greenhouse), when the differences in growth between the individual varieties show up clearly, and

Fig. 36. The same plants 9 days after
chilling
1 — Gordeiforme 10; 2 — Lutescens 62

frozen in an unheated greenhouse to which they were transferred from the cool greenhouse. They were kept in the unheated greenhouse from the middle to the end of December. During this time the lowest temperature was -15°. Fig. 38 shows the plants before they were frozen.

The results of freezing the plants one week after they were brought into a warm greenhouse were as follows. Spring wheat Lutescens 62 and Gordeiforme 10, wheat-wheatgrass hybrids 23086 and 34085, and winter wheat

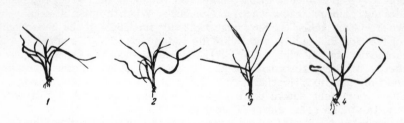

Fig. 37. Aftergrowth of winter wheat kept at -26°. 1 — Kooperatorka;
2 — Moskovskaya 2411; 3 — Gostianum 237; 4 — Lutescens 329

Fig. 38. Plants before chilling
1 — soft spring wheat Lutescens 62; 2 — hard
spring wheat Gordeiforme 10; 3 — wheat-wheatgrass hybrid 23086; 4 — wheat-wheatgrass
hybrid 34085; 5 - 12 — winter wheats:
Kooperatorka, Moskovskaya 2411, Sandomirka,
Khar'kovskaya 917, Gostianum 237, Krymka,
Borovichevskaya, Lutescens 329

Kooperatorka and Moskovskaya 2411 were dead. The survivors, arranged in order of degree of frost injury, were: Sandomirka (the most severely injured), Krymka, Gostianum 237, Khar'kovskaya 917, Borovichevskaya, Lutescens 329 (the least injured). Fig. 39 gives an idea of the condition of the plants, representing four of the varieties mentioned above, one and one-half months after freezing.

Fig. 39. Winter wheat after chilling
1 — Moskovskaya 2411; 2 — Krymka; 3 —
Khar'kovskaya 917; 4 — Borovichevskaya

Experiment 4. The wheat-wheatgrass hybrids were compared for hardiness with spring varieties and winter wheat Moskovskaya 2411. They all died at -15°. To determine the differences in hardiness, the plants were frozen at higher temperatures. We used plants from boxes in the cool greenhouse which were sown at the same time. They were frozen in the unheated greenhouse like the plants in the preceding experiment. The minimum temperature to which the plants were exposed was about -13°.

This was the picture one week after the plants were transferred to a warm greenhouse. All the spring Lutescens 62 were dead; only a few of the Gordeiforme 10 survived. Both wheat-wheatgrass hybrids remained alive, but badly injured, hybrid 23086 suffering most of all. Only the tips of the leaves of Moskovskaya 2411 (about one-third of the blade) were winterkilled.

Let us now sum up our tests of 12 wheat varieties. In ascending order of hardiness they are: Lutescens 62 (spring, early-ripening), Gordeiforme 10 (spring, late-ripening), wheat-wheatgrass hybrid 23086), wheat-wheatgrass hybrid 34085, Kooperatorka (one of the least hardy of the winter varieties), Khar'kovskaya 917, Borovichevskaya, Lutescens 329 (one of the hardiest of the winter varieties).

Let us now arrange them by growth using the same order as in the experiment with low temperatures: Lutescens 62, Gordeiforme 10, wheat-wheatgrass hybrid 23086, wheat-wheatgrass hybrid 34085, Kooperatorka, Moskovskaya 2411, Sandomirka, Khar'kovskaya 917, Gostianum 237, Krymka, Borovichevskaya, Lutescens 329.

The correspondence is almost complete, the only exception being Krymka. The hardiness of Krymka is not very great, in which respect it is only slightly superior to Moskovskaya 2411. In growth, however, Krymka was equal to that of the very hardy Borovichevskaya and very close to Lutescens 329, the hardiest of all. The reason for the exception is that Krymka has small leaves, which set it apart from the other varieties tested and which, naturally, affected the height of the plants.

4. FALL GROWTH AND HARDINESS IN OTHER PLANTS

The connection established between the arrest of growth in winter and spring wheat in the fall and development of hardiness impelled us to investigate other plants for the same phenomenon. At various times we studied winter rye, clover, aflfalfa, cereal grasses, winter rape, beets, cabbage, kohlrabi, etc. The picture turned out to be more or less as follows. Within each crop the varieties with relatively slower growth in the fall were less hardy. However, when different crops were compared, e.g., wheat and rye, there was no relationship between growth rate and hardiness. Here are two of our experiments.

Experiment 1. Vyatka winter rye and two species of wheatgrass — Agropyrum glaucum and Agropyrum junceum — were sown at the end of August in such a way that in each box two quarters of the area along the diagonal were occupied by rye or wheat and the other two quarters by wheatgrass. The seeds were germinated before planting. This was particularly important in the experiment with wheatgrass because dry seeds do not sprout for a long time nor do they do so simultaneously. Thus, wheatgrass sown at one time will be in different stages of growth.

Fig. 40 shows typical rye and wheatgrass plants just before winter. Judging by leaf size, the wheatgrass grew more slowly than the rye. Moreover, its root mass was no thicker.

Fig. 40. Plants before winter
1 — winter rye, variety Vyatka; 2 — Agropyrum glaucum

111

Fig. 41 is a photograph of plants in the box in which they grew and wintered, approximately a month after the snow melted. The winterkilled plants had already begun to rot while the survivors recovered and were sprouting. The plants wintered under a thin layer of snow and were exposed to temperatures as low as -19.5° in the zone of the tillering nodes. Except for some isolated plants the wheatgrass died during the winter. The rye came through in fairly good condition.

Fig. 41. Plants one month after melting of snow
Lower left quarter of the box — Agropyrum glaucum:
upper right quarter — Agropyrum junceum;
remainder — Vyatka winter rye

Equally instructive are the comparisons between winter wheat and wheatgrass in respect to growth and frost resistance. Fig. 42 shows Lutescens 329 and wheatgrass A. glaucum a month after the snow had melted. All the wheat grass leaves were dead, with only the tillering nodes surviving; in the winter wheat, however, they survived along with the bases of the young leaves. Yet the wheat grass during the fall, judging by the leaf mass, grew much more slowly than the wheat whose growth was likewise checked.

Experiment 2. The growth and hardiness of winter varieties of Omka and Vyatka rye, Borovichevskaya winter wheat, and four species of wheatgrass — A. glaucum, A. elongatum, A. junceum, and A. trichophorum. The experiment was set up the same way as experiment 1. Four boxes were sown September 4 with already germinated seeds. Both varieties of rye, wheat, and one species of wheatgrass were planted in each box. Growth and hardening took place outdoors. On January 14 the air temperature fell to -29° within a few hours. The plants subsequently brought into the greenhouse were severely injured. However, two weeks later the rye began to grow quite vigorously. An occasional winter wheat plant began to grow, but almost all the wheatgrass was dead.

Despite its slower fall growth, the wheatgrass proved to be less resistant to frost than the two rye varieties — Omka and Vyatka — and Borovichevskaya wheat.

Thus, our investigation of plants other than wheat revealed that slow growth in the fall is no indicator of hardiness, that it may be associated with less rather than greater hardiness.

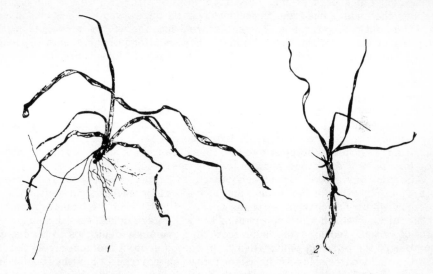

Fig. 42. Plants one month after melting of snow
1 — winter wheat, variety Lutescens 329; 2 — Agropyrum glaucum

5. FALL GROWTH AND DEVELOPMENT OF HARDINESS IN FRUIT TREES AND BERRIES

The most important growth characteristic of woody plants is the close connection between rate of cell formation and subsequent differentiation. This is true of herbaceous plants as well, but it is more pronounced in woody plants because of much greater cell differentiation. Specifically, it consists of the following: when growth proceeds fairly vigorously, cells of the growing parts become differentiated slowly; when growth proceeds sluggishly, newly formed cells are differentiated more rapidly. Surface tissues in rapidly growing shoots are usually insufficiently developed, and these shoots resemble the shoots of herbaceous plants in succulence and external appearance. As soon as the shoots stop growing, they lignify, become drier and tougher as they acquire a thick superficial layer of cork and "ripen".

The young shoots of woody plants normally "ripen" in the fall when the weather gets colder and growth ceases naturally. This process very often begins in the summer, depending on the species and age of the tree, fruit bearing, and external conditions. In old trees growth ceases earlier, other things being equal, than in young trees. Drought frequently causes growth to halt, but it resumes with the fall rains. In this event sometimes all the buds open and leafy as well as flowering and fruit trees in gardens assume a springlike appearance.

Late growth in woody plants, regardless of cause, always has an adverse effect on frost resistance. Here is an example from my own investigations of fruit trees in the Maritime Territory. There was a severe drought in the summer of 1949 and even young trees virtually stopped growing. Buds had formed on the shoots of many apple varieties. After rain fell at the end of August, the buds opened and the shoots began to grow again. This continued until the cold weather set in. The shoots went into the winter unripened, with clusters of leaves at the tips. Almost all the portions of the shoots that had grown during the fall were winterkilled. The trees of those varieties with no late shoot growth did not suffer during the winter.

In some trees the freezing of part of the newly grown young branches is a common phenomenon. It is exceptionally severe in transplants from other climates. In the Maritime Territory there is partial freezing every year of the young shoots of Lespedeza bicolor Turcz., Catalpa japonica, Sophora flavescens Ait., and other imports from the south. They can all grow in the Maritime Territory, but the overall mass increases very slowly because they lose part of the young growth every winter.

The vigorous growth of young shoots in the fall may lower frost resistance both of other parts of the branch and of the tree as a whole. One often sees trees in which the cortex below the necrosed portion of the branch is completely alive while the pith and part of the xylem are dead. And if a succession of cross sections is made from the obviously dead tips to the base, necrosis of the pith and part of the xylem can be seen in the underlying parts with the unaided eye. Moreover, all the pith of an apparently healthy branch is often brown. Sometimes an entire branch or even the whole plant may be injured by freezing, as a result of late growth. I.V. Michurin mentioned the Nerchinskiy apricot as an example of a fruit tree dying in winter because of late growth. Although it comes from an incomparably colder climate, a seedling of this apricot is nevertheless winterkilled in Michurinsk simply because "having finished its growth in mid-summer, the sap begins to move again by fall; it freezes before it can be 'harvested' " (vol. 1, p. 337).

However, just as in the case of herbaceous plants, not all trees and shrubs whose growth ceases in the fall are thus helped to develop hardiness. The cessation of growth due to plant exhaustion resulting, for example, from excessive fruit bearing always has an adverse effect on hardiness. A nutritional deficiency also inhibits growth and the development of hardiness.

6. FALL GROWTH AND DEVELOPMENT OF HARDINESS IN SUBTROPICAL PLANTS

The fall-winter period of dormancy that is so characteristic of most trees and shrubs in the temperate zone is very slight in subtropical plants. They grow, temperature permitting, until late in the fall and go into the winter insufficiently hardened with immature shoots. The lemon is noted for its particularly "unrestricted" growth which, most citrus experts say, is the main reason why it does not harden and has low frost resistance.

Sharp daily fluctuations in temperature are characteristic of our subtropics during the winter and early spring in clear weather. Plants quickly warmed by the sun in the day and then get chilled at night. These brupt changes affect plants adversely, particularly the leafy subtropical varieties which vigorously absorb the sun's rays and have no distinct period of winter dormancy. Sap movement and growth during the day reduce their hardiness so that they are prone to subsequent frost injury (S.M. Ivanov, 1939a, 1945). This is the main reason why citrus groves on the Black Sea coast are ruined from time to time.

Thus, for most subtropical plants as well as for the woody and herbaceous plants of the temperate zone the cessation of growth is a major factor in the development of hardiness. However, the importance of this factor must not be exaggerated. As we learned from B.S. Moshkov's research (1935), reducing the amount of natural light tends to halt the growth of woody plants in the temperate zone and build their resistance to frost. Halting of growth by no means increases the hardiness of all subtropical plants.

A.F. Lakhtionov and I conducted joint experiments in Vladivostok on Japanese persimmon seedlings of an unhardy variety with rapidly changing growth rate depending on the length of day. We only had to expose the young plants to nine hours of daylight for 10 days to check their growth and cause terminal buds to form, the best indicator of termination of growth. Plants exposed to a shortened day early in summer could be kept dormant for several months before the autumn frosts without any signs of growth whatever, but with continued and accumulating assimilation of reserve plastic substances by all parts of the plants. It was a fair assumption that these seedlings, grown under reduced light, would be much more resistant to frost than plants kept under normal conditions and ten times their size. Actually, however, the experimental plants, even though they were covered with snow, all died, just as did the controls. Total cessation of growth long before the onset of frosts failed to strengthen naturally unhardy plants. Despite complete suppression of growth, the Japanese persimmon did not even approach the pea in hardiness, individual plants of which under the same conditions were still alive at the end of March.

There was comparatively little change in the hardiness of other heat-loving plants of tropical origin even after growth was completely halted by photoperiodic action.

7. NATURE OF THE RELATIONSHIP BETWEEN HARDINESS AND FALL GROWTH

The growth phenomenon itself must be carefully examined before the nature of the relationship between hardiness and fall growth can be understood. Growth may be defined as an increase in the plant mass through the new formation of living matter — protoplasm. As a result of its vital activity protoplasm is destroyed and recreated. In a young growing cell the new formation of protoplasm prevails over the destructive process and thus causes growth. In a nongrowing working cell the new formation of protoplasm is in balance with the destructive process, but in an aging cell it fails to keep pace with it.

The new formation of protoplasm, which is basically a protein substance, is the end product of metabolism. Metabolism is more active in the growing parts of a plant than in those parts which are not growing. The same thing holds true for growing plants and for plants which have stopped growing as a whole. Plant growth is always associated with the specific areas where cell multiplication takes place. However, growth in one area does not necessarily affect the entire plant. The harmful effect of late fall growth of young tree shoots frequently shows up in lowered frost resistance not only in the growing parts of these shoots, but also in the parts below them. The main reason for this phenomenon is that growth is an indicator of the metabolic processes actively taking place in the plant. Even if there is no pronounced growth in the working cells, metabolism may nevertheless be intensified.

The new formation of protoplasm normally occurs only when all of its components are present. If any one of them is missing or is present in insufficient amounts, new formation halts and the entire metabolic process takes another direction. Instead of protoplasm its individual components now begin to accumulate — carbohydrates, oils, proteins or products of their assimilation. At the same time the appearance of the cell changes. If excessive, carbohydrates are deposited on the cell walls in the form of additional layers of hemicellulose and are later transformed, in whole or in part, into lignin or cork. If there is an excess of oils, the cells become oily, etc.

All types of cell differentiation are forms of such changes in protoplasm which are essential for individual development of the organism. Historically, however, these forms arose as a divergence from metabolism, the new formation of protoplasm being the final result. This is confirmed by the simplest of plants — fungi and algae — and by bacteria which, under favorable conditions, continuously accumulate protoplasm and multiply but which, under unfavorable conditions, are transformed into cysts, become covered with thick membranes, fill with carbohydrates, oils, and other reserve substances, and become dormant.

One more observation in conclusion. Whatever the significance of growth may be and, consequently, of the rate of metabolism associated with it, the characteristics of a plant, including resistance to frost, depend primarily on the nature of the protoplasm, its chemical composition, colloidal state, etc. peculiar to that plant. Growth is simply the manifestation of protoplasmic activity. Protein bodies constituting the basis of protoplasm are endlessly varied. Each organism has its characteristic protein. Depending on the properties of this protein and on the properties of its protoplasm, the plant acquires this or that set of characteristics. Thus, even with the same growth rate in the fall, plants will acquire different degrees of hardiness, as we have already seen.

We are now in a better position to understand the beneficial effect of cessation of growth in the fall on the development of hardiness. Arrested growth is primarily a manifestation of lowered plant activity and is thus conducive to strengthening resistance to frost. As already pointed out, the lower plants — fungi, algae — as well as bacteria become dormant when conditions cease to be favorable. This is equally applicable to the higher plants.

A reduced rate of growth also leads to greater differentiation of cells and tissues, thickening of cell walls, development of sheaths, deposition of cuticle, cork, etc., all of which promote frost resistance. Arrested growth is associated with changes in metabolism — accumulation of certain original products of protoplasmic formation such as amino acids, sugars, oils, etc. along with a reduction in the rate of new formation of protoplasm.

This, then, is the way in which cessation of growth in the fall affects the development of frost resistance in plants. It must be remembered, however, that we have oversimplified the situation, because frost resistance is a function of more than arrested growth.

CONCLUSION

Several specific examples were cited to show that cessation of plant growth in the fall (but not when due to nutritional deficiency) is an essential, though not exclusive, prerequisite of the development of hardiness in plants. Arrested growth affects different plants in different degrees.

We conclude from out analysis that growth as a process of increasing the amount of living matter — protoplasm — is merely a special case of the continuous self-renewal characteristic of protoplasm and is organically connected with the rate of metabolism. More vigorous growth is an indicator of more vigorous self-renewal of protoplasm and of more energetic metabolism in the parts closest to the growth zones or even in the plant as a whole. When subzero temperature halts the growth of a thriving plant in the fall, the protoplasm continues to renew itself. Although it actually diminishes as the temperature falls, self-renewal is relatively higher than before. Thus, the plant is insufficiently hardened to withstand frost.

The relationship between rate of fall growth and development of hardiness can therefore be understood only when the changes in protoplasm during the fall are analyzed.

CHAPTER 4

REŞERVE PLASTIC SUBSTANCES AND HARDINESS

One of the results of cessation of growth in the fall is the storage of plastic substances in the cells. All investigators regard this process as a prerequisite of successful plant wintering. The reserve of plastic substances is a source of energy enabling plants to live through the winter without photosynthesis. "Protective substances" are formed from them which enable protoplasm to resist cold and frost. Thanks to these substances herbaceous plants regenerate early in the spring, despite the loss of all their leaves during the winter, and woody plants open their buds. All this is familiar knowledge, yet the question of whether frost resistance is to be attributed solely to the storage of plastic substances and their protection of protoplasm is still unresolved.

1. STORAGE OF PLASTIC SUBSTANCES
IN RELATION TO THE DIFFERENCE IN GROWTH
BETWEEN WINTER AND SPRING WHEAT

We pointed out in the preceding chapter that individual varieties of winter and spring wheat grow at different rates when the temperature is low. Since plastic substances are used up mainly during growth, we assumed that the corresponding differences in storage of plastic substances are the direct consequence of the differences in growth.

The accumulation of plastic substances is usually judged from the content of the most important compounds. However, the regenerative capacity of a plant is another criterion. Loeb (1924) once set up a strict, almost mathematical relationship between the regenerative capacity of Bryophyllum slips and their content of plastic substances. More reliable results can be obtained by this method since all the plastic substances, not merely individual constituents regardless of their role in a plant, are involved in the regenerative process.

We ran special experiments using methods of determining all the plastic substances found in plants. One method was to calculate the green mass grown after the plants were cut at ground level. These plants were naturally able to grow only if their subsurface parts contained a reserve of plastic substances, the rate varying with the amount stored. Another method was to compare the viability of individual varieties kept in darkness for a long time — the smaller the reserve of the substances, the sooner the plants became exhausted.

Experiment 1. This experiment was performed on already familiar winter and spring wheat varieties. They were sown September 14 in boxes, four winter and four spring varieties in each. Our purpose was to compare the regrowth of the individual varieties. Accordingly, on November 16 all the plants in two boxes were cut down at soil level and the boxes placed in a dimly lit room. Before they were cut, all the wheat plants had five leaves on the main shoot and were bushy. There were 3–4 shoots on the winter wheat, 2–3 on the spring wheat. The latter had no sheaths. On December 1 the regrowth of leaves of each variety were cut, dried, and weighed (Table 9). Typical specimens were photographed (Fig. 43).

The second fresh weight of the winter wheat was much larger than that of the spring wheat. The amount of leaves in individual winter wheat varieties was inversely proportional to their rate of growth at low temperatures. Kooperatorka had the smallest mass of leaves, Moskovskaya 2411 had somewhat more, Gostianum 237 still more, and Lutescens 329 most of all. Gordeiforme 10, outstanding among the spring wheat varieties for low growth rate at low temperatures, had the largest regrowth of leaves.

Experiment 2. This experiment involved the same winter and spring varieties, which were sown at the same time. The plants were kept outdoors until October 3, at which time they were in the two-leaf stage with the third leaf just beginning to appear. Growth of the winter wheat clearly lagged behind that of the spring wheat. There was also a difference in growth between the individual spring varieties. On October 3 the plants were shifted to a cool greenhouse with a temperature of +6 to +8° and kept in darkness. Seventeen days later the individual varieties looked the way they are shown in Fig. 44. The spring wheat scarcely grew all the time it was in darkness. No new leaves or shoots appeared and many plants died. Gordeiforme looked the best of the spring varieties. The winter varieties grew perceptibly under the same conditions. Etiolated leaves of the fourth node appeared in all the Lutescens 329 and Gostianum 237. About half of Moskovskaya 2411 was so affected. In Kooperatorka only leaves of the third node grew for a while, but no new leaves appeared. All the spring wheat died after 20 days of remaining in darkness. Among the winter varieties Kooperatorka died almost com-

Table 9

Aftergrowth of leaves of spring and winter wheats

Wheat variety	Weight of aftergrowth of leaves of 20 plants, g
Spring	
Lutescens 62	0.025
Tsezium 111	0.028
Melanopus 69	0.042
Gordeiforme 10	0.058
Winter	
Kooperatorka	0.078
Moskovskaya 2411	0.137
Gostianum 237	0.156
Lutescens 329	0.160

pletely, just a few isolated plants surviving. Most of Moskovskaya 2411 survived, but in very poor condition. Gostianum 237 looked the best. Lutescens 329 turned out to be the most viable.

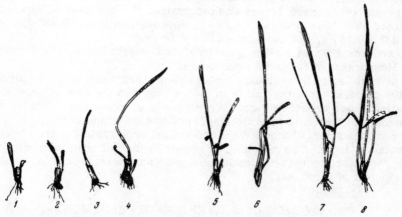

Fig. 43. Plants two weeks after cutting of the aerial mass
1 - 4 — spring wheats, from left to right: Lutescens 62, Tsezium 111, Melanopus 69, Gordeiforme 10; 5 - 8 — winter wheats, from left to right: Kooperatorka, Moskovskaya 2411, Gostianum 237, Lutescens 329

The experiment revealed the clear-cut differences among the individual varieties in reserve of plastic substances. Those varieties which not only survived but grew in the absence of photosynthesis naturally had the larger reserve. This difference is closely connected with the difference in growth of individual varieties at low temperatures already established. With photosynthesis excluded, the length of time a variety remained viable due to large stores of plastic substances was inversely proportional to the degree of suppression of growth in the presence of photosynthesis at low temperatures.

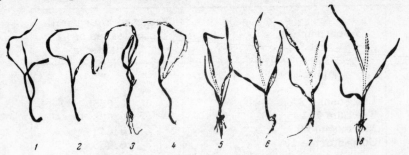

Fig. 44. Plants after two weeks in darkness. Dead parts of plants are darkened; dotted lines designate parts of leaves that grew after remaining some time in darkness
1 - 4 — spring wheats, from left to right: Lutescens 62, Tsezium 111, Gordeiforme 10, Melanopus 69; 5 - 8 — winter wheats, from left to right: Kooperatorka, Moskovskaya 2411, Gostianum 237, Lutescens 329

Experiment 3. The plants were first exhausted by being kept in darkness and then cut. Only the winter varieties were tested. The method of sowing and growing the plants was the same as in the preceding experiments, but the date of sowing was earlier — August 26. They were kept outdoors until they formed plants of 4-5 shoots when they were brought into a cool greenhouse at a temperature of +6 to +8°. On December 1, after 16 days of darkness, all the plants were cut at soil level and the boxes transferred to the laboratory. The dry weight of regrown leaves was determined 10 days later. The weight of 20 plants was: Kooperatorka - 0.034 g, Moskovskaya 2411 - 0.055 g, Gostianum 237 - 0.107 g, and Lutescens 329 - 0.188 g.

Lutescens 329 was first in quantity of fresh weight followed by Gostianum 237, Moskovskay 2411, and Kooperatorka.

The results of all these experiments show, therefore, that the storage of plastic substances in the fall is in inverse ratio to the rate of growth. The varieties whose growth is more severely inhibited by low temperatures store more and can therefore tolerate longer periods in darkness as well as put on better growth after being cut. We have seen that such varieties are also more resistant to frost. The checking of growth in the fall results in the plants storing greater amounts of plastic substances and these, in turn, promote the development of hardiness.

2. STORAGE OF SUGARS AND DEVELOPMENT OF HARDINESS IN WINTER AND SPRING GRAIN CROPS

Starch is the most important of the reserve plastic substances stored for the winter. But starch by itself is inert. It becomes active only when it is hydrolyzed and converted into soluble products, e.g., sugar. Sugars have an exceptionally significant part in plant hardiness. Let us consider in grains the relationship between fall storage of sugars and development of hardiness. In these plants, reserve plastic substances of the carbohydrate group are immediately deposited in the form of sugars. Starch as a reserve product is not present in the vegetative organs of bread grains.

Experiment 1. Vyatka winter rye, Kooperatorka winter wheat, and Lutescens 62 and Melanopus 69 spring wheat were sown in pots outdoors at the end of August — all four varieties in each pot to ensure complete uniformity of growth conditions for all the plants. The sugars were determined during the growth period by Hagedorn and Jensen's method in the leaves and tillering nodes separately (on the technique of analysis, cf. I.M. Vasil'yev, 1931b). Fig. 45 contains data on the sugar content of the tillering nodes. The results were similar in the leaves.

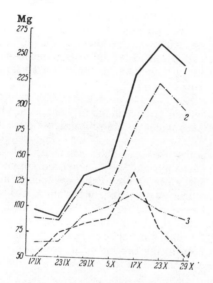

Fig. 45. Content of sugars (in milligrams per g of dry weight) in plants sown in August 1 — Vyatka winter rye; 2 — Kooperatorka winter wheat 3, 4 — Lutescens 62 and Melanopus 69 winter wheat

It is evident that the spring varieties differ sharply from the winter varieties in sugar storage. Throughout the fall the spring wheat had less sugar, which correlates well with their lesser hardiness. Among the winter varieties more sugar was found in the fall in the hardy rye than in the less resistant wheat. The maximum sugar content was noted in spring wheat on October 17, in winter wheat on October 23, i.e., at a time when the frost resistance of all the plants was growing very swiftly (chapter 2).

Let us now compare sugar content and hardiness in Melanopus 69 spring wheat on two dates — September 23 and October 23. The same plants were used to determine hardiness as were used for the sugar analysis. The plants were frozen in a refrigerator for 24 hours. The point corresponding to the sugar content in the September 23 test is on the ascending branch of the curve while the point corresponding to the sugar content in the October 23 test is on the descending branch. The amount of sugar in these tests was almost identical, whereas the degree of hardiness of the plants at these times was markedly different. On September 23 they were completely winterkilled at −8°, whereas on October 23 they were unaffected by −9° and remained alive even at −14°. The same pattern was observed when we compared the dynamics of sugars and frost resistance in other varieties as well. Hence, there is no direct connection between sugar content and frost resistance.

Changes in the rate of sugar storage in the fall are very important. The materials set forth in the preceding chapter on the comparative growth rates of winter and spring plants at low temperatures show that spring plants grow more rapidly under these circumstances than winter plants and thus accumulate smaller quantities of plastic substances. The break in the sugar content curves of spring wheat during the latter part of October indicates that more sugar is expended on growth and respiration than is manufactured in photosynthesis, which decreased at this time not only because of low temperatures but also because of a reduction in the duration and intensity of daylight. In winter plants the break in the sugar content curves was noted later in accordance with their slower rate of growth.

The experiment described above shows that the development of frost resistance by spring and winter plants in the fall is associated with the dynamics of sugar. However, frost resistance may grow even if the sugar content decreases.

Experiment 2. Vyatka winter rye and two wheat varieties — Moskovskaya 2411 and wheat-wheatgrass hybrid 599 — were compared. The hardiness of these varieties was determined several times both in the field and after artificial freezing. The rye was naturally the most resistant. Moskovskaya 2411 was slightly hardier than the hybrid. Plants from three sowing times — August 16, August 30, and September 16 — grown outdoors in Mitscherlich pots were used for the analysis. Specimens were taken at the beginning of winter. Table 10 presents the results of determining the sugar content (according to Bertrand) in the tillering nodes.

Table 10

Sugar content of tillering nodes of winter plants
(as % of dry weight)

Winter variety	Sowing date		
	16. VIII	30. VIII	16. IX
Vyatka rye	28.5	34.5	31.3
Moskovskaya 2411 wheat	23.5	31.5	23.1
Wheat-wheatgrass hybrid 599	27.7	32.5	25.6

It is evident from the table that the winter rye of all three sowing times had more sugar than either of the two winter wheats, which correlates perfectly with its higher frost resistance. When the two wheat varieties were compared with each other, the result was different. Moskovskaya 2411, as pointed out above, was somewhat hardier, yet it clearly had less sugar than the hybrid.

Experiment 3. The purpose of this experiment was to compare the amount of sugar stored during the fall in a relatively large number of winter wheat varieties. The latter were selected in accordance with the results of many years of testing them for hardiness both in the field and after chilling in a refrigerator. Table 11 shows them arranged in decreasing order of hardiness.

Table 11

Sugar content of wheats with differing hardiness
(as % of dry weight)

Wheat variety	Leaves	Tillering nodes
Lutescens 329	20.5	28.6
Wheat-rye hybrid 434/154	20.5	25.8
Lutescens 121	16.9	28.9
Wheat-rye hybrid 46/134	19.3	28.2
Erythrospermum 118	18.7	25.0
Gostianum 237/9	20.9	26.8
Gostianum 237	21.7	27.2
Wheat-rye hybrid 27/36	18.9	28.8
Kooperatorka	17.6	23.2

The sugars (monosaccharides and sucrose) were determined during the fall by Hagedorn and Jensen's method. Our interest here is in comparing the varieties by quantity of sugars during the period of maximum accumulation. The figures in Table 11 are average values obtained from four determinations in November (17, 19, 21, and 24) when the plants contained the greatest amount of sugars.

Any relationship between sugar content and hardiness, if it exists at all, is observable only by comparing varieties displaying extremes in hardiness, notable Lutescens 329 and Kooperatorka. The leaves and tillering nodes of the former clearly contain more sugar than those of the latter. In the other varieties, which differ less in hardiness, no such relationship can be observed. Consequently, the amount of sugars present during the period of maximum fall storage cannot be regarded as an indicator of the hardiness of individual varieties.

3. INTER-CONVERSION OF INDIVIDUAL FORMS OF SUGARS AND THE HARDINESS OF WINTER AND SPRING GRAINS

Bulk analysis of the sugars as reflected in our data naturally does not fully characterize the role played by these compounds in the frost resistance of plants. Sugars in winter and spring grains may be composed of monosaccharides and sucrose which are not equivalent in physiological action. Therefore, to make a more correct appraisal of their role in the frost resistance of grains, it is essential to examine data on changes in content of the individual forms of the sugars.

The determination of the dynamics of monosaccharides and sucrose in winter plants made by A.A. Rikhter (1927) is particularly noteworthy. Analysis of the plants sown in the field at the regular time showed a close interrelationship between the conversion of some forms of sugars into others and the influence of temperature on these conversions. A drop in temperature during the winter caused hydrolysis of sucrose and an increase in the amount of monosaccharides. As the temperature rose, the monosaccharide content decreased while the sucrose content increased. Rikhter concluded that monosaccharides perform the "dominant role in the chemical protection of plants from winterkilling" (p. 343). When sucrose is split into monosaccharides during periods of frost and the amount of monosaccharides ("molecular activity") in the cells is doubled, plant hardiness rises accordingly. To check Rikhter's conclusion, I set up a series of experiments on several winter wheat and rye varieties.

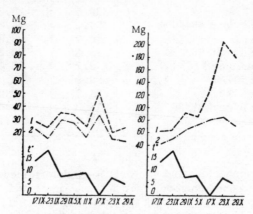

Fig. 46. Content (in milligrams per g of dry weight) of monosaccharides (on the left) and sucrose (on the right) in Kooperatorka winter wheat (1) and in Lutescens 62 spring wheat (2) t° — air temperature

Experiment 1. The objective of this experiment was to trace the dynamics of monosaccharides and sucrose as well as of hemicellulose during the fall growth period of winter and spring varieties. We used the plants in which we made the bulk analysis of sugar in the first experiment of the preceding section in this chapter, i.e., Vyatka spring rye, Kooperatorka winter wheat, Lutescens spring wheat 62, and Melanopus 69 spring wheat.

Fig. 46 shows that the monosaccharide content of both wheat varieties, which differ considerably in hardiness, changes uniformly during the fall and that changes in the sugars are closely connected with temperature changes. The sugar curves are almost a mirror reflection of the temperature curve. As the temperature falls, the amount of monosaccharides increases, and vice versa. Changes in the sucrose content appear quite different. Sucrose in both wheat varieties is steadily stored until October 23 regardless of temperature, after which it decreases. Winter wheat has much more sucrose than spring wheat. An unusually sharp difference was observed in the wheat varieties being compared from October on when the winter wheat begain to lag in growth, comparatively speaking, as is usually the case with this variety during the fall. The same thing occurred in Vyatka winter rye and Melanopus 69 spring wheat. Other investigators working with different winter varieties obtained approximately the same results (Tumanov, 1940).

Experiment 2. Let us now consider the dynamics of sugars and of hemicellulose in frozen plants when there is neither photosynthesis nor growth. The experiment was performed on the nine varieties of winter wheat listed above. The data on bulk analysis of their sugars were presented in Table 11. We shall limit ourselves to the two extremes — the most resistant, Lutescens 329, and the least resistant, Kooperatorka (Figs. 47, 48, 49, 50).

The hemicellulose content changes quite uniformly throughout the winter, and as a reserve carbohydrate it is not used either in the tillering nodes or in the leaves. The sugars in both forms were very mobile. As before, an increase in monosaccharides is accompanied each time by a corresponding decrease in sucrose, and vice versa. Sucrose serves as a reserve of simple sugars. The amount of monosaccharides changes inversely with changes in temperature, and the monosaccharide and temperature curves tend to be mirror reflections of each other. The sucrose content, on the other hand, increases and decreases in direct, though not always precise, conformity with the rise and fall in temperature (the temperature was determined not in the leaf zone, but above a thin layer of snow).

A comparison of the results of both experiments shows that during the period of fall growth and photosynthesis and during the winter, when there is neither growth nor photosynthesis and the plants are frozen, the monosaccharide content changes more or less evenly in close relation to the temperature. As the temperature falls, the monosaccharide content increases, and vice versa. Sucrose serves as a reserve sugar, which is particularly evident during the period of fall sugar storage.

However, the connection between changes in monosaccharide content and temperature is not a simple one. Note the following. Even if the temperature in the fall drops sharply, the monosaccharide content changes within fairly narrow limits and at the end of October is about the same as in the middle of September. In winter too the monosaccharide content changes in accordance with the temperature, but the absolute amount both in the leaves and in the tillering nodes at the end of March is about the same as in the middle of November. This suggests that while the monosaccharides play some part in strengthening frost resistance, there are other factors involved as well.

4. USE OF RESERVE PLASTIC SUBSTANCES BY WINTERING PLANTS FOR RESPIRATION

Like all living organisms, plants steadily use up plastic substances in the process of living. One activity which never ceases, even during the severest frosts, is respiration, although it naturally slows down as the temperature falls. It has been shown that sugars are the basic material for respiration. That is why grains in which reserve plastic substances are stored for the winter chiefly in the form of sugars are unusually convenient objects of study for this purpose.

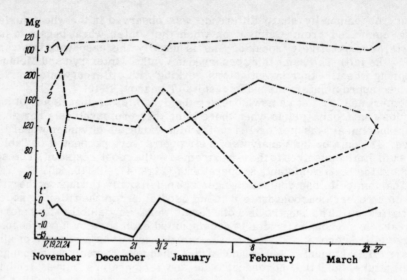

Fig. 47. Content of sugars and hemicellulose in the tillering
nodes of Kooperatorka winter wheat
1 — monosacchardies; 2 — sucrose; 3 — hemicellulose;
t° — air temperature

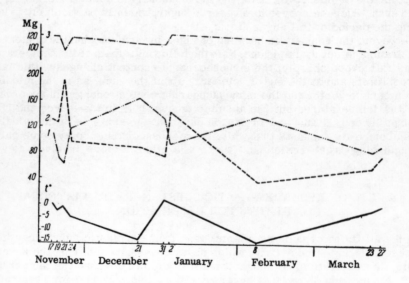

Fig. 48. Content of sugars and hemicellulose in the tillering
nodes of Lutescens 329 winter wheat
1 — monosaccharides; 2 — sucrose; 3 — hemicellulose;
t° — air temperature

126

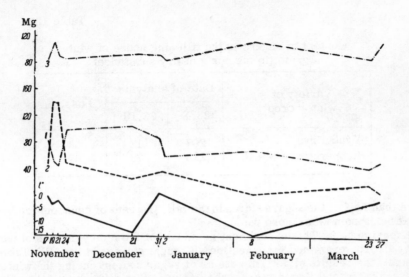

Fig. 49. Content of sugars and hemicellulose in Kooperatorka leaves
1 — monosaccharides; 2 — sucrose; 3 — hemicellulose; t° — air temperature

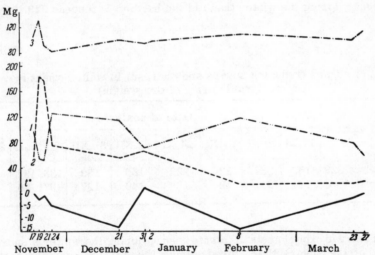

Fig. 50. Content of sugars and hemicellulose in Lutescens 329 leaves
1 — monosaccharides; 2 — sucrose; 3 — hemicellulose;
t° — air temperature

Experiment 1. This experiment was performed on Vyatka winter rye and Kooperatorka winter wheat. Part of the plants served for sugar analysis in the fall (experiment 1 in the second section of this chapter). The other plants were left to winter outdoors and were examined for sugar content as soon as the snow melted. Table 12 contains data on the sugar content of the tillering nodes five months after the initial investigation.

The table shows that during the winter both the rye and the wheat used up

Table 12

Content of sugars in the tillering nodes of winter
grain (in mg per g of dry substance)

Variety of winter crop	Date of analysis		Loss, %
	23.X	23.III	
Vyatka rye	267	112	58
Kooperatorka wheat	223	73	67

more than half of the sugars stored in the fall, the rate of consumption by the
wheat being somewhat more rapid.

Experiment 2. This experiment made use of the nine varieties of winter
wheat already examined in connection with sugar storage in the fall. Table 13
presents the results of determinations of sugar content during the winter of
Lutescens 329 and Kooperatorka, the two varieties differing most widely in
hardiness. The sugar content of both steadily decreased from November 19
on when the temperature fell below zero. The loss of sugars in Lutescens
329 was 66%, in Kooperatorka - 73%. The less hardy Kooperatorka expended
more sugar during the winter than did the hardier Lutescens 329.

Table 13

Content of sugars (reducing sugars and sucrose) in winter wheat leaves
(in milligrams per g of dry weight)

Wheat variety	Date of analysis								
	17.XI	19.XI	21.XI	24.XI	21.XII	31.XII	2.I	8.II	27.III
Lutescens 329	153	237	226	202	169	139	133	138	80
Kooperatorka	144	211	194	158	140	127	97	76	56

In these two experiments the plants used up during the winter a substantial
portion of the sugars they stored during the fall, but a portion remained.
Moreover, the hemicelluloses remained completely intact, their content, as
shown by Figs. 47–50, remaining virtually unchanged throughout the winter.
Yet the hemicelluloses serve as a source of sugar formation in the summer
when the plants may be suffering from a deficiency caused, for example, by
insufficient moisture (I.M. Vasil'yev and N.G. Vasil'yeva, 1934).

Plants, therefore, store up for the winter more plastic substances than
they actually need for protection from frost and for respiration. This is
readily understandable because it is due to these substances that plants begin
to grow in spring, develop buds, and partially renew the parts lost as a result
of unfavorable wintering conditions.

5. RESERVE PLASTIC SUBSTANCES AND HARDINESS
OF WINTERING TREES AND SHRUBS

Like herbaceous plants, woody plants store plastic substances for the winter, chiefly in the form of starch which frequently begins to accumulate in the summer. Starch is deposited in the bark and xylem of roots, trunks, and branches, usually in the oldest parts. If growth and fruit bearing end earlier, the deposition of starch begins earlier. When the cool fall weather sets in, the starch gradually disappears through conversion into sugar and oil. This process has long interested investigators who invariably postulated a direct connection between it and the development of hardiness (Russow, 1882; Baranetskiy, 1883; Grebnitskiy, 1884; Surozh, 1891).

The conversion of starch into sugar and oil is accompanied by the production of hemicelluloses from starch. This process was thoroughly studied by Schellenberg (1905) who demonstrated in many woody species that the disappearance of starch in the fall is always associated with a thickening of cell walls by hemicellulose deposited on their inner surface. By spring the hemicellulose disappears and the walls shrink by one-third or one-half. This shows up very clearly in the grapevine and black locust. When the protoplasm in the cells of these plants is destroyed during the winter, the hemicellulose deposited on the cell walls does not dissolve in the spring. Hemicellulose thickening of cell walls, according to Schellenberg, is a major condition of the maturing of young shoots in the fall.

A study of these and other published data on starch storage in woody plants in the fall and its conversion during the winter into sugar, oil, hemicelluloses, and other compounds like glucosides, resins, etc. leaves no doubt that all these processes are directly connected with the development of hardiness. However, there are some reasons for caution in evaluating the role of starch and its modifications. In one year old shoots, for example, starch is deposited mostly in the pith. Pith cells serve as a kind of storage bin for the shoots. However, they are the first to die in the winter from frost. These cells are the oldest in the shoots and their decreased viability is by no means fully compensated for by a large reserve of plastic substances.

An even better example is the fruit, which constitutes a special storage receptacle for plastic substances. While apples, for example, are ripening, they abound in sugars (about 24%), hemicelluloses, pectins, etc., yet the fruit of even the hardiest varieties scarcely hardens and is usually killed by the first frosts of -5 to -7° (Tserevitinov, 1949). The same thing holds true of other fruits and berries.

Consequently, without denying the importance of reserve plastic substances in the hardiness of wintering woody plants, we must point out that plastic substances do not always protect them from frost and that other factors like age of cells and nature of the organ are of great significance.

6. RESERVE PLASTIC SUBSTANCES AND HARDINESS
OF SUBTROPICAL AND HEAT-LOVING PLANTS

Subtropical evergreen plants are marked by comparatively weak development of so-called "storage tissues" in their trunks and branches. Plastic substances accumulate mainly in the older leaves that have stopped growing, i.e., just as in winter grains, cabbage, and other wintering herbaceous plants. Magnolia is a good example. F. F. Leysle (1948) showed through micro-chemical and chemical analysis that the previous year's leaves in magnolia are packed with starch early in spring. At this time starch fills up the parenchyma cells and only the epidermal cells remain free of it. In June and July the starch content is still very high, but is almost all gone in winter. Sugars simultaneously accumulate in large quantities — monosaccharides, sucrose, maltose — to 20% of the dry weight.

The sugars naturally make magnolia more frost resistant. Like other subtropical plants, magnolia can become hardened to a certain extent. However, the connection between hardiness and sugar accumulation is not as close as it is, less us say, in winter grains. As we have seen, only the most resistant varieties of winter wheat, e.g., Lutescens 329, store 20% sugar in their leaves in the fall. Yet Lutescens 329 leaves can tolerate temperatures as low as -20° in snowless weather, whereas the lowest temperature tolerated by magnolia leaves is -10 to -12°.

As another example, sugar is the principal reserve plastic substance in citrus. The quantity increases as the temperature falls. By spring the content diminishes as frost resistance changes. However, this connection between sugars and frost resistance in citrus is a broad one and sometimes difficult to discover in plants possessing similar degrees of resistance. Table 14 shows the results of one of S.M. Ivanov's experiments (1939) to determine the frost resistance and sugar content of mandarin, orange, and lemon leaves.

Table 14

Content of sugars in citrus hardiness

Plant	Content of sugars, %		Number of organs damaged by -8°, %	
	in branches	in leaves	branches	leaves
Unshiu mandarin	8.36	12.37	0	18
Oranges	8.64	8.73	8	55
Lemon	7.27	10.99	60	100

As usual, the mandarin was the most resistant followed by the orange and lemon in this order. The connection between frost resistance and sugar content could be traced only in the two extremes — mandarin and lemon. The sugar content of the orange, which is hardier than the lemon, was about 20% less.

Even better illustrations of the lack of correlation between accumulation of plastic substances and hardiness can be found among tropical plants. For example, the sugar cane stores in its stems more than 20% sugar (sucrose), but cannot tolerate cold at all. Ripe bananas also contain about 20% sugar (invert and sucrose), not counting starch. Yet neither the fruits nor the plant itself are hardy.

The same thing is true of imports from the tropics and subtropics cultivated in the U.S.S.R. The roots of the sugar beet, for example, contain from 18 to 25% sugar, but are winterkilled at -5 to -8°. Potato tubers abound in starch which is partly saccharified as the temperature falls so that they become sweet. However, this does not substantially strengthen their resistance to frost and they are killed as soon as they are frozen at -2 or -3°.

We have thus come to the conclusion that the connection between accumulation of plastic substances and frost resistance largely varies with the nature of the plants. In plants that are naturally unhardy, even the accumulation of large stores of plastic substances does not strengthen their resistance perceptibly.

7. DEPOSITION OF PLASTIC SUBSTANCES IN CELLS DURING THE WINTERING PERIOD AND SIGNIFICANCE OF THE PROCESS IN FROST RESISTANCE

The deposition and storage of plastic substances is an ordinary process in plants. During intense daytime photosynthesis, when the outflow of sugars from the green plastids lags behind the accumulation, sugars are converted into starch and are temporarily deposited here in the plastids. In plants which do not store starch in leaves, e.g., wheat, the excess of sugars is transported to the vacuoles. Thus, the dynamics of sugars in leaves during the day is normally shown by a curve rising in the morning and afternoon hours and falling by evening (I.M. Vasil'yev, 1932).

A great quantity of plastic substances is often deposited in summer in the vacuoles and the cell walls, but not in the protoplasm itself, at least not in the active cells. For example, there is ordinarily no sugar in living protoplasm (Kizel', 1940). In fall, when growth comes to a halt and in general when metabolism is arrested due to falling temperature the process takes place differently. At this time the flow of plastic substances into protoplasm exceeds the consumption of these substances so that they are accumulated throughout the protoplasm along with the usual deposition in the vacuoles, leukoplasts, and on the cell walls. Moreover, in fall there are excessive deposits of plastic substances not only in old cells, but in general in all active cells, including the youngest ones where this does not happen at other times of the year. The relatively severe inhibition of growth at low temperatures in the more resistant grain varieties as compared with the less resistant varieties, which we determined in the above-mentioned research, is an important precondition of the break between inflow and consumption of plastic substances. These naturally accumulate in greater quantity in the protoplasm of grains with more arrested growth.

It is a well known fact that plants can harden only at low temperatures. They do not do so at high temperatures regardless of how rich they may be in plastic substances. At high temperatures and if all other conditions are favorable, protoplasm makes full use of all the plastic substances available. This, among other reasons, is why even the hardiest of plants have little or no frost resistance in summer. The role of plastic substances in frost resistance is therefore largely due to the fact that they are stored in protoplasm.

CONCLUSION

Using winter grains, wintering trees and shrubs of the temperate zone and subtropical plants, we have shown that the fall storage of plastic substances is a prerequisite of the development of frost resistance. These substances accumulate in greater quantity in many hardier plants. But the connection between frost resistance and accumulation of plastic substances is far from fixed, especially in heat-loving plants. Large quantities of these substances may be deposited in the vegetative and reproductive organs of these plants, but there is no significant increase in their hardiness as a result. The same holds true for certain varieties of temperate zone wintering plants.

The extent of influence exerted by plastic substances on the development of hardiness depends on many factors, chiefly the nature of the plants themselves. In those which are naturally less resistant to frost, plastic substances are less involved in the development of hardiness. Thus, nonwintering or wintering organs exposed to light frosts in even the most resistant plants turn out to be unhardy, despite the fact that at times they abound in reserve plastic substances.

The form of the plastic substances too is significant. Starch, stored by plants in summer, strengthens frost resistance only when converted into sugars, hemicelluloses, oils, and other compounds, which takes place with the advent of cool fall weather. Among the sugars the monosaccharides are most important in frost resistance, at least in grains, whereas sucrose serves simply as the reserve of these sugars.

The deposition of plastic substances is particularly important for plants. In summer they are stored in the vacuoles and cell walls. In fall they are also stored in protoplasm because they are not fully used up in growth and other vital functions due to the fall in temperature, especially at night. An abundance of plastic substances in protoplasm prevents winterkilling.

CHAPTER 5

CHANGES IN WATER CONTENT, OSMOTIC PRESSURE, AND pH IN RELATION TO HARDINESS

1. WATER CONTENT AND HARDINESS IN WINTERING HERBACEOUS PLANTS

Low water content of cells is considered a major factor in frost resistance and in general resistance to unfavorable external conditions. A usual example is seeds which when air-dried can safely withstand even the severest of frosts, including chilling in liquid air (-190°) and in liquid helium (-269°). As seeds swell, their frost resistance diminishes; the resistance of seeds that have begun to germinate is about the same as that of the vegetative parts of the plant. We could cite many other examples of the beneficial effect of low water content on plant hardiness. There are, however, some exceptions. Here are some experiments testifying to the relationship between hardiness and water content in wintering grains and grasses.

Experiment 1. Water content was determined in the tillering nodes of Moskovskaya 2411 winter wheat, wheat-wheatgrass hybrid 599, perennial wheat 2 and wheatgrass (A. glaucum) as well as in the aerial parts of green leaves and in the rhizomes of tall wheatgrass (A. elongatum). All the plants were sown in pots and kept outdoors. The wheat was sown at the end of August, the wheatgrass in the middle of July. Samples were taken October 19 (Table 15).

Table 15

Water content of winter wheat and wheatgrass
(as of % of dry weight)

Variety	Part investigated	Water, %
Perennial wheat 2	Tillering nodes	77.7
Winter wheat-wheatgrass hybrid 599	Tillering nodes	77.1
Winter wheat Moskovskaya 2411	Tillering nodes	76.0
Wheatgrass A. glaucum	Tillering nodes	70.6
Wheatgrass A. elongatum	Green leaves	77.1
The same	Rhizomes	26.5

We are focussing our attention primarily on the low water content in the bases of the leaves of A. glaucum, as compared with the wheats, and on the comparatively high water content in the green leaves and very low content in the rhizomes of A. elongatum. This tallies with the fact that the underground parts of wheatgrass are much more resistant than its green leaves (cf. Part 2, chapter 3). The very hardy wheatgrass rhizomes are unusually low in water. Even in regions with severe winters and little snow wheatgrass rhizomes pulled out with a harrow are known to escape winterkilling. Among the wheat varieties tested Moskovskaya 2411, whch is more deficient in water than the others, proved to be the most hardy. Perennial wheat 2, with more water than any of the others, was the least hardy.

Experiment 2. Water content was determined in the tillering nodes of Vyatka winter rye, Moskovskaya 2411 winter wheat, and winter wheat-wheatgrass hybrid 599 sown at three times — August 16, 30, and September 16. The plants were sown and grown in pots outdoors just as in the preceding experiment. Samples were taken at the end of November. The results are presented in Table 16.

The varieties are shown in the table in descending order of hardiness, the rye being the most resistant. The later the sowing, the greater the degree of hardiness.

The correlation of comparative hardiness of the varieties with water content is complete here. The hardy rye of all three sowing times contains the least amount of water. The wheats are similar in water content as well as in hardiness; Moskovskaya 2411 which is somewhat superior to hybrid 599 in hardiness has a little less water. The result is quite different when plants sown at different times are compared. With late sowing the water content of each variety rises for the obvious reason that when the samples were taken the plants of the later sowing were younger. However, an increase in the water content of young plants of the later sowings coincides with an increase rather than a decrease in their hardiness.

Table 16

Water content of tillering nodes of winter grains
(as a % of dry weight)

Winter crop variety	Sowing time		
	16. VIII	30. VIII	16. IX
Vyatka rye	74.8	75.6	75.8
Wheat Moskovskaya 2411	77.1	77.3	79.6
Wheat-wheatgrass hybrid 599	77.5	77.8	80.6

Thus, these experiments show both the existence and lack of a connection between water content and hardiness. A connection is found when comparing rye and wheat varieties differing in hardiness and even when different parts of the same plant are compared, such as green and underground parts of leaves and rhizomes of wheatgrass. In all these cases the more resistant plants and their parts contain less water. No connection can be found when comparing plants sown at different times. The younger plants sown later have more water, but are less hardy.

2. DYNAMICS OF OSMOTIC PRESSURE DURING THE WINTERING PERIOD OF WINTER WHEAT VARIETIES DIFFERING IN HARDINESS

Osmotic pressure of cell sap is considered the most universal indicator of plant hardiness. There are numerous published reports on the dynamics of osmotic pressure. Let us add some of our own observations on varieties of winter wheat differing in hardiness.

Plants of the nine varieties mentioned above were planted in a field. Osmotic pressure was determined by the cryoscopic method in the sap of killed plants according to Walter (1931). Samples were taken in the fall and winter. All the leaves were incorporated in the analysis.

The general pattern of changes in osmotic pressure in wheat as shown in Fig. 51 for two extremes is comparatively simple. The more hardy Lutescens 329 also had the higher osmotic pressure of the cell sap. Osmotic pressure in both varieties increased fairly rapidly during November and decreased more slowly during the winter months. The rise in osmotic pressure coincided with the fall in temperature from +3.7 to -15.2°. The drop in osmotic pressure at the end of December was due to a thaw. The subsequent fall in temperature after the thaw did not cause the osmotic pressure to rise again (Table 17).

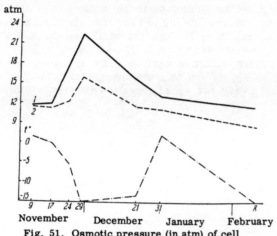

Fig. 51. Osmotic pressure (in atm) of cell
sap of winter wheat
1 — Lutescens 329; 2 — Kooperatorka;
t° — air temperature

With one exception, these data justify our establishing a direct connection
between osmotic pressure and hardiness in the varieties compared, especially
the maximum values at the end of November. The rate of increase in osmotic
pressure during the fall and its decrease during the winter differs from
variety to variety according to its hardiness.

Table 17

Osmotic pressure in wheat leaves (in atm)

Wheat variety	Date sample obtained for analysis						
	9.XI	17.XI	24.XI	29.XI	21.XII	31.XII	8.I
Lutescens 329	12.2	12.5	18.6	23.2	16.1	13.5	12.1
Wheat-rye hybrid 434/154	13.3	14.6	16.9	22.1	——	11.8	12.0
Lutescens 121	14.3	14.6	18.9	20.8	15.3	11.9	——
Wheat-rye hybrid 46/131	13.2	14.3	16.1	19.5	13.9	10.7	9.3
Erythrospermum 118	12.5	13.7	14.9	18.5	16.1	11.1	——
Gostianum 237/9	12.5	15.1	17.6	18.7	17.0	12.7	9.6
Gostianum 237	12.0	13.7	17.6	18.0	15.7	10.1	——
Wheat-rye hybrid 27/36	12.4	14.6	16.3	17.4	16.3	12.9	11.2
Kooperatorka	11.8	12.0	12.7	16.4	11.9	11.4	8.8

3. CHANGES IN CONCENTRATION OF ALL SUBSTANCES
DISSOLVED IN THE CELL SAP DURING THE WINTERING PERIOD
OF WINTER WHEAT VARIETIES DIFFERING IN HARDINESS

Besides osmotically active substances, cell sap always contains colloid-
soluble substances which can be determined at the same time as osmotically
active substances by means of a refractometer. The most convenient type for

135

this purpose is a refractometer on whose scale are plotted the percentages of dry substances corresponding to the refractive index. We present below the results of determining the content of all sap-soluble substances in the nine varieties of wheat listed above. The sap from killed plants, which also served for the determination of osmotic pressure, was used in the analyses.

The curves in Fig. 52 indicate the changes in content of substances dissolved in the cell sap of two wheat varieties differing widely in hardiness —

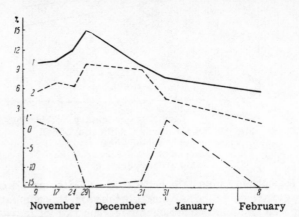

Fig. 52. Content of dry substance in wheat
cell sap
1 — Lutescens 329; 2 — Kooperatorka;
t° — air temperature

Table 18

Content of dry substance in winter wheat cell sap (as %)

Wheat variety	Date sample obtained for analysis						
	9.XI	17. XI	24.XI	29.XI	21.XII	31.XII	8.II
Lutescens 329	9.8	10.3	12.0	15.2	9.8	7.7	5.7
Wheat hybrid 434/154	9.0	9.6	10.1	15.2	—	7.3	5.5
Lutescens 121	9.5	10.1	12.1	14.0	8.7	6.3	4.1
Wheat-rye hybrid 46/131	8.2	9.2	10.0	12.8	7.5	5.5	3.7
Erythrospermum 118	7.8	9.2	9.6	12.6	9.6	5.7	—
Gostianum 237/9	7.8	9.9	9.0	12.2	9.8	6.8	2.5
Gostianum 237	6.9	8.5	10.8	11.9	9.7	7.9	2.3
Wheat-rye hybrid 27/36	6.0	9.1	10.8	11.0	9.2	6.9	2.2
Kooperatorka	5.5	6.9	6.4	9.8	9.1	4.6	1.9

Lutescens 329 and Kooperatorka. Table 18 is a summation of the data for all the wheat varieties studied.

The curves reflecting changes in the concentration of dry substances in cell sap are somewhat reminiscent of the osmotic pressure curves. The content of dry substance increased as the temperature fell in November and then decreased during the winter, despite the thaw at the end of December. It is important to note the difference between this curve and the curve of changes in sugar content of the same wheat varieties. The sugar content reached a maximum in the fall earlier than the content of the other substances dissolved in the cell sap and began to decrease while the content of the latter was still increasing. This shows that even in wheat, where it is believed that the sugars constitute the principal protective plastic substances, the sugars actually determine neither the contents of cell sap nor its osmotic pressure.

Table 18 enables us to establish a fairly close correlation between the content of dry substance in cell sap and hardiness of the varieties, especially when the maximum and minimum values are compared. For the indicated periods of the maximum and minimum the arrangement of varieties by degree of hardiness coincides with the order in which they are arranged by concentration of dry substance. Deviations from this order are appreciable at other times.

4. CHANGES IN CONCENTRATION OF HYDROGEN IONS (pH) DURING THE WINTERING PERIOD OF WINTER WHEAT VARIETIES DIFFERING IN HARDINESS

The values cited below of concentration of hydrogen ions were obtained from the same wheat varieties used in the investigations already described. The pH of the sap pressed from killed plants was determined electrometric-ally using a quinhydrone electrode. The results are shown in Fig. 53 and Table 19. It is evident from the figure that the nature of the pH changes during the experiment from November 9 to February 8 was fairly similar in

Table 19

pH of cell sap in winter wheat

Wheat variety	Date sample obtained for analysis						
	9.XI	17.XI	24.XI	29.XI	21. XII	31.XII	8. II
Lutescens 329	6.3	6.3	6.4	6.4	6.2	6.0	5.9
Wheat-rye hybrid 434/154	6.9	6.2	6.1	6.4	—	5.6	—
Lutescens 121	6.6	6.2	6.5	6.2	6.0	6.0	5.7
Wheat-rye hybrid 46/131	6.4	6.5	6.3	6.6	6.0	6.0	5.7
Erythrospermum 118	6.1	6.2	6.4	6.7	6.0	6.0	5.8
Gostianum 237/9	6.4	6.2	6.8	5.1	6.0	6.0	5.8
Gostianum 237	6.2	6.5	6.2	6.0	6.0	6.0	6.0
Wheat-rye hybrid 27/36	6.1	6.3	6.4	6.0	6.0	6.1	5.9
Kooperatorka	6.3	6.3	6.3	6.1	6.1	6.0	5.6

varieties widely differing in hardiness. The pH increased at first and then decreased. The increase in alkalinity of the sap in Lutescens 329 was paralleled by the rise in osmotic pressure and concentration of dry substance. In Kooperatorka the change toward sap acidification began earlier than the change in osmotic pressure and concentration of dry substance.

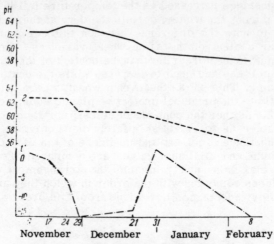

Fig. 53. pH of cell sap in winter wheat
1 — Lutescens 329; 2 — Kooperatorka;
t° — air temperature

The table shows that the pH also changes during the winter in the other varieties as well. From the end of November on, the cell sap became increasingly acid, somewhat earlier in the less hardy varieties, somewhat later in the hardier varieties. During the winter the sap is usually more acid in the less hardy varieties than in the hardier varieties.

5. CHANGES IN WATER CONTENT AND OSMOTIC PRESSURE IN RELATION TO HARDINESS OF WINTERING TREES AND SHRUBS

Let us first consider the data on the water content in the parts of woody plants above the snow during the wintering period. In December 1947 after familiarizing myself with the work of the Sverdlovsk Fruit and Berry Experimental Station, I was permitted to obtain a sample of tips of branches of the small-fruited apple common in Sverdlovsk oblast. The leaf buds cut off seemed completely viable. The water content of the buds minus the scales was 72%, which did not prevent them from safely withstanding a frost of –43° for several days.

The same picture is observed in pine needles, which generally have less water than ordinary leaves. Thus, according to Meyer (1928, 1932), in pitch pine, the common representative of coniferous trees in Ohio, the water content of the needles as a percentage of dry weight was: in October – 63%, in November – 61.8%, in January – 62%, in April – 60.6%, in May – 58.2%, and in June – 60.6%. During the wintering period, (before May) due to the difficulty in taking up water from frozen soil, the needles were dehydrated, but by the beginning of summer they were again filled with water, although the fluctuations in amount were comparatively slight. The high frost resistance of pine needles in winter is evidently not closely related to regular changes in their water content.

Let us turn now to osmotic pressure — the most important physicochemical indicator of the properties of cell sap. Fig. 54 shows the annual pattern of osmotic pressure in three species of pine investigated by Gail (1926) in Ohio.

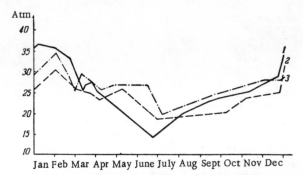

Fig. 54. Osmotic pressure (in atm) in cell sap of coniferous needles during the year (according to Hale, 1926) 1 — in Abies grandis; 2 — in Pinus ponderosa; 3 — in Pseudotsuga taxifolia

In all plants osmotic pressure drops until the middle of summer, then rises, attaining its maximum in the middle of winter. The maximum values of osmotic pressure reach 30 atm or more, whereas in the most resistant of the winter wheat varieties, Lutescens 329, it failed to exceed 23.2 atm in the experiments previously described. The reason for this, aside from the differences in nature of the plants, is apparently to be found in the wintering conditions. Winter plants are normally covered with snow by November so that their leaves are not exposed to such frosts as pine needles.

The higher osmotic pressure of woody plants as compared with herbaceous plants can be more justifiably correlated with the greater hardiness of the parts above the snow. No herbaceous plant can withstand the frosts endured by the branches, buds or nondeciduous leaves of trees and shrubs. However, we find no such correlation when we study species of woody plants differing among themselves, especially if they are systematically and geographically remote. Walter's data (1931) may serve as an illustration. Walter compared the dynamics of osmotic pressure during the winter and spring in three species of plants — Pinus silvestris, Buxus sempervirens, and Hedera helix. The pine is quite different from the other two comparatively unhardy plants in that it possesses a high degree of resistance to frost. Yet at the end of winter osmotic pressure in Buxus sempervirens was more than 70 atm, but only 25 atm in Pinus silvestris. The incomparably less hardy ivy exhibited the same osmotic pressure. This example is convincing proof of the futility of routinely correlating the hardiness of plants with the osmotic pressure of their cell sap.

6. CHANGES IN WATER CONTENT AND OSMOTIC PRESSURE IN RELATION TO HARDINESS IN SUBTROPICAL AND HEAT-LOVING PLANTS

Let us consider the connection between hardiness and properties of cell sap in subtropical plants in the light of F.F. Leysle's research on citrus (1948) on our Black Sea littoral.

Water content and osmotic pressure were determined in the leaves of small lemon and mandarin trees grown in pots outdoors. On November 26 the plants were artificially chilled. The temperature was maintained for the first two days at +4°, the next three days at +2°, the next two days at 0°, one day at -2°, one day at -3.5°, one day at -6°. The results are shown in Table 20.

Table 20

Water content and osmotic pressure in mandarin and lemon leaves

Experimental conditions	Water, % of dry weight		Osmotic pressure, atm	
	mandarin	lemon	mandarin	lemon
Before chilling in the chamber	64.2	63.4	8.7	9.4
After exposure to +4, +2, 0°	63.6	65.2	13.7	11.3
After exposure to -3.5°	62.0	65.2	13.8	12.9
After exposure to -6°	49.5	62.4	16.2	13.0

It is evident from the table that in comparatively unhardy subtropical plants as in very hardy plants of the temperate zone osmotic pressure rises as the temperature falls as long as the plants are alive.

The absolute values of osmotic pressure in subtropical plants may be much higher than shown in Table 20. For freely growing trees in the botanical garden of Batum in the winter of 1936 Leysle established an osmotic pressure of about 21.5 atm in the mandarin and about 18.7 atm in the lemon. According to Leysle and S. Ya. Sokolov (Leysle, 1948) who conducted investigations at the same time under the conditions of a colder winter in the Sochi area, osmotic pressure reached 27.6 atm in the mandarin and 26.7 atm in the lemon. Thus, when frost resistance is intensified, osmotic pressure in citrus increases much more rapidly than in winter grains.

There is an even greater noncorrespondence between osmotic pressure and hardiness, which is common to all plants, when osmotic pressure is compared in the periods of summer drought and in the winter months. According to Leysle, in February the osmotic pressure of the cell sap in one year old leaves of Citrus aurantium L. was 17.8 atm as compared with 18.2 atm in July; in Citrus deliciosum Tan. the corresponding figures were 16.6 and 16.2 atm in one year old leaves, and 15.9 and 17.6 atm in two year old leaves. Consequently, unhardened plants may exhibit the same (or even greater) osmotic pressure in the summer as hardened plants do in the winter.

High osmotic pressure may develop in the cells of naturally completely unhardy heat-loving plants, especially in arid regions and on saline soils. Osmotic pressure in many Saharan plants is measured in tenths of an atmosphere (Stocker, 1928). In plants of tropical regions with alternating wet and dry seasons osmotic pressure regularly changes over a year just as in temperate zone plants. However, changes in osmotic pressure there are due not to temperature, but to moisture.

Osmotic pressure, therefore, is an indicator both of the temperature conditions affecting plants and of moisture conditions. To the same degree, osmotic pressure may be considered an indicator of the conditions of photosynthesis and mineral nutrition.

7. NATURE OF THE RELATIONSHIP BETWEEN PLANT HARDINESS AND CHANGES IN WATER CONTENT AND OSMOTIC PRESSURE

Preparation for the winter is always associated more or less with a decrease in the water content of the plants. The water is partly squeezed from the cells when chilled due to contraction and increased permeability of the protoplasm. This process can be clearly observed when unicellular organisms are chilled in oil: as the temperature falls, droplets of water appear on the surface of the cells and are visible because they do not mix with the oil (Greely, 1902). At the same time water is pressed from the vacuoles by insoluble plastic substances deposited there. Cells become most dehydrated as soon as the plants are frozen. The water, so to speak, is sucked out of the cells by ice forming in the intercellular spaces. Up to 70-80% or more of all the water contained in the cells turns into ice (Sulukadze, 1945).

Even if all the water of the cell sap is lost, cell dehydration may under certain circumstances leave the protoplasm intact. This occurs when seeds ripen. The vacuoles of the aleurone layer, for example, become filled with protein substances alone and yet remain alive. The vacuoles of many woody plants are filled with oil all winter. The same thing happens in lower plants. Total or near total dehydration of the vacuoles sharply increases the resistance of the plants if the water is displaced by plastic substances with no significant contraction of the vacuoles. This last is always dangerous, because it causes the protoplasm to contract with possible deformation and rupture.

However, the complete extrusion of water and its displacement by plastic substances during the wintering period are not characteristic of all plants. As we saw, the water content of the leaves of winter crops, apple buds, and pine needles in the winter is about the same as in the summer. Consequently, plants may go into the winter and develop their normal resistance even with a normal water content in the vacuoles. In this case the hardiness of protoplasm varies with the physicochemical changes in the cell sap. The nature of this relationship is apparently as follows.

The first thing that happens in hardening is that the cell sap becomes more concentrated. This process is partly but not entirely determined by cell dehydration. The drop in temperature in the fall plays a major role and, just like dehydration, it intensifies the hydrolytic processes in the cells. Many previously insoluble compounds now turn into a genuine or colloidal solution as a result of which osmotic pressure increases and also the imbibition pressure of the cells. This pressure prevents ice from forming in the vacuoles when the water is frozen. We have, as it were, an automatic mechanism whose protective function comes into play as the temperature drops and more and more water is frozen out of the vacuoles. However, this functions only up to a point: after extreme dehydration the vacuoles contract markedly causing tension in the protoplasm, which may ultimately destroy it. An unusually high concentration of cell sap is toxic to protoplasm. A strong increase in the suction pressure of the cell sap with respect to the water in the protoplasm is also harmful.

Thus, the physicochemical changes in cell sap have only relative significance in the development of plant hardiness and show up only during the winter in certain plants accustomed to wintering and to a specific degree for each plant. In the summer, however, the same factors are inoperative while in heat-loving plants they have no connection whatsoever with frost resistance.

CONCLUSION

Raising osmotic pressure and total concentration and lowering cell sap acidity condition to some extent the development of frost resistance. On the other hand, lowering osmotic pressure and total concentration and raising acidity tend to reduce frost resistance. Another pattern emerges when comparing changes in osmotic pressure with changes in frost resistance in individual plants. In winter grains, as we saw, there is a relationship but only of a general kind; this relationship shows up clearly only in varieties differing widely in hardiness. When comparing systematically and geographically distant plants we see that there is no connection between osmotic pressure and hardiness, as in the case of heat-loving plants. The same thing happens when we compare osmotic pressure and hardiness in temperate zone plants in the summer: osmotic pressure may be very high, but hardiness is always extremely low.

It follows, then, that all the changes in osmotic pressure noted have significance, if at all, only in the winter and with respect to each plant separately. The significance of changes in cell sap cannot be reduced to a rule. Elevated osmotic pressure is usually associated with high frost resistance. However, extreme values of osmotic pressure become a negative factor and often are the direct cause of the death of plants.

Water in the vacuoles plays a special role in plant hardiness. This water in the winter must be regarded in general as a negative factor. Abrupt changes in water content, which invariably take place when plants are frozen, may be and frequently are the cause of destruction of protoplasm due to change in the size of cells and intracellular formation of ice. Therefore, water in the vacuoles is often displaced by some plastic substances, mostly oil, especially when the plants or individual parts are exposed to bitter frosts and winds.

CHAPTER 6

COLLOID CHEMICAL CHANGES IN PROTOPLASM AND PLANT HARDINESS

The study of colloid chemical properties of protoplasm in relation to plant hardiness has scarecely begun. Achievements in this field are still small, but we do know a little.

1. PROPERTIES OF WATER IN PROTOPLASM AND PLANT HARDINESS

Water may be found in colloidal systems either in free or bound form. Free water constitutes a dispersion medium, while bound water forms a part of a colloidal micelle. The molecules of bound water form a watery sphere around each particle organically connected with a colloidal particle. In contrast to the disorder in free water all the molecules of bound water in a micelle are strictly oriented and polarized. That is why bound water can be evaporated, frozen, or forced out under pressure only with great difficulty. It is very dense and loses its properties as a solvent to a large extent (Dumanskiy, 1937).

The difficulty of freezing bound water is particularly noteworthy in connection with plant hardiness. John's experiment (1931) in freezing albumin is instructive. Using the calorimetric method, John discovered that when he lowered the temperature to -12.5°, the water in the egg white rapidly froze and the amount of unfrozen water diminished accordingly. At -12.5° there was an abrupt change and when the temperature was further lowered to -35°, the water no longer froze. All told, 74% of the water in the albumin froze while 26% remained liquid, the latter, in John's opinion, being bound.

Actually the boundary between free and bound water cannot be drawn too sharply. Water bound by colloidal particles, especially on the margin of water films, does not lose all the characteristics of water in general and it can be pulled away with comparative ease. Only the molecules of water closest to the colloidal particle are capable of withstanding a great force of about 25,000 atm. Moreover, free water is not all free and part of it is retained by osmotically active substances dissolved in it. Capillaries too are highly significant in preventing water from freezing. The water which fills, for example, the intermicellar spaces in the cell walls may be kept there by powerful forces. The unfreezability of bacterial cells at very low temperatures is due to capillary attraction (Grayevskiy and Medvedeva, 1948).

These and other modifications of the theory of dividing water in colloidal systems into free and bound do not, however, exclude the possibility that some part of the water here is closely bound with colloidal particles and thus stabilizes the colloidal state. This fully applies to protoplasm as well. There is even reason for believing that protoplasm is completely lacking in free water so that any substantial loss thereof inevitably will destroy it. The formation of large quantities of ice in the intercellular spaces is the result of freezing of water in the cell sap of the vacuoles which passes through the protoplasm; however, the water bound with the protoplasmic colloids is not affected to any significant degree (Lepeshkin, 1937; Phillis and Mason, 1951; Frey-Wyssling, 1950).

Growth in plant hardiness is marked by an increase in the amount of bound water, as has been demonstrated by numerous investigations. A good example is seen in the experiments of V.A. Novikov (1928) who studied the oleaster, mulberry, black locust, and Siberian acacia which are very common in Saratov oblast. After chilling branches of these trees in a refrigerator during the fall hardening period, Novikov found that water in the hardiest Siberian acacia did not freeze even at -21.3°.

The absolute amount of bound water in protoplasm increases along with the growth in water-holding power during hardening. This is proved by the expansion of protoplasm, especially the nucleus, which, according to Kessler and Ruhland (1936), increases at this time to almost double its size (cf. too Scarth, 1941). Thus, part of the water in vacuole sap passes into protoplasm, a phenomenon due in part to the storage in protoplasm of plastic substances not required for its vital activity, as discussed in Part II, chapter 4.

All research to date indicates that water in protoplasm does not freeze as long as the protoplasm is living. Only when it dies does the bulk of the previously bound water become free and turn into ice. Thus, the freezing of water in protoplasm must be regarded not only as an indicator of the relative content of bound water, but also as a sign of incipient destruction of protoplasm. The only exception is rapid freezing of protoplasm at very low temperatures when all the liquid solidifies, frequently without crystallization, as we pointed out in Part I, chapter 1 and Part II, chapter 1. Such cases do not contribute to a solution of the problem of possible freezing of protoplasm under ordinary circumstances.

2. VISCOSITY OF PROTOPLASM AND HARDINESS

Viscosity is one of the main colloid chemical properties of protoplasm. Protoplasm ordinarily has low viscosity almost equal to that of water (Rubinstein, 1947; Danzhar, 1950). As the temperature falls, the viscosity of protoplasm increases, exerting a significant effect on all chemical changes occurring in protoplasm and, consequently, on metabolism and activity of protoplasm.

Kessler (1935) made an extensive investigation of protoplasmic viscosity in plants during the winter. Both from measurements of the displacement of starch grains in protoplasm (as a result of centrifuging leaves) and the time it took for the protoplast to round up after tissue sections were immersed in a plasmolytic, Kessler clearly succeeded in proving that protoplasmic viscosity was increased by cool fall weather. This process developed in close association with the entrance of plants into dormancy and the development of frost resistance.

Harvey (1933) and Martin (1934) observed a similar increase in protoplasmic viscosity in cabbage and clover root cells, respectively. Liquid in consistency and freely flowing during summer, the protoplasm became more viscous and less mobile during winter. Many other investigators have made the same observation.

Such an increase in viscosity tends to strengthen frost resistance and improve the plants' chances of wintering successfully. Viscosity checks the vital activity (but not viability) of protoplasm and helps plants to become relatively dormant so that they become more resistant to all kinds of unfavorable external factors. In dry seeds protoplasm is very viscous and thus passive; this is of positive value in the retention of viability.

However, increased viscosity is not always beneficial, and in heat-loving plants it may even be a direct cause of death. This is the conclusion, for example, of P.A. Genkel' and K.P. Margolin (1949) who experimented on cucumbers and other plants. The authors found that chilling them at 0° sharply increased viscosity and killed them. They assume that the cause of death is the slowing up of metabolism and coagulation of protoplasmic colloids.

3. PERMEABILITY OF PROTOPLASM AND HARDINESS

Limited permeability — still called semipermeability — is a major indicator of the viability of protoplasm. When protoplasm is injured, its permeability increases, becoming unlimited if it dies. It is a well known fact that root cells of the sugar beet die as soon as they are warmed in water, which is stained red. This means that the pigment formerly present in the cell sap of the vacuoles has passed into the protoplasm whence it is washed out into the water.

Protoplasmic permeability to water is of great significance in plant hardiness. The chilling of plants with formation of ice in the intercellular spaces is usually caused, as we have seen, by the vacuole water which naturally passes through the protoplasm before entering the intercellular spaces. If freezing begins in the intercellular spaces after a quick drop in temperature and the water does not manage to filter through the protoplasm, it freezes within the cells. Intracellular freezing in unhardened plants occurs largely as a result of the limited permeability of protoplasm to water. Hardening along with other changes is also accompanied by an increase in protoplasmic permeability to water.

Levitt and Scarth (1936a, 1936b; Levitt, 1939) made a thorough study of the problem while determining permeability from the rate of cell plasmolysis and deplasmolysis. They discovered that as the temperature falls, protoplasmic permeability to water increases, to a greater degree in the more resistant than in the less resistant plants. The authors conclude that high permeability to water is a basic prerequisite of hardiness because it prevents intracellular freezing.

However, their finding is not completely applicable, e.g., to heat-loving plants. As Pantanelli observed (1919), a drop in temperature to 0° abruptly raises protoplasmic permeability to water, causes extreme dehydration and ultimately death. But even in the most naturally hardy plants very pronounced permeability to water may be a negative rather than positive sign indicative of incipient destruction of protoplasm (Lepeschkin, 1937).

As the temperature falls, protoplasmic permeability to organic and nonorganic compounds also changes, although not to the same extent as to water. B.M. Golush (1937a, 1938) made a special study of several winter wheat varieties and one winter rye variety. Young plants grown at room temperature were frozen at various temperatures in cryohydrate solutions after which their water was removed by centrifuging along with that of the unchilled controls. Use of an interferometer to determine the substances washed from the cells and passing into the water extract made it possible to judge the permeability of the protoplasm. Golush discovered that plants chilled without preliminary hardening exhibit an abrupt increase in permeability to substances dissolved in water. In hardened plants permeability after freezing likewise increases, but not to the same extent as in unhardened plants. Permeability of more resistant varieties increases less after freezing.

The shortcoming of these and other similar investigations of protoplasmic permeability after cold and frost (Dexter, 1935) is that they fail to distinguish between permeability and the desorption of electrolytes and nonelectrolytes previously bound with protoplasm. Under unfavorable circumstances they become free and are washed out with the water.

4. ADSORPTIVE CAPACITY OF PROTOPLASM AND HARDINESS

Protoplasmic colloids possess marked adsorptive capacity. Many mineral ions and enzymes are included among the substances adsorbed on protoplasm. Let us examine several specific examples of changes in protoplasmic adsorptive capacity for enzymes following the exposure of plants to cold and frost. In white cyclamen, A.L. Kursanov, N.N. Kryukova, and A.S. Morozov (1938) determined that at room temperature the synthetic activity of invertase when the temperature falls to +5° is equal to the hydrolytic action, but with subsequent drops in temperature develops into hydrolytic activity. In other words, at room temperature invertase is chiefly in a condition adsorbed on protoplasm while at temperatures below +5° it is chiefly free.

A similar pattern was noted by B.A. Rubin and N.M. Sisakyan (1949) who determined invertase and proteinase in the leaves of two apple varieties — the more resistant Bordorf-kitayka and the less resistant Kandil'-kitayka. As the temperature was lowered, the synthetic activity of the enzymes in both varieties diminished and at subzero temperatures ceased altogether, whereas hydrolytic activity continued. The difference in reaction of each variety is quite significant. In the less resistant Kandil'-kitayka total cessation of synthetic activity of both ferments took place sooner than in the more resistant Bordorf-kitayka. Consequently, adsorptive capacity of protoplasm in the former for the aforementioned enzymes was lost sooner.

This loss was graphically shown in the experiment of A.L. Kursanov and N.N. Kryukova (1939) with seedlings of two cinchona species. One was somewhat more frost resistant and tolerated as much as -3° outdoors while the other died at +2°. When the plants were chilled to 0°, the activity of invertase in both species fell abruptly, but in the resistant species it was wholly restored when the temperature was elevated, whereas in the other only

ydrolytic activity was partially restored, synthetic activity being completely
st. The protoplasm injured by the low temperature could no longer adsorb
e enzyme.

The capacity of protoplasm exposed to cold and frost to adsorb elec-
rolytes may also change. S.M. Ivanov (1931) determined the electrical
onductivity of sap pressed from living plants before and after injury by
ost. Differences in frost resistance were investigated in varieties of winter
heat and cabbage. It turned out that electrical conductivity of sap increases
frozen plants with greater visible frost injury. Under identical conditions
freezing the process was less pronounced in the more resistant varieties.
he author attributes the increased conductivity of the sap to detachment
rom the protoplasm of the electrolytes previously bound to it. Desorption
f electrolytes, according to the author, is initially reversible, but beyond
ertain limits becomes irreversible and causes the protoplasm to die.

The loss of protoplasmic capacity to adsorb ferments, electrolytes, and
ther substances physically bound to it is undoubtedly a manifestation of its
estruction. A.N. Bakh (1936) thought that everything helping to free enzymes
rom the adsorbed state results in their destruction. However, this very
estruction may be a partial means of preserving the viability of protoplasm.
'ompounds that have become soluble function as protective substances for
rotoplasm. This is the way enzymes in the desorbed state act, causing
ydrolysis and formation of osmotically active substances. The same is true
f electrolytes. This shows the complex and contradictory nature of plant
esistance to frost and to other unfavorable external factors.

5. ACTIVITY OF ENZYMES AND HARDINESS

According to A.V. Blagoveshchenskiy, frost resistance is directly related
o the rate of metabolism and, consequently, to the activity of the enzymes.
'he greater the enzymic activity, the less dependent is the catalyzed reaction
n the inflow of energy from without and, consequently, on the temperature.
Ience, in more resistant plants enzymic activity does not decrease as rapidly
vhen the temperature falls. Hardy plants have low values of the temperature
oefficient Q_{10}. Thus, in the mandarin, Q_{10} is 1.61, but — 2.57 in the lemon
Blagoveshchenskiy, 1938, 1945, 1949, 1950).

Virtually all research to date confirms the existence of relatively higher
nzymic activity in the more frost resistant plants. The difference shows up
ven in unhardy plants and their sprouts. Ye. G. Kling (1931), determining
he activity of proteolytic enzymes in sprouts of winter rye, variety
Yeliseyevskaya, and of winter wheat, varieties Lutescens 329 and Koopera-
orka, determined that the most resistant rye possesses the most active
roteolytic enzymes, whereas the least resistant wheat, Kooperatorka, has
he lowest indices of proteolytic activity.

Of unusual interest is the research on comparative activity of enzymes in
lants during the hardening process. Investigating winter wheat varieties
liffering in hardiness — Minhardi, Turetskaya, and Fulcaster — Newton and
Brown (1931) discovered that the activity of catalase increases during the
all simultaneously with the accumulation of sugars before the end of October
und then decreases by mid-December. In other words, catalase activity
varies with frost resistance. It further turned out that in almost all the
leterminations during the fall and winter — with but one exception — the most

active catalase was found in the most resistant wheat, Minhardi, the lea$\!$ active catalase in the least resistant Fulcaster (cf. also Protsenko ar Polishchuk, 1948).

Of even greater importance in understanding the nature of enzymic activ ity and its relation to frost resistance is the discovery by B.A. Rubin ar V. Ye. Sokolova (1949) of the unusual hardening of the enzymes themselve to low temperatures. The authors determined the temperature optimum fc the synthesis of starch in potatoes during the summer and early fall. The found that it is not constant, but changes with the temperature and is differer in the leaves and tubers. As the weather turns cooler at the end of summe and fall, the temperature optimum for the synthesis of starch drops, th drop being particularly marked in the tubers which are more adapted to lo temperatures than the leaves. For example, early in August the optim$\!$ temperature for synthesis of starch in tubers was 40°, but only 19° b September 20.

6. PHYSIOLOGICALLY ACTIVE SUBSTANCES AND HARDINESS

One of the commonest activators present in plant and animal cells $\!$ glutathione, a compound of cysteine, glycocol, and glutamic acid. Due to th presence in glutathione of the sulfhydryl SH group it is easily oxidized an reduced. Being the activator of the proteolytic enzyme papain, glutathione i directly involved in protein metabolism. Reduced glutathione with the S group is responsible for the hydrolytic effect of papain and, accordingly, c protein decomposition. Oxidized glutathione with the SS group, on the othe hand, stimulates the synthetic activity of papain and thus increases the amour of proteins. The glutathione content is particularly high wherever there i rapid growth and intense respiration (Mothes, 1931; Guthrie, 1933; Prokoshe\ 1934; Stroganov, 1940).

S.M. Ivanov (1939a) determined glutathione in plants exposed to cold an frost. He showed that during the hardening process of citrus — mandarin orange, and lemon — the content of reduced glutathione increases, but no uniformly in different plants and in different parts. The mandarin, the hardi est of all, had in its hardened state the least amount of reduced glutathione whereas the lemon, the least hardy, had the largest amount. Relativel$\!$ resistant branches of the spring growth of the mandarin contained less re duced glutathione than the less resistant branches of the summer growth The latter, in turn, had less reduced gluthathione than the least resistan branches of the fall growth. The branches of ten year old trees had les reduced glutathione than the branches of two year old and less resistan trees. There was less reduced glutathione in the less frost damaged bas tissues of the branches than in the tissues of the leaves.

Thus, according to Ivanov, there was a very close connection between the hardiness of plants, their individual organs and tissues and the content o reduced gluthathione. In all cases great hardiness was combined with lo\ content of reduced gluthathione and proportionately high content of oxidize$\!$ glutathione but with relatively low hydrolysis and intensified synthesis o proteins, the basic constituent of protoplasm.

The connection between vitamins and frost resistance has been littl$\!$ studied in general. We shall speak briefly only about vitamin C, ascorbi$\!$

id. The role of ascorbic acid in the development of frost resistance, like
at of glutathione, is related to its ready oxidizability and reducibility and,
erefore, its ability to oxidize and reduce other substances. Ascorbic acid
especially abundant in the most active parts of plants.

Here is an example from one of our own investigations conducted jointly
ith R.L. Vinokur in the Institute of Plant Physiology. Ascorbic acid was
etermined in the leaves of winter rape differing in age. The plants were
rown in pots and kept in the open from the time they were sown on June 20
ntil the end of fall. Four age groups were represented in the leaves taken
r analysis: (1) the youngest, in the initial, still undeveloped stage; (2) com-
letely formed, young, healthy leaves; (3) aging leaves; (4) clearly aged
aves, already quite yellow. The results are presented in Table 21.

Table 21

Ascorbic acid content of winter rape leaves
(in mg % of dry weight)

Age of leaves	Date leaves obtained for analysis				
	14.VIII	30.IX	25.X	30.X	12.XI
Youngest leaves (I)	944	1164	943	889	769
Completely formed, young, vital leaves (II)	1130	1194	890	790	683
Aging leaves (III)	718	1068	590	449	345
Clearly aged, largely yellowed leaves (IV	442	761	419	228	—

It is evident from the table that the amount of ascorbic acid in the leaves
f all ages increases by the end of September and decreases during October
nd the first half of November. In other words, during the first phase of
ardening, when the plants are still growing and storing plastic substances,
he ascorbic acid content increases.

Note too the difference in ascorbic content of the leaves of different ages,
which has a bearing on the problem, as will be discussed in the next chapter.
The uppermost, youngest, and healthiest leaves, except those still unopened,
s in the sample taken August 14, contains more ascorbic acid than the more
mature, aging, or very old leaves, i.e., age influences the ascorbic acid
ontent of leaves as well as hardening.

Some idea of the significance of ascorbic acid in hardiness is provided by
he research of S.O. Grebinskiy (1940) who made comparative determinations
f ascorbic acid content, activity of catalase and peroxidase in a great many
ultivated and uncultivated plants in the vicinity of Alma-Ata (800 m above
sea level) and in the mountains before the glacier of Tyuyuk-Su (3100 m above
sea level). Grebinskiy found a sharp increase in ascorbic acid content and
ctivity of catalase and peroxidase in plants at altitudes of 2400 and 3100 m
above sea level. As the temperature falls, dryness of air increases, and
nsolation intensifies with altitude, all of which promote the development of
ardiness, and the oxidation-reduction potential in the cells increases. At the
same time plant growth is suppressed.

These data supplement the work of V.A. Kirsanova (1944) who determine
the ascorbic acid content of alfalfa in Uzbekistan at different times of th
year. It turned out that young plants were particularly rich in ascorbic aci
in early spring, in fall, and on warm winter days, i.e., when conditions ar
more favorable for hardening.

Grebinskiy (1941a) discovered that a high oxidation potential in plant cell
arising from the storage of ascorbic acid and intensification of the activit
of oxidation enzymes is directly related to the predominance of synthesi
processes over hydrolysis. By determining protein and soluble nitrogen i
mountain plants, the author found that with increasing altitude above sea leve
and consequent growth of the oxidation potential the plants become relativel
rich in protein nitrogen and poorer in non-protein, soluble nitrogen. Thi
pecularity of high-altitude plants — absence of decomposition of protein
and, consequently, of protoplasm — is regarded by the author as the mai
adaptive mechanism of plants for unfavorable mountain conditions.

The so-called phytohormones or growth substances have been even les
studied for their significance in plant hardiness. They differ from othe
physiologically active substances that catalyze most individual reactions i
that they are involved in the complex processes resulting in the origin o
living matter. The role of growth substances in hardiness is determined b
the fact that they are present wherever there is growth which, as we sav
above, has an adverse effect on the development of frost resistance

Let us first consider the work of I.I. Tumanov (1948) who ascribe
exceptional importance to growth substances in plant hardiness. Whil
investigating fruit trees — peach, apricot, and apple in Kirghizia — Tumano
found that late girdling of branches invariably decreases their resistance t
frost, despite the resulting evident accumulation of plastic substances abov
the ring. This led him to reconsider his former position on the value o
reserve plastic substances in frost resistance and to conclude that th
physiologically active substances, including auxin, connected with growth pla
a more important part.

Tumanov conceives of the situation in this way. The physiologically activ
substances responsible for growth are present in the growing parts of plants
They exclude by their very presence the possibility of these parts' developin
frost resistance. That is why late fall growth of shoots always results in a
decrease in their hardiness. To increase the hardiness of growing parts, it i
necessary for the physiologically active substances to become inactive o
move to other parts. This process normally takes place in the fall whe
growth ceases. However, when growing branches are girdled, the outflow o
physiologically active substances is checked and frost resistance does no
develop properly.

The future alone will determine how correct Tumanov's views are. Currently available data both support and contradict them. For example,
P.S. Belikov (1947), after treating kok-saghyz cuttings in the fall with heteroauxin, noted a sharp decrease in frost resistance during the winter. In this
instance artificial augmentation of the growth substances and resultant root
growth in the fall were naturally followed by lowered resistance on the part
of the cuttings.

However, such results are not invariable. There are cases where treating plants with growth substances does not increase, but instead stunts
growth, thereby affecting frost resistance. A good illustration of this is an
experiment conducted at the Sochi Experimental Station by N.G. Kholodnyy and

. Ye. Kocherzhenko (1948) who sprayed growing lemon branches with a solution of a higher than usual concentration of α-naphthyl acetate. The sprayed branches stopped growing, produced more fruit, and gained some hardiness.

V.A. Mirimanyan performed a similar experiment at the Sukhumi Experimental Station. By spraying growing lemon branches with highly concentrated solutions of growth substances, he succeeded in suppressing growth and increasing the hardiness of the parts of the branches affected. At the same time the hardiness of the trunk diminished, and the trunks of sprayed trees suffered considerably from frost throughout the winter. The reason was the more rapid growth of the trunk at the expense of the plastic substances stored by the plants in the fall which were not used for the growth of the branches. The more rapid growth of some parts of a plant with arrested growth of other parts is a very common phenomenon. It has to be reckoned with when pinching the tops of plants.

The above-mentioned instances of changes in frost resistance due to the use of growth substances show that the latter work indirectly through their influence on growth. These substances neither increase nor decrease resistance but affect the growth process as a whole in cooperation with other growth substances.

The growth substances also include the so-called biogenic stimulators, the therapeutic value of which has been brilliantly demonstrated by V.P. Filatov's eye surgery. According to A.V. Blagoveshchenskiy and his colleagues (Blagoveshchenskiy and Kologrivova, 1945a, 1945b), biogenic stimulators originate in animal and plant tissues when cells are near death as a result of low temperature. They tend to block death and in so doing resemble the lysates, products of protein decomposition, which also have potent therapeutic action. The activating effect of the biogens on catalase and proteinase is now fairly well known. In Filatov's eye operations they stimulate the healing of tissues.

7. NATURE OF THE RELATIONSHIP BETWEEN HARDINESS AND COLLOID CHEMICAL PROPERTIES OF PROTOPLASM

Modern knowledge of the colloid chemical properties of protoplasm justifies the conclusion that it is a colloidal system with heterogeneous parts.

One of the most important colloid chemical properties of protoplasm is its high degree of dispersion which, however, does not remain constant. Protoplasm may even partly coagulate as in the case of chromosome formation, but this coagulation is reversible. Protoplasm dies only when coagulation is irreversible (Danzhar, 1950; Frey-Wyssling, 1950; Makarov, 1953).

A major condition determining the resistance of protoplasmic colloids to irreversible coagulation is the presence of films of water around the colloidal particles. Living protoplasm is hydrophilic and a dehydrated state is inconceivable; as noted previously, water is a constituent of protoplasm. The amount of water changes very slightly, if at all, with the activity of protoplasm. The latter naturally gives off some of its water when the concentration of cell sap in the vacuoles increases and, on the other hand, draws additional water to itself when the concentration of cell sap decreases. This water exchange between protoplasm and cell sap is essential because the water-holding power of protoplasm and the vacuoles is in balance (Walter, 1924,

1931). But this exchange is relatively small. When protoplasm begins to lose water, the force holding water in it increases to an incomparably greater degree than the force holding water in cell sap. That is why the amplitude of variations in protoplasmic water content is much less than in the case of the vacuoles. Plasmolysis, for example, has only a minor effect on the water content of protoplasm (Lepeschkin, 1910, 1930).

The formation of ice in the intercellular spaces likewise has little effect on protoplasmic water. As we pointed out above, this ice is formed almost entirely from water in the cell sap of the vacuoles, whereas a substantial part of the protoplasmic water remains unchanged. And even in the bitterest frosts water does not freeze in protoplasm, remaining liquid owing to the vast power of adsorption on the colloidal particles. At the same time the colloidal particles are kept from coagulating. This explains the major role in plant hardiness of the water-holding power of protoplasmic colloids. We have seen that one of the consequences of the hardening effect of external conditions in the fall and early winter on the physicochemical condition of protoplasm is an increase in this power, i.e., a strengthening of the hydrophilic nature of protoplasm.

Strengthening of the hydrophilic nature of protoplasm in hardening provides a clue to understanding the essence of frost resistance. The process of strengthening the hydrophilic nature of protoplasm must intensify its vital activity; young cells are more hydrophilic than old ones. But in the hardening period new conditions are created which result in decreasing rather than in increasing the vital activity of plants by the very lowering of temperature. The outcome is high vital activity in potency, or high vitality. And the more this vitality develops, the greater becomes the hardiness and general resistance to winter.

Let us consider from this point of view all the other colloid chemical changes in protoplasm during the hardening of plants. We have already seen that the viscosity due to the higher degree of hydrophily avoids the danger of coagulation of protoplasmic colloids because of the thick films of water. At the same time it acts as another inhibitor of protoplasmic activity and promotes it transition to dormancy. All processes in viscous protoplasm naturally slow down.

Higher permeability of protoplasm acts in the same way. It leads to dehydration of the vacuoles and lowering of protoplasmic activity. It is a well known fact that wilting during droughts checks such manifestations of vital activity as photosynthesis and growth (Maksimov, 1939; Alekseyev, 1948). At the same time the very existence of high protoplasmic permeability in hardened plants reflects to a certain extent their greater vitality. In young cells protoplasm is more permeable than in old cells which have not yet begun to die (Maksimov and Mozhayeva, 1944). This is due to the more intense hydrophilic nature of protoplasm in young cells. Hydrophobic formations in and on protoplasm are impermeable to water.

Of major significance in understanding plant hardiness is the change in ability of protoplasm to adsorb enzymes, electrolytes, and the like. The first phase in the hardening process is always related to the heightened adsorptive capacity of protoplasm. This is suggested by the accumulation of plastic substances and the fact that they are stored in polymer form. As we saw in Part II, chapter 4, sugars accumulate in winter wheat throughout September and most of October and are stored in the form of sucrose; in other plants they accumulate and are stored as starch. This is a manifestation of synthesis and, consequently, of the heightened adsorptive capacity of protoplasm.

If the temperature falls further, the hydrolytic processes begin to predominate over the synthetic processes. The second phase of hardening is marked by intensified hydrolysis and conversion of complex into simpler reserve plastic substances with a larger coefficient of osmotic activity. This process is naturally associated with the transition of part of the enzymes from the adsorptive state to the free state. However, the freeing of some enzymes which hydrolyze reserve carbohydrates may occur simultaneously with the adsorption of other enzymes. It will be recalled that in many woody plants oil is synthesized in the second phase of hardening from starch hydrolyzed to sugars. This is also true of pentosans and many other colloidal substances significant in the development of frost resistance. The research of N.M. Sisakyan and T.P. Verkhovtseva (1948) showed that the accumulation of osmotically active substances in the cells, e.g., in connection with the hydrolysis of sucrose, strengthens the adsorptive capacity of protoplasm at low temperatures.

However, when plants are exposed to cold and frost, we encounter the absolute loss of protoplasmic adsorptive capacity, which serves as an indicator of its partial destruction. This occurs in the latest phase of the hardening process. Protoplasm can be partly destroyed, of course, without losing its viability. In this event the disintegration products separated from protoplasm may function as protective substances like electrolytes, which increase osmotic pressure. It will be noted that electrical conductivity of water extracts from chilled tissues rises appreciably only when frost has already injured the cells, even if the signs are still not apparent.

Very important confirmation of the viewpoint set out above on the increased vitality of protoplasm during the hardening process comes from research on the activity of enzymes and physiologically active substances. We have already seen that during hardening enzymes become more active while the temperature optimum falls. At the same time the oxidation potential of plants grows — a graphic indicator of increased vitality. The fact is that we also find among physiologically active substances growth substances which in certain concentrations stimulate growth while reducing frost resistance. However, during hardening these substances become inactivated and they pass from a free into a bound state, as demonstrated by Oserkowsky (1942) for auxin and by K.T. Sukhorukov and K. Bol'shakova (1946) for bios [inositol]. The latter showed that bios is freed in the winter only after plants are winter-killed, when the proteins of the protoplasm are destroyed.

Our conclusion, therefore, is that the strengthening of the hydrophilic nature of protoplasm during hardening inevitably results in increased vitality. It is reinforced by other colloid chemical changes in protoplasm effecting viscosity, permeability, and adsorptive capacity as well as changes in the activity of enzymes and the content of physiologically active substances.

The hardening process, to be sure, consists of more than these colloid chemical changes in protoplasm; undoubtedly other changes, notably in chemical structure, are likewise of significance. We still know very little about this. We assume, however, that data on the conversion of nitrogenous substances (the quantitative decrease in proteins and the increase in their decomposition products) at low temperatures apply chiefly to reserve proteins. It is difficult to reconcile the increased vitality of protoplasm, which is confirmed by the colloid chemical indicators enumerated above, with the destruction of its constituent protein, i.e., that basic protoplasmic substance with which life itself is bound up.

Nevertheless, the destruction of the constituent protein in frost resistance cannot be wholly excluded. Frost resistance may occasionally be sustained, apparently, at the expense of partial destruction of protoplasm. We know that when an organism starves, part of its constituent proteins are used up as nutrients. Destruction of protoplasm at the initial phase, like removal of part of the bound water, may even be beneficial for frost resistance, although it later turns out to be lethal. However, partial disintegration of protoplasm as a result of detachment from the proteins of substances physically bound with it may be quite safe. The lipids, for example, are apparently bound with protoplasm not chemically but, apparently, physically, by adsorption (Kizel', 1940). The formation of a lipid layer on the surface of protoplasm as plants go into fall-winter dormancy and storage of oils in the cells of many plants during the hardening period are advantageous to the plants. The same thing may be true of the electrolytes, the separation of which is to a certain extent reversible. However, this is only a hypothesis, for the appropriate investigations have not yet been made.

CONCLUSION

The hardening process of plants is closely connected with colloid chemical changes in protoplasm. Frost resistance is built up by strengthening the hydrophilic nature and viscosity of protoplasm, increasing its permeability and adsorptive capacity, intensifying the activity of enzymes and growth of the oxidation-reduction potential. Protoplasm becomes more vital, rejuvenated as it were, in the hardening process.

CHAPTER 7

AGE AND HARDINESS IN PLANTS

The aging of a living organism is determined not only by age, i.e., number of days and years lived, but also by the conditions of life, and the less favorable these conditions are, the quicker the organism ages, and vice versa. That is why in determining the aging condition the term agedness rather than age is used.

Aging may slow down and for a time an organism or its individual parts may even become rejuvenated. As applied to plants, all newly developing metameric organs — leaves, buds, new shoots — may be rejuvenated. So too newly formed cells. However, each succeeding wave of rejuvenescence becomes weaker and ever shorter in duration. The process of aging in plants is cyclical, with alternating rejuvenescence but on a diminishing curve. It is only the emergence of a new organism from a fertilized germ cell that represents total rejuvenescence (Krenke, 1940; Lysenko, 1949). Aging exerts great influence on the frost resistance of every plant and its individual parts.

1. EFFECT OF FROST ON PLANTS AND PARTS OF PLANTS IN RELATION TO AGE

The relationship between frost resistance and age is most pronounced in unicellular organisms whose resistance declines as the cells develop and age. This was demonstrated many years ago. Schumacher, for example, froze yeast and found that when fully developed, vacuolized cells died, young cells without vacuoles survived. According to P. V. Butyagin (1909), young bacterial cultures of various species were invariably more frost resistant than old cultures. The same relationship between resistance and age has also been noted in many multicellular organisms, e.g., mold fungi (Bartetzko, 1909) and moss (Irmscher, 1912).

The influence of frost on herbaceous and woody plants is more complex. In such grains as winter wheat, variety Moskovskaya 2411 (Fig. 1), the young top leaves are the most resistant. In trees and shrubs, on the other hand, frost usually kills the tips of young branches before the old skeletal branches and trunks. Hardiness, therefore, is not always in inverse relationship to age so that we must not limit ourselves to a comparison of hardiness in plants and parts of various ages. We must go into the subject a little more deeply.

2. REJUVENESCENCE AND HARDINESS

Vigorous or even severe pruning has been recognized from ancient times as a method of renewing trees and shrubs. Younger and more active parts develop at the places where the aging parts have been pruned. This is the way apple and other fruit trees, tea bushes, etc. are usually renewed. Grasses are renewed by mowing. While studying winter grains and grasses I observed that the new leaves of mowed plants are more viable and frost resistant than the corresponding leaves of unmowed plants.

Experiment 1. The purpose of the experiment was to compare the viability of leaves in mowed and unmowed perennial wheat, variety 34085, which shows particularly good growth after mowing. Seeds were planted August 14 in Mitscherlich pots outdoors. Four leaves formed on each by September 5 and some of the plants were cut at the base. They immediately began to grow back and six new leaves appeared on each by mid-October. The leaves appeared at about the same time that the next leaves on the uncut plants developed.

The difference in viability between the two sets of plants became more pronounced the longer the leaves continued to grow. The uncut plants aged more rapidly, as shown by earlier yellowing of the leaves while the cut plants looked fresher and greener. Fig. 55 shows the main shoots of typical cut and uncut plants. The sketch was made October 10 when growth came to a halt.

Fig. 55. Main shoot of perennial wheat 34085 after termination of growth
1 — control plant; 2 — plant cut at base September 5. Blackened leaves —
dead, crosshatched leaves — yellowed

Perennial wheat 34085 is a winter crop and it usually comes to ear only after the wintering period, although it just bushes out by fall if planted very early in the summer. This helps to explain the relatively rapid aging of the uncut plants in this experiment. When a winter plant does not come to ear for a long time, it ages comparatively quickly, as everyone knows who has observed winter crops sown in the spring or summer. Even under highly favorable conditions of growth the dead leaves by the end of summer usually impart to such plants a brown background variegated by the green of only the youngest leaves.

Experiment 2. This experiment was a comparative study of frost resistance in mowed and unmowed winter plants. Vyatka winter rye was sown July 17 in Mitscherlich pots. The plants were cut four times: August 15, 30, September 15, 30. They wintered outdoors under light snow to prevent desiccation and experienced frost of about -22.5° near the tillering nodes.

When the plants were moved into a greenhouse in early spring it was noted that all the uncut control plants died owing to lowered frost resistance caused by extremely early sowing. The cut plants remained alive for some time and died later, as is often the case with crops severely damaged by frost. Judging by external appearance, the plants cut September 15 were relatively more resistant; those cut August 15 and 30 were less resistant, while those cut September 30 were the least resistant of all.

The experiment thus showed an appreciable, if not outstanding, rise in the hardiness of plants rejuvenated by cutting as compared with uncut plants. There was also a difference in resistance in relation to the time of cutting.

3. HARDINESS OF WINTER PLANTS SOWN AT DIFFERENT TIMES

The significance of age becomes clearer when plants sown at different times are compared. Let us examine the hardiness of plants rejuvenated by cutting and young plants grown from seeds.

Experiment 1. This experiment was closely connected with the above. A few days before the next time the plants were due to be cut we sowed more rye in previously prepared pots in such a way that the appearance of the shoots would coincide with the start of the new growth of the cut plants. Our purpose was to ensure the uniformity of external growth conditions for the new leaves of all the plants. The only difference was that the leaves of the cut plants were of a higher order, i.e., they were preceded by a larger number of leaves than in the plants developing from seeds. Fig. 56 shows the results of the experiment after Vyatka winter rye had wintered under precisely the same conditions as those in the preceding experiment.

Fig. 56. Vyatka winter rye exposed to -22.5° (photographed 3 weeks
after transfer to a greenhouse Feb. 8)
1 - 4 — left to right: sown August 14, 29, September 13, 26

The frost resistance of the plants was greater than in the preceding experiment. A number of plants in most of the series survived a frost of -22.5°, whereas all the plants in the preceding experiment died. The plants sown August 14 were the least resistant, all dying during the winter. The plants sown September 13 were the most resistant; those sown August 29 and September 26 were less resistant. The experiment demonstrated, therefore, that as compared with the preceding experiment plants grown from seed are more resistant than those rejuvenated by cutting. It also showed definite differences in resistance in relation to the time of sowing.

Experiment 2. The purpose of the experiment was to check the results obtained in the preceding experiment. Beds were prepared in the summer. The soil was removed to a depth of 40 cm, finely screened, fertilized, and put back, as is done with pots, thereby ensuring uniformity of conditions for the growth of the plants throughout the beds. Winter wheat, variety 599 (wheat-wheatgrass hybrid) was sown five times: August 14, 30, September 13, October 10, 23. The plants sown August 14 were thick bushes by frost time and were naturally the "oldest." Those sown October 23, which put out only shoots, were the youngest.

Before the onset of cold weather all the plants were examined and any found injured to the slightest extent by insects (midges, wire worms, etc.) were discarded. The October plants which had not come up by frost time were selectively inspected in individual rows. A second check was made in the spring and the survivors tallied. The results of the experiment are shown in Table 22.

The plants of the September 13 sowing proved to be the most resistant; those sown earlier and especially those sown later were less so. In other words, the greatest resistance was displayed, just as in the preceding experiment, by neither the oldest nor the youngest plants, but by the "middle-aged" plants.

Table 22

Effect of sowing time on wintering of winter wheat

Date of sowing	Plants that went into the winter	Plants that overwintered	Survivors, %
14. VIII	326	154	47
30. VIII	1799	1230	68
13. IX	354	254	72
10. X	800	0	0
23. X	350	0	0

4. RELATIONSHIP BETWEEN HARDINESS AND SEED VIABILITY

The most important change that takes place as an organism grows older is in viability. This is quite evident in stored seeds. All seeds are known to suffer gradual loss of germinating power and vigor with time. Let us compare the frost resistance of shoots growing from seeds differing in viability.

Experiment 1. Half a kilogram each of the following seeds — spring wheat, variety Lutescens 62, and winter wheat, varieties Kooperatorka and Moskovskaya 2411 — were grown in the laboratory until the most vigorous seeds formed rootlets about 0.5 cm long. We then selected the most vigorous of the sprouted seeds from each variety as well as the weakest (rootlets 0.1-0.2 cm long) in which the germ had just broken through the coat. The difference in length reflected the difference in vigor of seed germination.

The shoots were kept on ice several days for hardening and then frozen. The survivors were counted two weeks after freezing (Table 23).

Table 23

Relationship between wheat hardiness and vigor of seed germination

Length of time sprouts kept on ice, days	Temperature of chilling sprouts, °C	Lutescens 62 Spring		Kooperatorka Winter		Moskovskaya 2411 Winter	
		Surviving sprouts (%) with rootlets					
		short	long	short	long	short	long
4	−6.0	78	93	99	99	98	98
6	−6.6	58	86	63	92	85	93
8	−9.6	27	62	55	81	51	76
9	−10.8	25	27	28	47	22	61

It is evident that shoots from the more vigorous germinating seeds were the more frost resistant.

Experiment 2. The experiment was performed simultaneously with the above. The experimental materials were winter wheat varieties known to differ in germinating power: Gostianum 237 - 96% germinating power - and Lutescens 329 - 71% germinating power. The results of chilling are shown in Table 24.

Table 24

Relationship between winter wheat hardiness and germinating
power and vigor of seed germination

Length of time sprouts kept on ice, days	Temperature of chilling sprouts, C°	Gostianum 237		Lutescens 329	
		Surviving sprouts (%) with rootlets			
		short	long	short	long
4	–6.0	98	97	82	85
6	–6.6	64	79	40	51
8	–6.6	57	72	29	44
9	–10.8	10	39	10	23

As in the preceding experiment, in both varieties sprouts from more vigorously germinating seeds were hardier. It also turned out that the shoots of Lutescens 329 with lower germinating power were less hardy than the shoots of Gostianum 237. Yet Lutescens 329 is characterized in general by greater hardiness than Gostianum 237.

Experiment 3. A study was made of frost resistance in five wheat varieties known to differ in germinating power and vigor: spring wheat, variety Lutescens 62, and winter wheat, varieties Kooperatorka, Moskovskaya 2411, Gostianum 238, and Lutescens 329 (Fig. 57).

Fig. 57. Sprouts from seeds with different germinating power and
vigor of germination
1 — spring wheat Lutescens 62; 2, 3, 4, 5 — winter wheats, from left
to right: Kooperatorka, Moskovskaya 2411, Gostianum 237,
Lutescens 329

One hundred seeds of each were sown on moist filter paper in dishes. Germination took place at room temperature in the light. The difference in bushiness of the varieties being compared testifies to the germinating power of the seeds while the differences in height are indicative of their vigor. The germinating power of the individual seed varieties was as follows: Lutescens 62 - 57%; Kooperatorka - 90%; Moskovskaya 2411 - 97%; Gostianum 237 - 95%; Lutescens 329 - 71%.

Frost resistance was determined in seeds (800 of each variety) five days after germinating without dividing them into groups with short and long rootlets. The shoots were kept on ice for a day and then chilled for another day at –6.6°. The number of live shoots from the original number was: in Moskovskaya 2411 – 73%; in Gostianum 238 – 69%; in Kooperatorka – 69%; in Lutescens 329 – 63%; in Lutescens 62 – 57%. The varieties are listed here in descending order of germinating power and vigor, which corresponds with the drop in frost resistance of the shoots. The decrease in germinating power and vigor was due to the decrease in hardiness.

Thus, the results of all the above-described experiments indicate that there is a relationship between the hardiness of shoots and the viability of the seeds from which they grow. In actively photosynthesizing plants this relationship can be detected as soon as the hardiness of leaves of different ages is compared. Young leaves are more vigorous than old and, as we have seen, they are also more resistant to frost.

However, some exceptions are encountered in experiments with photosynthesizing green plants. When comparing winter grains of different ages sown at different times, we discovered that lower resistance is associated not with older but with younger age. The great vigor characteristic of younger plants is sometimes apparently a negative rather than a positive factor.

To clarify this contradiction, let us first examine the results of research on the storage of reserve plastic substances in plants.

5. RESERVE PLASTIC SUBSTANCES AND THEIR ROLE IN THE HARDINESS OF VARIABLE AGE PLANTS AND THEIR PARTS

In Part II, chapter 3 we discussed the importance in plant hardiness of fall storage of reserve plastic substances. The rapid utilization of these substances during growth of the germ deprives the sprouts of the possibility of having, under normal circumstances, any substantial store of plastic substances even in the fall. That is why the advent of cold weather finds mature plants with an adequate supply for the winter while young plants in the form of shoots or sprouts are about as they were in the summer. If the caryopses are removed from sprouts that have not yet broken through the soil, these sprouts will not regenerate after their leaves are cut off, for they have no reserve for this purpose. The shoots of winter crops too, even with the caryopses, but largely exhausted, especially when sown too deeply, almost never regenerate after being cut. If gnawed by mice during the winter, they invariably die.

Such is the nature of the growth of young plants which explains why sprouts and shoots harden poorly and are less frost resistant. The reason is that they do not contain the plastic substances needed for the development of hardiness. Although potentially more resistant than mature plants, they are actually less so.

However, it does not follow from the above that young plants and their parts cannot store substantial amounts of plastic substances and thus harden effectively. If sprouts of winter crops are kept for some time on ice, they become more resistant to frost (Vasil'yev, 1937). The plastic substances apparently shift from the endosperm of the seed to the cells of the germ. The reason is that at 0° the germ virtually does not grow, whereas hydrolysis of the seed's reserve substances and their movement into the germ continue.

Hence, reserve substances not used up in growth are deposited in the germ, although not in as abundant quantities as in the hardening period of mature green plants.

Plastic substances are incomparably more abundant in the young shoots of wintering woody plants, provided, however, that their fall growth comes to an end soon enough. The advantage of these shoots as compared with young plants developing from seeds is that they have an inexhaustible source of plastic substances — the leaves. As a result, fully ripened young shoots are very resistant and in northern hardy species they are capable of enduring temperatures of -50 and lower. Very often, however, especially in southern species, the young shoots do not "ripen" in the fall and go into the winter with an inadequate supply of plastic substances and poorly developed surface tissues to protect them from evaporation. This makes them less hardy and in general less winter resistant than the older branches.

Analysis in accordance with the above viewpoint of any fact bearing on the difference in frost resistance of plants of different ages, individual parts, and cells clearly reveals that there is a necessary correlation between youthfulness and greater frost resistance if the corresponding plants or their parts and cells have been filled at the right time with reserve plastic substances. Thus, in well hardened trees, even if injured by frost, the cambial cells are the last to be damaged. These cells are relatively more resistant than the others. M.I. Saltykovskiy (1929) showed that in the tillering nodes of winter grains the youngest cells are likewise the most hardy.

However, in addition to storage of reserve plastic substances appropriate changes in the protoplasm itself are required to ensure frost resistance. That is why we must know the changes in protoplasm with age if we are to understand the relationship between hardiness and the age of plants.

6. COLLOID CHEMICAL CHARACTERISTICS
OF PROTOPLASM IN YOUNG AND HARDENED PLANTS

Young, newly formed cells have only the rudiments of vacuoles in the form of small mucilaginous formations. These formations enlarge only with time as they become filled with watery sap partially from protoplasmic water (Guilliermond, 1941).

The dehydration of protoplasm and increase in the water content of vacuoles continues even after the so-called stage of elongation, when the size of the vacuoles grows very rapidly. As the cells age, the cavities occupied by the vacuoles enlarge while the amount of protoplasm keeps on diminishing. And in old, but still living cells the protoplasm is simply a thin layer next to the membrane from which strands extend to the nucleus usually found in the center of the cell. Thus, the water content of protoplasm decreases during the process of aging and decreased cell activity.

In plant hardening we encounter an apparent contradiction: protoplasmic activity in hardened plants is low while water content, on the other hand, is high. However, this is not a genuine contradiction. It is created purely by the nature of the external conditions during the hardening period, chiefly low temperatures. Actually, as noted in the preceding chapter, protoplasm during hardening becomes more active, but only potentially because this activity cannot manifest itself under the given circumstances. Consequently, according to one of the major physicochemical indicators of protoplasm — water content — hardened plants can logically be likened to rejuvenated plants. The same thing is also true of other physicochemical indicators.

Protoplasm changes with age in many respects. Homogeneous and optically empty in young and active cells, it becomes less disperse and thickens as it gets older while microscopically visible granules of all kinds form; droplets of oil as well as starch and aleurone grains are very frequently seen. The appearance of these formations in cytoplasm largely depends on external conditions and on the nature of the plants, but they never show up in young active cells, for their appearance is primarily a function of age. If there are heavy accumulations of these formations, the protoplasm degenerates. Oil degeneration, starch degeneration, protein degeneration, etc. are distinguished according to the substances deposited. Once in a while lignified protoplasm can be found (Aleksandrov, 1949, 1954; Rokhlina, 1936; Tauson, 1948), but these are rare cases of aging and degeneration. The aging of protoplasm is usually due to increased viscosity and reduced permeability. However, in very old cells where intensified hydrolysis takes place, permeability is again increased, but this is due to a moribund state (Maksimov and Mozhayeva, 1944a, 1944b; Grammatikati, 1948).

The adsorptive power of protoplasm also changes with age. Several investigators of enzymes have shown that the synthetic processes predominate in the younger leaves, an indicator of the fact that enzymes are adsorbed on protoplasm. In the older eaves, on the other hand, the hydrolytic processes always predominate so that the enzymes show up in a relatively free state (Kursanov and Bryushkova, 1940a). In hardened plants, at least in the first phase, protoplasmic adsorptive power is higher so that synthesis, as in young plants, predominates.

The activity of enzymes likewise changes with age. N. M. Sisakyan and B.A. Rubin, among others, have demonstrated that in later and thus less rapidly aging varieties of vegetables enzymes are more active than in earlier, relatively rapidly aging varieties. The authors believe that this is the reason for the higher survival rate of the later varieties in winter storage (Rubin, 1936, 1939; Sisakyan and Rubin, 1944).

The greater enzymic activity in young plants and their parts than in old plants is partially responsible for their greater vitality. The activity of enzymes is likewise greater in hardened plants; the enzymes are more stable and are inactivated later when the temperature is low.

The oxidation potential becomes high in young plants, as shown by Bukin and Stupak (1938) in early and late cabbage varieties. There was more ascorbic acid in the late, better preserved varieites. This was indicated by the analysis given in an earlier chapter of the ascorbic acid content of winter rape leaves of different ages, the younger leaves of which had more ascorbic acid in the summer and fall. The oxidation potential too is higher in hardened than in unhardened plants.

It follows from the above that by such important physicochemical indicators of protoplasm as adsorptive capacity, enzymic activity, and oxidation potential, hardened plants may fairly be likened to rejuvenated plants. The difference between them is that in hardened plants at low temperatures heightened activity is transformed into heightened vitality.

CONCLUSION

While aging plants lose the capacity for resistance to frost, old plants and their parts are always less resistant than young plants, provided that the latter have an adequate reserve of plastic substances.

Thus, there is an organic connection between aging (the opposite of rejuvenescence) and frost resistance. Viability is based on the processes of renewal and hardening: the more viable the plant and its individual parts, the more potentially frost resistant it is, other things being equal. Renewal invariably improves the capacity of the renewed parts to harden. This is particularly apparent in the case of seeds and total renewal of the plants. It also explains why plants grown from seeds are always more viable and hardy than those grown from slips, cuttings, etc.

The viability of plants is primarily due to the properties of protoplasm. The more viable protoplasm of young cells is more hydrophilic and thus contains more water, possesses higher adsorptive power, more active enzymes, and greater oxidation potential. Protoplasm in the cells of frost-resistant plants has the same indicators. Hardening, at least in the initial phase, is caused by these changes in protoplasm. Thus, hardening can justly be compared to rejuvenescence. Yet there is a difference between the two. Rejuvenescence is essentially associated with the renewal of protoplasm, including its elimination of so-called paraplasmatic (i.e., not, strictly speaking, forming part of protoplasm) formations like reserve plastic substances. Yet hardening is inseparably bound up with the storage in protoplasm of plastic substances not consumed in its vital activity. Therefore, in speaking of the resemblance between rejuvenescence and hardening, we must not forget the differences. For, hardening is not fully inclusive of rejuvenescence, it merely embraces some elements of it.

CHAPTER 8

FALL-WINTER DORMANCY AND WINTER HARDINESS

It has long been observed that different plants go into fall-winter dormancy at different times and that relatively early transition to dormancy is associated with greater hardiness, whereas continued growth in the fall results in partial or even total destruction of plants during the winter.

1. FALL-WINTER DORMANCY

Coville's research (1920) gives a good idea of fall-winter dormancy. The following observation stimulated the research. Several blueberry bushes were brought into a greenhouse at the end of one summer to permit work to continue during the winter. Despite the favorable growing conditions, however, all the plants lost their leaves in the fall. Even more surprising was the fact that after remaining in a warm place all winter these plants failed to start growth in the spring like the plants that wintered outdoors and they remained without leaves for many months. Attempts to change the situation by brief chilling were futile. Only two to three months of temperatures somewhat above zero restored their growth capacity. The same thing happened with other wintering trees and shrubs, many species of which were later tested by the author.

Analysis of the stimulating effect of cold on dormant plants showed that it is strictly localized and that only those parts of a plant start growth which are directly exposed to cold. In the experiments with the blueberries brought into the greenhouse at the end of summer, one branch was allowed to protrude through an opening in the glass and remain exposed to air. And when spring came only that branch started to grow. In another experiment, the reverse happened, i.e., a single branch of the plant was brought into the greenhouse through an opening, and in the spring the entire plant began to grow with the exception of the one branch that wintered in the greenhouse, which remained dormant.

It was further discovered that dormancy can be overcome by various mechanical injuries to tissue as well as by cold. Pruning, girdling, removal of parts of the bark and xylem invariably induced growth of buds nearest the wounds. Stimulation also occurred due to the death of the upper branches after the dormant plants were kept in the greenhouse for some time. The buds on branches underneath began to grow.

Such in outline is fall-winter dormancy in plants. A more detailed examination discloses a number of peculiarities varying from plant to plant. We shall study the phenomenon in the three main groups of wintering plants — trees and shrubs of the northern and temperature zones, grasses, and subtropical plants.

2. FALL-WINTER DORMANCY IN WINTERING TREES AND SHRUBS OF THE NORTHERN AND TEMPERATE ZONES

Fall-winter dormancy is particularly pronounced in wintering trees and shrubs of the northern and temperate zones so that they provide excellent material for a study of the phenomenon. To begin with, dormancy is never absolute. Activity does not come to a complete halt in winter; metabolism continues as does growth. This was proved long ago by N.I. Zheleznov (1851) who showed in several trees in the Moscow Botanical Garden that the buds grow larger during the winter, their water and ash content increases, the ovaries, egg-cells, and anthers become larger and pollen forms in the anthers. We know now that even without growing, buds never remain unchanged but develop, albeit slowly; they may also pass from the vegetative into the reproductive stage.

Fall-winter dormancy never involves the entire plant and it differs in degree from part to part. Young annual buds enter the deepest dormancy. It is most difficult to force growth when the plant or individual branches are brought into a greenhouse during the winter. Perennial buds frequently have no dormancy period at all and start growth as soon as the external conditions are favorable. The suppression of growth in these buds is usually due to an insufficient supply of plastic substances. The parenchymal cells of the bark of the trunk and branches are almost never dormant and under certain conditions they may begin to divide at any time and form cambium. Roots too have comparatively little dormancy. They normally continue to grow late in the fall until the ground freezes; their growth is subsequently halted mostly by frost. Dormancy is pronounced, as in young buds, only in the cambium of the trunk and, above all, in young branches (Simon, 1906; Aleksandrov, 1948; Metlitskiy, 1949).

The duration of dormancy varies with the species and origin of the plants. Ye. S. Moroz's research (1948) is very instructive in this connection. Moroz studied dormancy in 123 species of ornamental trees growing outdoors in the Leningrad Botanical Garden and in 116 varieties of fruit trees and bushes from several fruit and berry stations in the European part of the U.S.S.R. Branches were cut in the fall and kept for several days at temperatures ranging from 0° to +5° or as long as necessary to induce the buds to open. The branches of some trees and bushes required 60 days at low temperature, 30 to 45 days were enough for others, 15 days for a third group. Finally, there were some branches that put on growth without any additional chilling as soon as they were brouht into a warm room.

According to Moroz, genera with the most distinct dormancy period included: Acer, Alnus, Amelanchier, Corylus, Crataegus, Fraxinus, Tilia, Ulmus, Quercus; to a lesser degree — Malus, Prunus, Pyrus, Populus, Betula, Caragana, Salix; to an even lesser degree — Berberis, Spiraea, Syringa, Muladelphios, Physocarpus, etc. Among the fruit trees, the cherry required the shortest dormancy, the apple the longest. There is no assured criterion and, as Moroz writes, "the duration of chilling required by individual species within a single genus may be quite different and not at all characteristic of most species of the given genus" (p. 313). Much more definite is the connection between dormancy and origin of the plants and conditions of the habitat. Thus, all apple, cherry, and plum varieties from Krasnodar kray had a longer period of dormancy than varieties from Leningrad oblast. Hence the author concludes: "The more southerly the regions in which the variety is cultivated, the longer the period of chilling needed for dormancy, and conversely, varieties cultivated in the more northerly regions end the dormant period quickly and require less chilling" (p. 319).

Such are the characteristics of fall-winter dormancy in wintering trees and shrubs of the northern and temperate zone.

3. FALL-WINTER DORMANCY IN WINTERING HERBACEOUS PLANTS

There are frequent statements in the literature to the effect that wintering herbaceous plants do not become dormant in the fall. This is explained on the grounds that the plants are capable of growing any time of the year as long as the external conditions are favorable. As we shall see below, herbaceous plants do have a dormant period, only it is not very pronounced.

A.I. Stebut was the first to note fall-winter dormancy in these plants. Observing several winter wheat varieties in the fall at the former Saratov Experimental Station, he learned that with the advent of cold weather growth of the more frost-resistant local varieties slows down more perceptibly than the growth of frost-resistant varieties from other regions. Stebut called this characteristic of local varieties "anabiosis". However, his conclusion regarding "anabiosis" of winter plants was not based on precise research and the author himself termed it speculative (Stebut, 1916). There is now available experimental proof of the existence of a fall–winter dormant period in wintering herbaceous plants. For example, as discussed above, winter wheat displayed the maximum suppression of growth at low temperatures as compared with the spring varieties while it was more marked in the hardy as compared with the unhardy varieties. This kind of difference between winter and spring varieties is also found in their storage of dry substance in the fall. Let us familiarize outselves with the research on this problem.

Vyatka winter rye, Kooperatorka winter wheat, soft spring wheat Lutescens 62, and hard winter wheat Melanopus 69 were grown in Mitscherlich pots, seven plants of each variety per pot. Already germinated seeds were sown August 31. To determine the green mass, each sample of one variety consisted of 100 or more plants from 16 adjacent pots. The green mass was weighted during the fall seven times at three periods: (1) before tillering and at the beginning of tillering with an identical number of shoots of winter and spring varieties; (2) when the winter varieties had outstripped the spring varieties in bushiness; (3) just before the onset of frost.

Table 25 shows the dry weight of the green mass of plants from each variety before tillering (September 17) and at the beginning of tillering (September 23).

Table 25

Dry weight of winter and spring grains
(in grams per 100 plants)

Data sample obtained	Winter		Spring	
	Vyatka rye	Kooperatorka wheat	Lutescens 62 wheat	Melanopus 69 wheat
17. IX	3.45	3.05	3.60	4.26
23. IX	9.10	8.47	9.64	10.80

Leaving aside the analysis of the differences between the individual varieties within the winter and spring groups, we can state that the green mass in the winter rye and wheat with an equal number of shoots per bush was less than the green mass in the soft and hard spring wheat, i.e., the vigor in storing dry substance in the winter crops in the fall was less than in the spring crops.

By the time of the second comparison of the green mass (October 5) the winter rye and wheat were quite thick with 4–6 shoots each. The spring wheats were noticeably lagging in tillering, but they had the bigger shoots. Table 26 gives an idea of these differences between the winter and spring varieties.

Due to the heavy tillering of the winter varieties the weight of their bushes increased and was now comparable to that of the spring varieties. But there was often a very sharp difference in the weight of the individual shoots. An average shoot in a winter variety weighed half as much as an average shoot in a spring variety. Tillering lagged in the spring varieties, but each shoot acquired a green mass much sooner.

Of special interest is the green mass in the plants at the end of October and first part of November. By this time the winter varieties had thickened

Table 26

Condition of winter and spring grains October 5

Indicator	Winter		Spring	
	Vyatka rye	Kooper-atorka wheat	Lutescens 62	Malanopus 69
Weight 100 bushes, g	22.9	22.0	22.0	22.6
Average number of shoots per bush	5.5	4.6	2.1	2.7
Weight of average shoots, g	4.2	4.8	11.0	8.5

out more — there were 6-7 shoots per bush. The spring varieties changed comparatively little because after mid-October they passed into the stem-extension stage so that tillering came to a complete halt (Table 27).

Dry weight of winter and spring grains (in g per 100 bushes)

Table 27

Date sample obtained	Winter		Spring	
	Vyatka rye	Kooperatorka wheat	Lutescens 62	Melanopus 69
23.X	42.6	43.5	39.4	38.5
29.X	46.1	46.4	47.0	45.8
4.XI	48.9	46.2	49.0	50.3
10.XI	48.5	46.2	53.3	55.1

Judging by these data, the increase in dry substance in the winter rye and winter wheat came to a complete halt by the beginning of November. Meanwhile it was continuing in both varieties of spring wheat and the weight of the plants rose until November 10. As a result, the weight of the spring varieties was equal to that of the winter varieties and then exceeded it. On November 4 and 10 the spring varieties, although they were less than half as bushy, weighed more than the winter varieties.

These data leave no room for doubt that all the viable growing and working cells of winter wheat become dormant in the fall. The plants become less active and cease entirely to store dry substance, whereas, as long as the temperature permits, the same process is still quite apparent in the spring varieties.

Fall-winter dormancy of wintering herbaceous plants was investigated by P.A. Genkel' and L.S. Litvinov (1930). The authors determined seasonal changes in photosynthesis in the hazelwort and strawberry. They discovered that the leaves of these plants brought into a warm room in the fall do not immediately begin to store dry substances even if the conditions are favorable for photosynthesis. At first there was only respiration and it wasn't until the leaves were kept warm for several days or more and given warm baths that their weight increased appreciably as a result of photosynthesis. The same thing was observed when determining changes in dry weight of leaves outdoors early in the spring.

4. FALL-WINTER DORMANCY IN SUBTROPICAL PLANTS

Fall-winter dormancy in subtropical plants, as in wintering herbaceous plants, is not very pronounced. However, the group is not homogeneous. Some have virtually no dormant period and stop growing only when the temperature falls steeply while others have a marked dormant period. For example, the lemon has scarcely any dormant period and only ceases to grow with the onset of frost. As soon as the weather warms up, it almost immediately resumes growth. On the other hand, the mandarin has a distinct period of dormancy. The various forms of tea differ in depth of dormancy. For example, the Indian (Assamese) forms in Ajaria do not become dormant at all, whereas certain Chinese forms have a dormant period and stop growing even before the cold weather sets in (Pokrovskiy and Merabyan, 1936).

In woody subtropical plants, as in woody plants of the northern and moderate zones, fall-winter dormancy is closely related to the place of origin, but this relationship is manifested in a different way. Plants from the more southerly regions of the subtropical zone, where winters are very mild, generally have no dormant period, whereas plants from the more northern regions of this zone with colder winters have a distinct dormant period. That is why there is a direct connection between dormancy and frost resistance in subtropical plants, unlike trees and shrubs of the northern and temperate zones. Those forms of plants in which dormancy is deeper have greater frost resistance. This relationship is well known to every horticulturist on our Black Sea coast, and the hardiness of subtropical plants is usually appraised here from the standpoint of whether they have a fall-winter dormant period (Nadaraya, 1938; Gocholashvili, 1940b).

This view has a firm basis in fact, and arrested growth in the fall, if not caused by inadequate food, always promotes the development of frost resistance. Subtropical plants are no exception to this rule. However, it would be completely wrong to reduce frost resistance in subtropical plants solely to a matter of their having a dormant period, for the latter is not an invariable precondition of the development of frost resistance. Here are some examples.

Part II, chapter 3 contained a description of an experiment with the Japanese persimmon, a plant that is very sensitive to changes in the photoperiod. A short day of 9 or 10 hours induced dormancy in seedlings any time during the summer. Moreover, dormancy continued for several weeks after they were exposed to natural light. Yet this dormancy had no appreciable effect on their hardiness. Both the short-day plants that became dormant and the controls that did not become dormant died with the first fall frosts.

An excellent example of the lack of direct connection between frost resistance and dormancy is provided by our potato, an import from the subtropical zone. The tubers have a well defined dormant period, yet, as is well known, they are not particularly hardy and are winterkilled as soon as ice forms in them at -2° or -3°. This is also true of the roots of beets and carrots — other imports from the subtropics — which have a relatively well defined fall-winter dormant period but are not very hardy.

All this shows that there is no clear-cut connection between frost resistance and dormancy. In some plants dormancy definitely promotes the development of hardiness, whereas in others it seems to have no appreciable effect.

5. INTRACELLULAR CHANGES IN CONNECTION WITH FALL-WINTER DORMANCY

Kraus discovered in 1874 that in the leaves of orchardgrass, meadow-grass, barley, and rye as well as in the bark of the oak, poplar, linden, and other wintering trees plastids that are normally distributed uniformly in the cytoplasm during the summer crowd together inside the cells when the fall frosts begin (at -2 to -8°). In 1930 A.V. Ryantsev (1930) studied this phenomenon in detail on plants from the environs of the city of Molotov. He discovered that in the pine, cedar, juniper, red bilberry, cranberry, wild rosemary, andromeda, etc. all the plastids with part of the protoplasm and the nucleus actually move inside the cells in the fall while the vacuoles are squeezed out. At the same time the size of the plastids changes. In the summer the stroma of the plastids is enlarged by grains of starch but in the fall, when the starch disappears, it contracts and the plastids shrink. The shift of chloroplasts from the winter to summer position also took place every time the leaves were brought into a warm room in the winter and left there 15 to 48 hours. Exposed to temperatures of +1 to -4°, they shifted to the winter position within 20 to 48 hours. The plastids did not move in leaves frozen at -5°.

Harvey (1933) observed that the cells of winter wheat, cabbage, and some other wintering plants seem to turn into cysts in the fall due to steadily falling temperatures, i.e., they are covered with thick membranes and cease normal activity. At first the protoplasm stops moving, then the protoplasm seems to lose its ability to hold water, slides off and partially moves away from the membrane. At the same time a new membrane forms on the outer surface of the protoplasm next to the old one so that the latter appears very thick. The result is the isolated cell-cysts so characteristic of resting bacterial and algal cells.

This observation of Harvey's was confirmed and developed by P.A. Genkel' and Ye. Z. Oknina (1945). The authors discovered there is separation of the protoplasm from the membrane and isolation of each protoplast in the fall in the cells of hazelwort, wheatgrass, red bilberry leaves, in the needles of the white cedar, pine, and spruce, and in the leaves and growing points of wheat and rye. The authors called this process "isolation of protoplasm." However, unlike Harvey, Genkel' and Oknina found that the protoplast is covered on top not with a new cellulose membrane, but with a lipoid layer impermeable to water which also covers the tonoplast delimiting the vacuoles. As a result the protoplasm is no longer able to swell when the cells are placed in water and it becomes dehydrated much more slowly under conditions favoring the evaporation or freezing of water. The isolation of protoplasm is further reinforced by the fact that the plasmodesma which always joins the individual cells is now drawn within the protoplast. The entire plant loses the organization of a single whole and becomes a column of numerous cells thus isolated.

Such is the picture of visible intracellular changes in plants, as drawn from various sources, that take place in fall-winter dormancy. It is natural to expect that these changes will also affect cell functions. L.A. Ivanov and L.M. Orlov (1931), determining the ability of pines growing near Leningrad to assimilate carbon dioxide in the wintering period, found that the needles brought into the laboratory from outside remained inactive, despite the presence of the conditions needed for photosynthesis. Only after the cut branches were kept in a warm place for several days were the plastids ready for photosynthesis. The authors found that the chloroplasts become inactive as early as November, reaching a maximum in December–January. The capacity for photosynthesis is gradually restored in March and by mid-May reaches the summer level. L.A. Ivanov (1941) later found that the protoplast as a whole is inactivated when the plant becomes dormant.

Data on plant respiration are likewise important in the physiology of fall-winter dormancy. Respiratory differences between winter and spring grains were described by L.I. Govorov (1922-1923). In an attempt to find the reason for the greater frost resistance displayed by winter plants as compared with spring plants, Govorov learned that the former respire less rapidly at low temperatures than the latter and thus use up their sugar reserve more economically.

While determining the respiration in one year old apple twigs cut in the winter from mature trees in a garden, De Long, Beaumont, and Willman (1930) noted that the respiratory rate rose abruptly as soon as they were brought into a warm room. For example, in one of the experiments, twigs kept 10 days in a refrigerator at -2° released 20 times more carbon dioxide during the first few hours after they were shifted to a room with a temperature of +6° than they did afterwards. The temporary increase in amount of carbon dioxide released by plants when brought indoors or moved from a cold into a warm room is due to the decreased solubility of carbon dioxide in cell sap when the temperature is elevated. This phenomenon has long been known (1885), but De Long, Beaumont, and Willman found that in some of the 11 apple varieties they studied this temporary rise in the amount of carbon dioxide released when the twigs were moved from a cold place to a warm one was slight, whereas it was very marked in others. Consequently, some varieties stored comparatively small amounts of carbon dioxide, others very large amounts, and their cell sap was saturated with it. It is obvious that the varieties storing little carbon dioxide in the winter respired less rapidly, the other varieties storing a good deal of carbon dioxide respired more rapidly. A comparison of these data with the hardiness of different varieties showed the larger accumulation of carbon dioxide in the cells was associated with lesser frost resistance.

The research just described suggests that fall-winter dormancy causes the reorganization of cell contents whereby the cells tend to become dehydrated and isolated as they become cyst-like. This condition is an indication of "organic" dormancy as contrasted with "enforced" dormancy which befalls all plants, including nonwintering varieties, when external conditions become unfavorable. They differ in that organic dormancy is caused by certain structural changes in the cells, whereas there are no such changes in enforced dormancy so that normal cell activity resumes as soon as the conditions become favorable.

6. NATURAL COURSE AND ARTIFICIAL INTERRUPTION OF FALL-WINTER DORMANCY

The factors chiefly responsible for dormancy are low temperatures and shorter and less intense daylight. Soil moisture, proportion of nutrients, and other conditions also play a major part in the process. It is a well known fact that restricting the water supply of trees in the fall may substantially hasten the start of dormancy while abundant water may arrest or even interrupt it. Changing the soil nutrient regime may similarly hasten or delay the start of dormancy. For example, too much potassium fertilizer brings on dormancy sooner, whereas too much nitrogenous fertilizer delays and sometimes interrupts it.

The plants gradually emerge from dormancy by spring, aided by the processes at work in the plants during winter. Compare, for example, the dynamics of changes in reserve plastic substances in fall and in winter. In fall they are deposited chiefly in the form of complex, insoluble compounds not only in the vacuoles and on the walls but in the protoplasm itself. In the course of the winter low temperatures and cell dehydration convert a substantial portion of the plastic substances into simpler, soluble forms. Moreover, the quantity of these substances decreases as a result of cell activity, particularly in the protoplasm. The prerequisite of greater protoplasmic activity is thus established.

The protoplasm proper changes in the same direction and under the same influences — low temperatures and cell dehydration. It has been experimentally demonstrated that the amount of protein nitrogen in dormant cells decreases during winter, whereas the amount of nonprotein soluble nitrogen increases (McDermott, 1941). A good deal of the enzymes adsorbed in the fall and transformed into a zymogenic state changes into a free state, thus causing the processes of hydrolysis to predominate over synthesis in the winter (Bukin and Stupak, 1938; Kursanov and Bryushkova, 1940a, 1940b); bios associated with fall is released (Sukhorukov and Bol'shakova, 1946), etc. As a result protoplasm in the spring is different from what it was in the fall. In conjunction with this change those properties of the cells change which are primarily responsible for organic dormancy.

Dormancy can sometimes be artificially interrupted. The principal method is to penetrate the airtight and water-impermeable cell coats and membranes by external mechanical and chemical means. For example, scarification terminates dormancy in nonsprouting "hard" leguminous seeds (clover and alfalfa) and increases the germinating power of freshly harvested grain seeds (Kretovich, 1941; Lysenko, 1949). The same method can be used on potato tubers whose eyes are insulated from air during dormancy (Ivanovskaya, 1947; Chelyadinova, 1947). Removing the coat may cause dormant apple seeds to germinate.

Dormancy can be interrupted by other means, e.g., specifically irritating or injuring protoplasm in dormant cells. The popular practical presowing method of air warming of grain seeds, as suggested by T.D. Lysenko (1945), is based on this principle. Intense and prolonged light (including electric light) is sometimes very effective. Klebs (1914) used it to the exclusion of everything else to terminate the dormancy of beech buds. So too Z.P. Bulgakova (1937), on a number of trees. Familiar techniques, especially in floriculture, but unknown to plants in their natural habitat, are etherization, warm baths, treatment with tobacco smoke, gasification with the fumes of sulfuric acid, use of ethylene chlorohydrin, etc.

The mechanism involved in terminating dormancy by the methods mentioned above was elucidated by S. M. Prokoshev and Ye. I. Danchev (1947). The authors showed that the well known phenomenon of suberization of the wounds of dormant potato tubers is based on the various processes preceding it — forming sugar from starch increased activity of peroxydase, intensification of respiration, biosynthesis of ascorbic acid, proteins, etc. As soon as a wound is inflicted, the activity of all the adjacent cells changes abruptly and they cease to be dormant. Among the effective substances are the so-called wound hormones — protoplasmic disintegration products of wounded cells. This type of physiologically active substances called "biogens" are formed when the cells are violently depressed and on the verge of death. Their role as stimulants of healthy cells is highlighted by the epochal investigations of V.P. Filatov in the field of tissue therapy.

Cells are evidently stimulated into activity when dormant plants are given warm baths, exposed to tobacco smoke, etc.

7. SIGNIFICANCE OF FALL-WINTER DORMANCY IN ADAPTATION

The physiological characteristics of fall-winter dormancy just described apparently lead to the conclusion that there is always an organic connection between dormancy and frost resistance. This is the view, for example, of Kessler and Ruhland (Kessler, 1935; Kessler and Ruhland, 1938). They regard Kessler's experiments as quite convincing. Completely dormant saxifrage retained its characteristic fall hardiness even though kept in a warm room for two months. According to the authors, viscosity, hydration, and permeability of protoplasm are intensified during hardening and onset of dormancy. Protoplasm tends to become inert as far as external factors are concerned.

Yet there is contradictory evidence. For example, despite the dormancy of potato tubers, cabbage, carrot and chicory roots, they are far from being frost resistant. The potato is winterkilled as soon as the temperature in its cells falls to -2 or -3°. Dormancy ensures frost resistance neither in the tuber as a whole nor in its buds. Nevertheless, all the above-described features are to be found in dormant tuber buds — the isolation of protoplasm, etc. that are characteristic of hardy plants in a dormant state.

Let us consider the postharvest ripening of seeds. This too is fall-winter dormancy analogous to that in potato tubers and carrot roots. Air-dried seeds of winter and other plants are very hardy and under normal storage conditions are scarcely affected by frost. But in all the seeds hardiness depends wholly on enforced dormancy caused by the dehydrated condition of the cells. They are equally hardy whether found in the postharvest ripening stage or past it. The presence or absence of organic dormancy is unimportant as far as the hardiness of air-dried seeds are concerned.

Let us recall the above-described research of Ye. S. Moroz who compared the duration of dormancy in several apple, cherry, and plum varieties from Krasnodar kray, Tambov oblast, and Leningrad oblast. Moroz concluded that dormancy in each variety depends on their habitat and is more pronounced the further south it is cultivated. In these instances dormancy is in inverse rather than direct relationship to frost action on plants.

It is evident from what we have said that it is impossible to regard fall-winter dormancy as a prerequisite of the development of hardiness, although the latter is undoubtedly strengthened by those changes in cell contents which take place with the onset of dormancy — dehydration of protoplasm, formation of a thick cellulose membrane or lipoid layer over it, etc. (Krayevoy and Oknina, 1954; Krayevoy, Oknina, and Kpekdzhiyan, 1954; Tyrina, 1952).

Wherein lies the adaptive value of fall-winter dormancy? Organic dormancy prevents seeds from sprouting under conditions that would be dangerous for the particular plants, e.g., frost, drought, too deep planting, etc. Dormancy is very pronounced in uncultivated plants and weeds. Dormant seeds can remain that way for many years until conditions become favorable for them. The difference in this respect between dormant winter and spring grain seeds and grass seeds is very instructive. Winter grains go through the winter in the green state, spring grains in the form of seeds, because seed dormancy in the former is less pronounced than in the latter. Deep seed dormancy is thus the winter adaptive mechanism for spring varieties. This is also our conclusion with regard to potato tuber dormancy, which ensures the viability of the potato during the wintering period. Tubers left in the ground will be warmed by the soil and frequently winter successfully no matter how cold the weather as long as there is snow. If potatoes kept in the field start to grow in the fall then, of course, they are eventually killed by frost.

Dormancy serves the same purpose in wintering trees and shrubs. The growth of dormant plants is checked in the fall as reserve plastic substances build up. Nondormant plants are likely to be stimulated into growth by winter and early spring thaws, thus exposing them to destruction by even mild frosts.

CONCLUSION

Analysis of fall-winter dormancy leads to the conclusion that it more or less suppresses the vital activity of cells. Dormant cells do not grow or, at any rate, do so slowly. Such vital functions as photosynthesis and storage of dry substance are inhibited or halted, respiration weakens, etc. Dormant plants are, as it were, in a state of hibernation for some time even when the external conditions are favorable for their activity.

The difference between organic dormancy, which we shall discuss below, and enforced dormancy, which all plants enter when the external conditions are unfavorable, is determined by the presence of structural changes in cell contents occasioned by the onset of organic dormancy. When the cells of a multicellular plant are transformed into isolated cell-cysts, they are no longer interconnected. They become dehydrated and a thick cellulose membrane or water-impermeable lipoid layer forms, etc. so that they become less active. Exchange of substances between these cells halts while it diminishes within the cells proper. That is why organic dormancy is always deeper, for the plants remain that way even when the external conditions are favorable for a higher level of activity. The activity of plants in enforced dormancy increases as soon as there is a favorable change in external conditions.

Wintering plants survive the cold weather because of a variety of adaptive devices, direct and indirect. Fall-winter dormancy is essentially an indirect adaptation because the plants become inactive and unable to grow during winter and early spring thaws.

When plants are stimulated by a winter thaw, not only the growing cells, but also all the cells of the various tissues and organs in general become active, thus undermining their resistance to subsequent frosts. With arrested growth these processes are reduced to a minimum. Arrested growth helps render all the cells inactive. Even photosynthesis in green parenchymal cells is restricted with arrested growth in the fall because they become saturated with assimilates not expended on growth.

It was pointed out in earlier chapters that arrested growth in the fall is a prerequisite of the development of frost resistance. We see now that arrested growth in the fall and prevention of growth during winter and early spring thaws are caused by fall-winter dormancy. An analysis of dormancy will further show the exceptional importance of arrested growth as a factor in frost resistance as well as in the broader phenomenon of cold resistance.

CHAPTER 9

HIBERNATION AND COLD RESISTANCE

The term hibernation has long been applied to the arrested formation of fruit-bearing organs in wintering plants. It is quite apparent in winter grains. Sown at the end of summer, they merely bush out before the cold weather and do not go into the stem-extension stage, i.e., they do not form culms and ears. Spring varieties sown at the same time are usually in the shooting stage by winter. There is the same delay in forming the fruit-bearing organs of wintering cereal and leguminous grasses, all cultivated root crops, cabbage, kohlrabi, and other wintering plants the year they are sown.

The nature of hibernation was elucidated by T.D. Lysenko. He called the first two stages of development the vernalization and light stages. Passage through these stages determines the transition of plants from the vegetative into the reproductive state (Lysenko, 1928, 1929, 1932, 1935a, b, 1949).

1. HIBERNATION IN WINTERING PLANTS

Leaving aside the well known facts relating to the hibernation of winter grains and root crops, cabbage, and other biennial plants, we shall focus on woody plants. The peach is particularly instructive in this respect. Like other fruit seeds, peach seeds do not germinate as soon as the fruits ripen but go through a long period of postharvest maturation. If the germs of such seeds are allowed to have free access to air, they germinate, but seedlings display a growth anomaly. Their leaves are broad and shortened, the internodes of the stem do not develop and the plants assume a rosette form, resembling in habit nonvernalized winter grains. These anomalies do not occur if the seeds are first kept for 10 to 12 weeks at +3 to +5°. In this event the embryos go through the vernalization stage along with postharvest ripening (Turkey and Carlson, 1945).

2. CHARACTERISTICS OF THE VERNALIZATION
STAGE IN WINTERING PLANTS

As demonstrated by Lysenko and other investigators, notably on winter grains, the vernalization stage in wintering plants is best if the temperature is about 0°; above this temperature vernalization is checked. And it is mainly for this reason that only individual plants of winter varieties sown in spring enter the stem-extension stage by the end of summer and come in to ear. The same thing can be said of the bolting of wintering biennials — beets, carrots, etc. (Avakyan, 1950). Vernalization is inhibited even more if the temperature is below 0°, as can be seen in Fig. 58 (photograph made by my former co-worker in the Institute of Grain Raising of the Nonchernozem Belt, O.I. Drozdova).

Fig. 58. Growth of Kooperatorka winter
wheat from sprouts vernalized for 40 days
at various temperatures
On the left — vernalization at +3°; on the
right — vernalization at -3°

A little over two months from the time they were sown Kooperatorka winter wheat plants, vernalized in the sprout stage at about +3°, all came into ear; they merely became bushy at -3°.

Vernalization takes place over a given period of time characteristic of each plant. Thereafter even highly favorable conditions do not accelerate development. It is evident from Fig. 59 that 50 days is the optimum period of vernalization for Lutescens 329 winter wheat. Subsequent exposure of the sprouts to above-zero temperatures has no effect on their growth.

It has been demonstrated that wintering plants differ from one another in length of vernalization stage. For example, it lasts 50 days in Lutescens 329, whereas it is completely over in Kooperatorka after 40 days. A detailed analysis of vernalization in various winter and spring wheats reveals a grad-ual transition from winter to spring varieties. The difference between the two is purely quantitative. This was the conclusion reached by T.D. Lysenko and D.A. Dolgushin back in 1929. Among the winter wheat varieties the longest vernalization stage (60 to 70 days) is found in plants from Sweden, Norway, Finland, and Northern Germany.

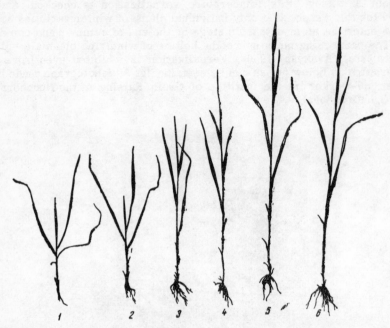

Fig. 59. Growth of Lutescens winter wheat Lutescens 329 with different periods of vernalization of sprouts (sowing of May 4, photographed June 28) 1 — plant from nonvernalized sprout; 2 - 6 — plants from sprouts vernalized at temperatures ranging from 0 to 2° for 24, 30, 40, 50, and 60 days

The vernalization stage takes longer in winter wheat than in winter rye. This is clearly shown in Fig. 60 where one can see sketches of Vyatka winter rye and several winter wheat varieties growing from nonvernalized seeds planted in the spring. The rye came more fully into ear and in greater numbers than any of the winter wheat plants. And even in the relatively unhardy Kooperatorka the rate of development in the nonvernalized state was much slower than in Vyatka rye.

Such, in brief, are the main characteristics of vernalization in wintering plants.

3. CHARACTERISTICS OF THE LIGHT STAGE IN WINTERING PLANTS

The temperature and light demands of wintering plants in the light stage are very exacting. In the fall and during winter thaws the light stage is much more difficult for winter than for spring plants. Hence, spring plants, as mentioned above, when sown in the fall often reach the stem-extension stage

Fig. 60. Development of plants from nonvernalized seeds (sowing of
May 5, photographed September 25)
1 — Vyatka winter rye; 2 - 5 — winter wheats, from left to right:
Lutescens 239, Moskovskaya 2411, Gostianum 237, Kooperatorka

by the onset of frost despite the low temperature, weak light, and short day
while winter plants under the same conditions, even when vernalized seeds
are sown, generally do not reach this stage.

I made an interesting observation in this connection while studying winter
sowing in February 1948 in Rostov oblast, Stavropol and Krasnodar krays.
Due to the unusually warm winter here the crops maintained almost continuous if very slow growth until mid-February. In any event they remained for a
long time neither frozen nor covered with snow. By February they had completely passed through the vernalization stage into the light stage. However,
even the winter crops sown very early, in August, failed to reach the stem-
extension stage, although the terminal growing point had already become
differentiated as a rudimentary ear. The spring crops, windfall of spring
grains, and spring weeds presented another picture. All the spring grains
had definitely reached the stem-extension stage with visibly separated internodes of the culm sometimes several centimeters long. On the floodplain of
the Kuban River there was a good deal of winter cress — a typical spring
weed in the flowering state — among the winter crops.

The close connection between light stage and duration of daylight was
demonstrated by the research of O.I. Drozdova. Fig. 61 shows the main
shoots of Kooperatorka winter wheat grown from vernalized seeds planted in
the spring before the start of differentiation of the vegetative cone in natural
daylight but thereafter with varying periods of daylight. When the photograph
was taken, the control plant, continuously exposed to natural light, had come

into ear, whereas earing of the plants exposed to a short day after the vegetative cone began to be differentiated, i.e., in the light stage, was retarded in direct proportion to the shortness of the day.

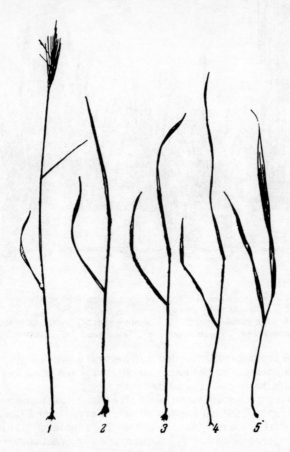

Fig. 61. Development of Kooperatorka winter wheat
from vernalized seeds
1 — natural summer day; 2 - 5 — after beginning of
differentiation of vegetative cone on a short day, from
left to right: 12-hour, 10-hour, 8-hour, 6-hour

The duration of the light stages varies from plant to plant. Hence, the same hibernation may be the result of vernalization and light stages of different duration. There are plants with relatively long vernalization and relatively short light stages, and vice versa. Pairs previously studied in this connection can be crossed to obtain both more and less winter-like varieties of plants. This is the basis of the stage analysis of parental pairs proposed by Lysenko and now widely used in selection (Lysenko, 1949).

4. VERNALIZATION, GROWTH, AND HARDINESS

Lysenko demonstrated that vernalization does not depend on growth. Growth is practically nonexistent in seeds vernalized at about 0°, whereas winter crops come into ear immediately afterward when sown in the spring. However, the conditions determining vernalization in wintering plants, especially low temperatures, are not without effect on their rate of growth. As a result there are changes in the properties depending on growth, e.g., frost resistance.

Experiment 1. The purpose of the experiment was to determine the effect of vernalization on frost resistance following total suppression of growth. We used the seeds of winter plants completely vernalized on ice and the seeds of winter plants that were not vernalized at all, merely those which germinated at room temperature. The results of the experiment are presented in Table 28.

Table 28

Effect of vernalization on winter wheat hardiness

Wheat variety	Surviving sprouts after chilling at -7°, %	
	Nonvernalized	Vernalized
Kooperatorka	0	72
Saratovskaya { 118	2	76
121	8	80

The germinated seeds taken from ice, although completely through the vernalization stage (checked by comparing the development of plants from these vernalized and nonvernalized sprouts), were hardier than the seeds nonvernalized but simply germinated at room temperature. We assumed that this was due to the difference in hardening of the sprouts. The vernalized sprouts kept on ice a long time were more hardened than the nonvernalized sprouts kept at room temperature. In this connection we performed the following experiment.

Experiment 2. We were interested in comparing the hardiness of sprouts of winter wheat kept on ice for varying periods of time while going through the vernalization stage. The design of the experiment and results are shown in Table 29.

Thus, our hypothesis was confirmed. Sprouts kept on ice not only go through the vernalization stage, but they also harden, the more so the longer they remain there, at least within the number of days used in the experiment.

In subsequent observations of the green plants we found that in the initial phases, somewhat before the appearance of the fourth leave, the growth of the vernalized plants was clearly slower than those of the nonvernalized plants; thereafter, on the other hand, it was more rapid.

Experiment 3. Winter wheat, variety Saratovskaya 121, was the experimental plant. Vernalized and nonvernalized seeds were sown in the fall at the same time in the same box in the greenhouse. Before sowing time the nonvernalized seeds were allowed to reach the same stage as the vernalized seeds in order to obtain sprouts simultaneously. Figs. 62, 63, and 64 show plants from vernalized and nonvernalized seeds in the two-leaf phase,

Table 29

Relationship between winter wheat hardiness and length
of time the plants were kept on ice

Wheat variety	Surviving sprouts after freezing at –6°, %		
	Not subjected to freezing	kept on ice	
		6 days	13 days
Kooperatorka	10	71	95
Moskovskaya 2411	39	82	87
Saratovskaya 121	43	80	98
Saratovskaya 118	25	80	100

three-leaf phase, and beginning of the stem–extension phase of the vernalized plants. In the first, second, and third leaf phases the plants from the vernalized seeds lag in growth with consequent formation of short, narrow leaves.

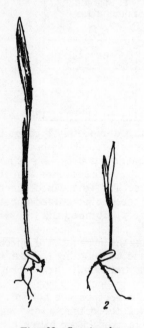

Fig. 62. Saratovskaya
121 winter wheat in the
two-leaf phase
1 — from a nonvernalized sprout; 2 — from a
vernalized sprout

Then each individual shoot among the vernalized plants grows more rapidly than the non-vernalized plants shoots, resulting in the formation of longer and broader leaves.

Experiment 4. The purpose of the experiment was to find out whether the arrested growth of vernalized plants following formation of the first leaves was due to their passage through the vernalization stage or to the germinated seeds being kept at low temperatures. We used the seeds of winter wheat, variety Saratovskaya 118: (a) germinated before sowing and not exposed to low temperatures; (b) kept in the sprout stage on ice at 0° to +2° for 55 days; (c) kept in the sprout stage on ice at these temperatures for 104 days. The seeds were nonvernalized in the first variant, completely vernalized in the second, the duration of vernalization being about 50 days; in the third variant the seeds remained on ice twice as long as was needed for them to pass through the vernalization stage. Fig. 65 shows the results of the experiment. The plants were photographed in the four–leaf phase 20 days after the seeds were sown.

The difference in growth from variant to variant is very marked, especially between the extremes. In the plants grown from seeds which lay on ice 55 days in the sprout stage, the blade of the first leaf was half as short as that of the control. The second leaf too was perceptibly shorter, but less so. The suppression of growth had scarcely any effect on the third leaf. In the plants from seeds chilled for 104 days the blade of the first leaf was six times smaller than that of the control, the blade of the second leaf twice as short and narrow, the blade of the third leaf one and one half times as short

Fig. 63. Saratovskaya 121 winter wheat in the three-leaf phase
On the left — plants from nonvernalized seeds; on the right — from
vernalized seeds

The experiment showed that suppression of growth in vernalized plants
fter formation of the first leaves is not caused by the vernalization stage but
y the length of time the germinated seeds are chilled. The longer such seeds
re exposed to low temperature, the more marked is the suppression of sub-
equent growth in the first phase of leaf formation.

Fig. 64. Saratovskaya 121 winter wheat in the
stem–extension phase of vernalized plants
On the left — plants from nonvernalized seeds:
on the right — from vernalized seeds

Let us now try to explain the well known fact established almost simul-
aneously by several investigators that plants from vernalized seeds are less
ardy than others (I.M. Vasil'yev, 1934; Kuperman, 1935; Saltykovskiy and
aprygina, 1935; Timofeyeva, 1935a, 1935b; Tumanov, 1937), citing first some
ata from our own experiments.

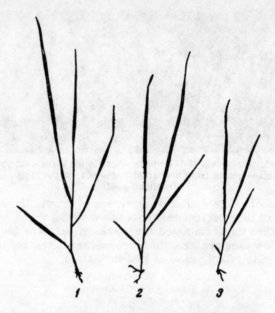

Fig. 65. Growth of Saratovskaya 118 winter wheat
from seeds exposed to cold
1 — control plant, 2 — plant from sprouted seed
on ice 55 days, 3 — plant from sprouted seed
on ice 104 days

Experiment 5. Vernalized and nonvernalized seeds kept 50 days on ice were sown together in a greenhouse in the fall. The plants were tested for frost resistance after they had stooled out somewhat. Before the test they were hardened first in a cool, light room, then outdoors at –4°. Table 30 presents the results of the experiment after the plants were frozen at –11° and then allowed to resume growth for 18 days in a warm greenhouse.

Table 30

Effect of vernalization of seeds on winter
wheat hardiness

Wheat variety		Surviving plants, %	
		Nonvernalized	vernalized
Ital'yanskaya		8	0
Saratovskaya	121	75	0
	27/36	93	0
	118	92	43

All the wheat plants from vernalized seeds were unhardy, most of them dying when the temperature fell to –11°. The Saratov varieties from nonvernalized seeds withstood this temperature with few losses and only the unhardy Ital'yanskaya suffered substantial damage.

Experiment 6. This experiment was designed to determine the hardiness of winter wheat from slightly hardened vernalized and nonvernalized seeds. Planted in the fall in a comparatively warm greenhouse, they were exposed to about -6° with no preliminary hardening at low above-zero temperatures. The differences in hardiness between the vernalized and nonvernalized plants are shown in Table 31.

Table 31

Effect of vernalization on the hardiness of poorly hardened winter wheat

Wheat variety	Surviving plants, %	
	nonvernalized	vernalized
Ital'yanskaya	17	0
Saratovskaya 118	100	36

I obtained the same results as the above in many similar experiments, as did the above-mentioned investigators who made comparative tests of vernalized and nonvernalized winter plants for frost resistance. Thus, the view that vernalization invariably reduces hardiness received support, but actually it is not correct. Here is proof.

Experiment 7. Vernalized and nonvernalized seeds of about 10 winter wheat varieties were sown in the fall in a cool greenhouse. Sprouts appeared fairly soon and at the same time. They were exposed to -10 to -12° outdoors a week later when a determination was made of the growth differences. After thawing in the greenhouse, all the plants from the nonvernalized seeds were found to have suffered severely from the frost, many of them remaining wilted a long time. Some of the less resistant varieties like Kooperatorka were clearly dead. On the other hand, the plants from the vernalized seeds looked better, few having suffered any injury or dying.

Similar experiments yielded identical results. Plants from vernalized seeds during the period of arrested growth were invariably more resistant than plants from nonvernalized seeds. We also ran some experiments in an effort to determine changes in frost resistance depending on whether plants come from nonvernalized, wholly vernalized, or partly vernalized seeds.

Experiment 8. Winter wheat, variety Lutescens 329, constituted the experimental plants. We sowed in pots on October 10: (a) completely nonvernalized seeds that germinated just before sowing; (b) seeds vernalized for 25 days; (c) seeds vernalized for 40 days; (d) seeds vernalized for 55 days. Vernalization was effected by keeping the germinated seeds on ice. Series 'b" and "c" seeds were not completely vernalized because Lutescens 329, as we have seen, requires about 50 days for the process. Series "d" sprouts were completely vernalized. The plants remained outdoors all the time and by the start of frosts had formed two leaves each. This was the phase in which they were subsequently tested for frost. There was a distinct difference in the growth of the plants in the individual series. The leaves, particularly the first ones, were smaller the longer the seeds had been exposed to low temperatures. The sharpest differences were noted between plants from the nonvernalized and completely vernalized seeds. Plants from the partly vernalized seeds occupied an intermediate position.

Testing for frost resistance was done outdoors. Frosts set in around mid-November, but the temperature did not fall below -10° for a month. It reached -26° the night of December 14-15, a very low temperature even for Lutescens 329. Eight hours later they were brought into a cool room for slow thawing and then into a greenhouse for further growth. We tallied the results of the experiment two weeks later and sketched typical plants in each series (Fig. 66). The effect of the frost was in inverse propotion to the length of time the seeds were chilled and the degree to which growth was suppressed during the period when the first and second leaves were forming. Thus, the lower leaves in the sketched plants from nonvernalized seeds died off completely, whereas they all survived in plants from vernalized seeds. The second leaves from the bottom in plants from nonvernalized seeds half died off and were the shortest of all, whereas they were fairly long in plants from vernalized seeds. Yet the situation was reversed by the time of the frosts. A change took place while the plants were in the greenhouse after they were frozen as a result of further growth of the second leaves from the bottom in the plants from the vernalized seeds.

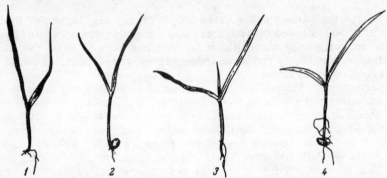

Fig. 66. Comparative hardiness of Lutescens 329 winter wheat in the two-leaf phase grown from sprouts with different degree of vernalization 1 — plant from nonvernalized sprout; 2, 3, 4 — plants from sprouts vernalized for 36, 50, and 55 days, respectively. Blackened areas are the dead parts of leaves, the crosshatched areas are living leaves, but injured by frost

The third leaf is the clearest indicator of differences in degree of hardiness. In plants from series "a" and "b" the rudiment of this leaf was injured by the frost and did not emerge from the sheath as long as the plants were in the greenhouse. This leaf in series "c" plants was viable and grew. It was more viable in series "d" plants from vernalized seeds and put on more growth by the time the picture was taken.

Experiment 9. Winter wheat, variety Lutescens 329, was the plant studied. We sowed on October 4 in pots in a cool greenhouse: (a) nonvernalized seeds, but sprouted to the state of the vernalized seeds before sowing; (b) seeds vernalized on ice for 25 days; (c) seeds vernalized for 35 days; (d) seeds vernalized for 45 days; (e) seeds vernalized for 55 days. Series "b" and "c" seeds were clearly not wholly vernalized, series "d" almost completely vernalized, series "e" completely vernalized. The plants were tested for frost when there were two or three shoots per plant and four leaves on the main shoot. The difference in growth between the series under comparison by the time they were chilled lay in the fact that the rate of growth was directly proportional to the degree of vernalization. The tallest plants were from completely vernalized seeds, the shortest from nonvernalized seeds. The plants were chilled for 24 hours in a refrigerator at a temperature of -11.7°. The results are shown in Fig. 67.

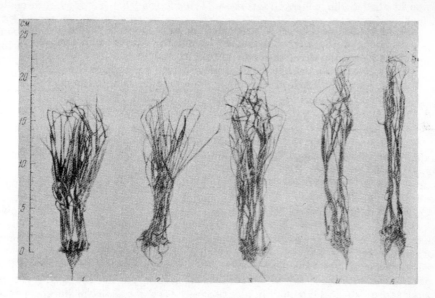

Fig. 67. Lutescens 329 winter wheat after freezing (photographed 10 days after plants were brought into a greenhouse)
1 — plants from nonvernalized sprouts; 2, 3 — plants from nonvernalized sprouts kept on ice only 25 and 35 days; 4 — plants from sprouts vernalized 45 days; 5 — plants from sprouts vernalized 55 days

The extent of frost injury varied with the rate of growth before freezing — the longer the seeds were kept on ice, i.e., the more vernalized they became, the more rapidly the plants grew in the four-leaf phase and the less hardy they were. In plants from nonvernalized seeds only the tips of the leaves were affected by the frost. Approximately one-third of the leaves died in plants from insufficiently vernalized seeds kept on ice for 25 days. The plants from seeds kept on ice for 45 and 55 days were completely winterkilled.

Experiment 10. This experiment differed from the preceding one in that the plants were kept outdoors before freezing rather than in the greenhouse. In addition, we used another method of appraising the degree of frost injury, i.e., by the new growth of the rootlets. This method is very helpful when applied to winter crops and is often employed both in scientific and practical work where it is known as the "water method of reviving winter plants". It involves essentially the removal of plants from the ground after freezing and thawing and then placing them in water. If frost didn't kill them, rootlets soon form. In severely injured plants the rootlets will be smaller or there will be none at all, even though part of the leaves remains green. This then was how we appraised plant hardiness in this experiment.

The plants were chilled for 24 hours in a refrigerator at -14.2°, thawed in a cool greenhouse, then transplanted into glasses of water. The water just covered the roots and tillering nodes and was changed daily. New roots soon developed which could be easily distinguished from the old ones because of their lighter color. The plants that formed new roots were counted 15 days after chilling. The number as a percentage of the total number was as follows: in series "a" without vernalization — 88; in series "b" (25 days of vernalization) — 60; in series "c" (35 days of vernalization) — 56; in series "d" (45 days of vernalization) — 8; in series "e" (55 days of vernalization) — 0. It is evident from these figures that the longer the seeds were exposed to low temperatures and the more rapid the rate of growth in the four-leaf phase, the less the regenerative capacity of the plants with respect to the formation of new leaves. In other words, in this as in the preceding experiment, the hardiness of plants from seeds vernalized in varying degree was closely connected with their growth rate prior to freezing, i.e., the more vigorous the growth, the lower the frost resistance.

To sum up, changes in the resistance of plants from vernalized seeds can be described as follows. Frost resistance depends, strictly speaking, not on vernalization of seeds, but on growth, the rate of which is affected by low temperatures. Low temperatures influence both the passage of plants through the vernalization stage and their subsequent growth. Growth in winter plants from vernalized seeds is arrested at first, but then becomes more rapid. Accordingly, these plants are more resistant than those from nonvernalized seeds. Resistance drops only with the formation of the fourth leaf by plants from vernalized seeds when the growth rate increases markedly.

The work of the aforementioned investigators as well as my own initial experiments in comparing the hardiness of plants from vernalized and non-vernalized seeds were based on plants from vernalized seeds which were in the four- or five-leaf stage and growing rapidly. That is what gave currency to the erroneous view that low frost resistance is characteristic of plants from vernalized seeds.

5. THE LIGHT STAGE, GROWTH, AND HARDINESS

Repeated tests of plants for hardiness in relation to the light stage have invariably shown that completion of the light stage reduces resistance to frost (Kuperman, 1935; Timofeyeva, 1935; Saprygina, 1935; Shestakov, 1936). My initial experiments yielded the same results.

Experiment 1. Vernalized Kooperatorka seeds were planted in pots in a greenhouse on September 10, some of the pots receiving natural short-day light, others long-day light in a section of the greenhouse with 500 watt bulbs. Thus, all the plants were able to go thrugh the light stage.

A month after the appearance of sprouts in the long-day plants a rudimentary ear began to form, quickly followed by elongation of the internodes of the culm. This showed that the light stage had passed. There were no such external signs in the control plants receiving natural light. A test for frost was made at this time over a 24-hour period in a refrigerator at -9.4°. The plants were hardened for three days at about 0° before being placed in the refrigerator. As a result of freezing all the plants that passed through the light stage died, whereas 90% of the plants that did not pass through this stage survived. Most of the initial survivors eventually died because they had been severely injured by frost. Yet it is possible to speak of the greater hardiness of plants in the light stage as compared with those that have already gone through it.

Experiment 2. A replicated experiment was performed 10 days later. The plants were hardened for five days at low temperatures and then frozen for 24 hours at –17 and –11.4°. All the plants were killed by –17°. The results of freezing at –11.4° are shown in Fig. 68. The plants that passed through the light stage turned out to be less hardy than those which had not.

I obtained the same results in a series of similar experiments, as did other investigators.

Fig. 68. Kooperatorka winter wheat after
freezing at –11.4°
1 — plants that did not go through the light
stage; 2 — plants that went through the
light stage

It is evident from Fig. 68 that winter wheat plants, variety Kooperatorka, which had passed through the light stage and were less hardy, also grew more rapidly before freezing. All the cases of strengthened hardiness of these plants described in the literature is attributed to their swifter growth. Yet swifter growth is not always the consequence of the plants' going through the light stage. They may go through this stage and thereafter be subjected to low temperatures for a long time when growth is suppressed while photosynthesis continues. The plants will then store plastic substances, harden, and become more resistant. This phenomenon is encountered, for example, when determining the dynamics of frost resistance of winter wheat sown in the fall.

They frequently go into the stem–extension stage by the time the frosts occur. Meanwhile they become increasingly hardy because growth is suppressed as a result of low temperatures. An example of this is the experiment I performed to determine the hardiness of wheat plants in the fall before they passed through the light stage, when the terminal growing point had not as yet been differentiated into a rudimentary ear, and after they passed through this stage, when a rudimentary ear had formed and there was visible elongation of the internodes of the culm.

Experiment 3. The experiment involved spring wheat — soft Lutescens 62 and hard Melanopus 69. Vyatka winter rye and Kooperatorka winter wheat were used for comparison. The seeds were sown August 31 in pots. The plants grew and hardened outdoors.

The plants were tested for frost the first time on September 22 when there were as yet no signs of differentiation of the vegetative cone into a rudimentary ear. The freezing was done in two refrigerators, one set at -8°, the other at -10°. Before this the plants grew at comparatively high temperatures; the daily average during the last week was +11.4° with a maximum of +15° or more, which was not conducive to hardening. As a result all the plants of both varieties of spring wheat were winterkilled at -8°. Only the winter varieties survived, although they were also severely damaged. By October 7 the vegetative cone in both spring wheats began to be differentiated. As is usual in such cases, it became elongated and crimped, showing that the plants had entered the light stage. The temperature was lowered further and did not exceed a daily average of +8°. Growth slowed down correspondingly. The plants were tested for frost at -8° and -11.5°. Six days after they were brought into a warm greenhouse it turned out that both varieties of spring wheat died at -11.5° but not at -8°. Entrance into the light stage, therefore, did not decrease their capacity for hardening. Frost resistance grew as the temperature fell. The winter crops — Vyatka rye and Kooperatorka wheat — proved to be more resistant.

A complete rudimentary ear formed in both spring wheat varieties by October 17. We could see through a magnifying glass the first separation of the nodes of the culm, and although the stem extension process had just begun, it indicated that the plants had completed the light stage. The condition for hardening were now even more favorable because the temperature remained for several days at an average daily level of +2 or +3° with light night frosts.

The plants were then tested for frost at -7.6 and -10.3°. Checking on the results of freezing a week later, we found that -7.6° caused no damage. All the plants withstood -10.3°, only the tips of the spring wheat leaves being winterkilled.

A week later, on October 23, I more or less repeated the test, but this time the temperatures were lower with regular night frosts of -4 and -5°, which naturally further hardened the plants. The plants had by this time completely stopped growing and there were no changes in their development. The temperature in one refrigerator was -9° and -14° in the other. The plants did not suffer from -9° and all survived -14°, but the spring wheat was severely injured. Fig. 69 shows the experimental plants 10 days after chilling at -9°.

We see, therefore, that going through the light stage need not reduce hardiness. The plants may harden after going through it and with the natural fall in temperature after the summer their frost resistance steadily rises. Spring wheat is no exception and behaves like the winter varieties.

Fig. 69. Plants after freezing at -9°
1 — Vyatka winter rye; 2 — Kooperatorka winter wheat; winter wheats;
3 — Lutescens 62; 4 — Melanopus 69

Here are some observations from practical experience.

In February 1948 there was a danger in the south that the winter crops would be killed due to the unseasonably warm weather and the frosts likely to set in at the end of that month. It was necessary to determine the hardiness of the commercial crops. In Rostov oblast the plants tested were Gostianum 237, Stavropol'skaya and Voroshilovskaya in Stavropol kray, and Voroshilovskaya, Krasnodarskaya, and Novoukrainskaya in Krasnodar kray. The plants were frozen in Rostov at -23°, in Stavropol at -13°, and in Krasnodar at -18.5°, the lowest temperatures that could be produced by local refrigerators. The results were highly favorable. The winter crops proved to be thoroughly hardened and my forecast was subsequently borne out. The frosts that set in late in February did no damage whatsoever in the southern areas of the European part of the U.S.S.R. Yet there were quite a few plants (from the very early August sowing) in which the growing point had already become differentiated into a rudimentary ear, as in the spring varieties described above.

These facts leave no doubt that changes in the hardiness of plants that have passed through the light stage are caused by growth rather than by the stage itself. We must examine from this viewpoint all the research to date, including our own, in which frost resistance proved to be greater after the plants had passed through the light stage. In these experiments in greenhouses and on small outdoor plots plants receive a long day of light by means of electric bulbs. Under such conditions they not only pass through the light stage, but also grow more rapidly due to the greater heat radiated by the bulbs. And when such plants are tested for frost, they naturally turn out to be less hardy than plants receiving the normal light of a short fall day and at much lower temperatures.

6. HIBERNATION AND FORMATION
OF REPRODUCTIVE ORGANS

Hibernation is most clearly reflected in the formation of the reproductive organs. Winter grains sown in the spring, as discussed above, merely stool out over a long period of time and grow an ever larger mass of leaves and roots, but do not form rudimentary ears or internodes of the culm which functions as a floriferous shoot. It is only at the end of summer that winter plants, and not all of them, pass from the vegetative into the reproductive state. This phenomenon is primarily associated with the peculiarities of the vernalization stage which in wintering plants takes place in the summer at relatively high temperatures only with great difficulty, and no signs of the reproductive organs appear until this stage is passed. The growing point of winter grains at this time looks like a gently sloping little hill with the rudiments of new leaves laid at its base one after the other. The first signs of a rudimentary ear in the form of an elongated and crimped cone can be observed in the vegetative cone only after the plants pass from the vernalization into the light stage. As time goes on this process becomes more vigorous and the rings of the cone turn into rudimentary ears. When the rudimentary ear is more or less formed, the internodes start to grow. The start of culm growth indicates that the winter plants have passed through the light stage.

This is essentially the way in which the reproductive organs are formed in other wintering plants as well. Perhaps the only difference is that the floriferous shoot and rudimentary flower buds on it grow not from the tillering nodes but on stems just above the soil as, e.g., in vetch and clover and in trees where each floral shoot develops from more mature branches.

Intracellular changes caused by the vernalization and light stages have been scarcely studied. People have long believed that rapid growth retards the formation of flower buds in trees, whereas suppression of growth is somewhat helpful in this respect. Thus, the nutritive regime of the soil and ·moisture, availability to the growing parts of plants of plastic substances and the quality of these substances are highly important, especially for fruit trees. An excess of nitrogenous fertilizer invariably intensifies growth of the vegetative parts and delays the formation of flowers. Too much potassium and phosphorus fertilizer with a nitrogen deficiency has the opposite effect and the plants begin to bear fruit sooner. Insufficient water does the same thing. Such methods as girdling, which retards the outflow of plastic substances to the roots from the branch above the ring and leads to the storage of these substances (particularly carbohydrates) in the growth zones of the branch and to the rapid formation of flower buds, are exceptionally effective.

These familiar facts were the basis of Klebs' theory [Klebs, 1913] of "flower maturity of plants" in relation to the so-called carbon:nitrogen ratio, i.e., the ratio of carbohydrates to nitrogenous substances in cells. A relative increase in the carbohydrates, according to Klebs, is a prerequisite of the growth process proceeding in the direction of formation of the reproductive organs. A relative increase in the nitrogenous substances, on the other hand, is a prerequisite of the formation of the vegetative organs. Klebs' theory now seems too primitive to justify going into it in detail. Moreover, Klebs by no means took into account everything that was known in his time about the growth and development of plants. A noteworthy piece of work was D.N. Pryanishnikov's (1891) "Connection between the Anatomical Structure of the Beetroot and Its Sugar Content and Tendency to Produce the Beet-Seed Stalk" in which he elucidated the relation of the beet-seed stalk both to the storage of sugars in root cells and to arrested growth and lignification of the cells.

Modern science attributes fruit bearing and resultant intracellular changes chiefly to qualitative changes in the protoplasm proper. The research of B.A. Rubin (1936a, b) on the biochemistry of late ripening (and consequently longer hibernation) and early ripening forms of the onion during storage can be usefully applied to wintering plants. Late ripening forms are marked by low activity of hydrolytic processes and higher indices of the oxidation system which, as we know, are the clearest manifestations of the vital activity of protoplasm. Plants are more thrifty when in a state of rapid vegetative growth or capable of such growth. Vigor diminishes when the plants begin to bear fruit. This is why plants bear fruits more rapidly when external conditions become unfavorable.

Winter plants in the vernalization stage can develop only leaves and roots, whereas in the light stage, in addition to leaves and roots, they can also develop the rudiments of the fruit-bearing organs. However, special conditions are needed for the growth of these organs. Leaves, for example, can grow in fairly dry air, whereas roots require a water-saturated atmosphere. The fruit-bearing organs too grow only when external conditions are favorable. When very suitable for the growth of the reproductive organs, they appear in usually large numbers and, contrariwise, when unsuitable they become abnormal and turn into other organs. There are many such cases. Here are some examples from our own investigations. Fig. 70 shows two ears of winter wheat, variety Moskovskaya 2411. This wheat was sown in the spring and it passed through the vernalization and light stages by the time of autumn frosts. The plants came through the winter intact and in the spring resumed their growth. Some time later I noticed a number of ears at the bases of the main ears. The main ears were formed in the fall, the lateral ears in the spring after they had overwintered, when winter crops usually go through the light stage.

Fig. 71 presents an entirely different picture. In the experiment performed by O. I. Drozdova, vernalized winter wheat seeds were sown in the spring. After the light stage the plants were exposed to an artificially shortened day. As a result the rudimentary ears already formed began to grow abnormally and in a little while there was a cluster of leaves on the culm instead of an ear.

It is well to keep in mind that the natural consequence of suppressing the formation of reproductive organs in wintering plants with long vernalization and light stages in a greater yield provided that external conditions are favorable. That is why late forms with longer hibernation are also more productive. The only exception is when the crops mature during a drought, early frost, prevalence of plant diseases, insect invasion, etc.

7. ADAPTATION VALUE OF HIBERNATION FOR WINTER HARDINESS

Hibernation is the result of plant adaptation to wintering. It shows up very clearly at the vernalization stage. This stage is related to wintering because all wintering plants become vernalized at low temperatures. However, vernalization is not a direct adaptation to frost, for varieties with a long period of vernalization are not necessarily hardier than other crops. As pointed out above, vernalization is shorter in many winter rye varieties than in wheat varieties, yet rye is more frost resistant than wheat. As a result of four years of studying the stages and hardiness of 800 specimens of winter wheat from the worldwide collection of the Institute of Plant Growing I. Kh. Shmelev (1940) discovered that wheat from Western and Northwestern

Fig. 70. Ears of Moskovskaya 2411
winter wheat sown in the spring,
after overwintering

Fig. 71. Abnormal ear of winter
wheat

Europe, which is not very hardy, has the longest period of vernalization.

Thus, the existence of a vernalization stage tends to strengthen winter hardiness rather than frost resistance because it represents a developmental period that delays their entering the reproductive state. It is quite apparent that this adaptive mechanism functions only when there are no frosts. Frosts automatically check all processes of development. The value of vernalization for winter hardiness increases the longer the frostless period in the fall and winter lasts, as is the case in those regions where winter varieties with long vernalization stage originate.

It is important to stress that vernalization takes place when the temperature is low, not when the plants are frozen. Consequently, low above-zero weather, against which the purely protective action of vernalization is directed, "removes" this stage. At first glance this looks like a contradiction. However, we have met this contradiction many times, especially when analyzing fall-winter dormancy in wintering trees and shrubs. We saw that dormancy inhibits growth at low above-zero temperatures, although these temperatures (but not frost) remove dormancy. The resemblance between vernalization and dormancy is enhanced by the fact that dormancy is also pronounced in plants from regions with a long frostless fall and regular winter thaws.

Vernalization is contradictory in still another respect. When seeds are vernalized at low temperatures, plant growth is checked. Seeds kept on ice at 0 to +2° scarcely grow, but this enables them to harden and resist frost. Low temperatures have an aftereffect that lasts for some time. In the experiments described above this was reflected in the suppression of growth of plants from vernalized seeds prior to the appearance of the third leaf. At the same time processes are taking place which will eventually show up in much more vigorous growth, as we observed when comparing the growth of plants from vernalized and nonvernalized seeds in the four-leaf stage and later. In other words, two contradictory influences are at work in wintering plants going through vernalization at low temperatures, one inhibitory, the other intensifying. The latter remains latent while the plants are directly exposed to low temperatures and for some time thereafter, coming to the fore only when the external conditions are favorable. This normally occurs in the spring when the soil and air begin to warm up.

The mechanism of this complex process which invariably accompanies vernalization is best regarded as a result of plant adaptation to wintering. In the fall, when seeds have started to grow or green plants are passing through the vernalization stage, they grow more slowly and harden under the direct influence of low temperatures. The process of passing through the vernalization stage at this time does not diminish the plants' hardiness, but prolonged vernalization prevents the formation of rudimentary ears so that every shoot is shortened and the terminal growing point remains concealed in the tillering node. The same thing happens during winter thaws. When the snow melts early in spring the growth-suppressing aftereffect of low temperatures becomes apparent so that on unusually warm days growth is not vigorous, thereby enabling the plants to survive the normal spring frosts. It is only after the warm weather sets in permanently that winter crops start to grow rapidly and the growing point of each vernalized shoot is soon differentiated into a rudimentary ear.

The adaptation value of vernalization is clearly shown in arid regions. Here due to rapid growth the plants early in spring make better use of soil moisture supplied by winter and spring rains. The temperature is not so high as to dry them out. It is a well known fact that the onset of seasonally warm weather stimulates winter plants to rapid growth and in a few days they become unrecognizable. The green mass is a good protection from summer drought. In northern and mountainous regions with short growing season overwintering plants, due to their characteristic rapid spring growth and entrance into the light stage as soon as the temperature rises, are able to complete their life cycle in a short summer and produce completely ripe seeds by fall.

Let us now turn to the light stage. This stage constitutes a partial reserve in connection with plant adaptation to wintering. It takes place in wintering plants only when the temperature is fairly high and the day is long. That is why winter crops sown very early in the fall, for example, or during prolonged winter thaws have a light stage that never completely ends in the winter and the plants do not enter the stem-extension stage before spring. This stage sets in only after spring sowing, when after a period of high temperatures winter crops nevertheless pass through the vernalization stage and reach the light stage long before the beginning of cool weather in the fall. The same phenomenon is observed when vernalized seeds are sown at the regular time for winter crops. High temperatures and relatively long days are the major factors responsible for the adaptation value of the light stage in wintering. The difference in this respect between wintering and nonwintering plants, particularly between winter and spring varieties of grain, is noteworthy. In the spring varieties, as we have seen, the light stage may begin and come to a complete halt in the fall or during periods of winter thaws. Hence, spring varieties sown simultaneously with winter varieties at the end of summer go into the stem-extension stage before winter and many spring weeds even flower during periods of protracted winter thaws. Their temperature and daylight requirements at the light stage are thus not very exacting. This suggests that the light stage in wintering plants is a means of adaptation to wintering.

A comparison inevitably rises in the mind between winter and spring varieties with respect to the temperature required for the light stage and for growth. We noted in Part II, chapter 4 that temperature is more significant for the winter varieties and that as it falls in the autumn their growth slows up more than that of the spring varieties, thereby enabling them to harden and adapt better to winter conditions. Temperature requirements are also more exacting while they are in the light stage, another means of adaptation that delays stem extension and prevents the rudimentary ear from appearing above the soil late in the fall or during winter thaws.

CONCLUSION

Hibernation checks the development of fruit-bearing organs in wintering plants by prolonged vernalization and light stages. Its adaptation value lies in the fact that it prevents the formation and growth of rudimentary fruit-bearing organs in the fall before frost and during winter thaws. As a result green herbaceous plants winter as rosettes; their terminal buds do not appear on the soil and are thus protected from destructive frosts. Hibernation is most pronounced in plants from regions with a long fall and frequent winter thaws. There is no direct connection between frost resistance and hibernation. Winter rye has a shorter rest period and yet is hardier than winter wheat.

Hibernation is the result of adaptation of plants to the wintering conditions in which they were formed. In some plants now grown with spring crops, e.g., annual lupine, hibernation determined by the length of the vernalization stage survives as a relic of the days when they wintered under natural conditions. Thus, hibernation in modern late-ripening spring plants is a partial indication of past cultiviation as winter crops, e.g., late-ripening spring wheat varieties, vetch, lentils, annual lupine, and others. Moreover, hibernation is not a permanent characteristic and it can be changed by exposing plants during the vernalization and light stages to unfavorable conditions. This is the basis of the method proposed by T.D. Lysenko for transforming winter varieties into spring varieties and vice versa.

CHAPTER 10

PRINCIPLES FOR STRENGTHENING
THE WINTER HARDINESS OF PLANTS

Plants can be affected in three ways: through the soil, through the air, and directly. Let us examine each in relation to the problem of strengthening winter hardiness.

1. STRENGTHENING HARDINESS THROUGH THE SOIL

Hardening — the development of winter hardiness in the fall and early winter — is the consequence both of weather and of soil nutrition, water, and air. Skillful cultivation and fertilization along with optimum water and air conditions can strengthen hardening significantly.

The possibility of affecting hardiness through the soil has been known a long time. Every locality has worked out its own methods. For example, it is customary in the central belt of the U.S.S.R. not to sow winter crops earlier than two to three weeks after the second plowing of fallow land to permit the soil to subside. Failure to follow this rule invariably results in lowered winter resistance. It is widely recognized that the best precursor of winter crops when snow is adequate is a well manured bare fallow, for too little or too much soil moisture adversely affects the wintering of plants. However, this knowledge was purely empirical. The reason why a given measure had this or that effect on winter hardiness was not always clear. As science progressed and offered sound explanations for the various phenomena, more efficient techniques were worked out.

We now know that plants must be provided before winter with all the essential soil nutrients, water, and air in order to obtain the highest yield. They are the best means of enabling the plants to withstand unfavorable wintering conditions.

As we have seen, the first prerequisite of the development of winter hardiness is the storage of reserve plastic substances in cells during fall. This is achieved only if photosynthesis is comparatively rapid and growth is inhibited. A deficiency in any nutrient, water, or air checks photosynthesis. If a plant accumulates carbohydrates rapidly during photosynthesis but uses them up equally rapidly on growth, as happends, for example, if there is an excess of nitrogen in the soil, the cells do not obtain enough plastic substances and they fail to develop hardiness as they should. To ensure the highest rate of photo-synthesis under given weather conditions with simultaneous suppression of growth is the problem to be solved during the pre-winter period of wintering plants. There may be some objections to this theoretical position. Agronomists and fruit growers often use phosphates or potassium salts alone rather than a complete fertilizer to increase winter hardiness. The soil in orchards is permitted to dry a little even if it isn't too moist to begin with so as to limit fall growth as much as possible and hasten the "ripening" of young shoots. However, these and similar measures are taken only when plants have to be "treated".

Let us analyze the phenomenon of late fall growth in fruit trees, which is essentially a problem for plant pathologists. It occurs only when a tree has done poorly during the summer owing to a nutritional deficiency or disturbance in the water-air regime. Fall rains stimulate it into vigorous growth as though to compensate for lack of growth during the summer. A tree that has grown normally because all of its requirements were met ceases to grow in the fall and it is not easy to make it continue to do so. By providing trees in the summer with everything they need we prevent late growth regardless of the conditions that may obtain in the fall. There is no necessity for checking growth by using phosphates or potassium fertilizers alone or by allowing the soil to dry out.

Low winter hardiness in fruit trees may also be due to excessive fruit bearing. It is a well known fact that high yields always result in severe injury if conditions during the winter are unfavorable. The trees are exhausted, especially if the fruits are not harvested until late autumn, because they use up more plastic substances than they store in the process of photosynthesis. Neither phosphorus nor potassium fertilizer alone, particularly if the soil is poor in nitrogen, nor desiccation is helpful. The best thing to do under the circumstances is to apply as early as possible large amounts of a complete fertilizer (or better yet manure) and see to it that the trees have enough water and air. The reason is simple. If trees expend a good deal of their plastic substances in forming the fruit-bearing organs, it is necessary to create the conditions that will enable them to accumulate these substances more rapidly. This can be done only by furnishing them whatever they need in the way of food, water, and air throughout the summer, which is the principle underlying efficient crop management, as mentioned above.

This approach is the second major prerequisite of hardiness — increased vigor. Plants are always less vigorous on infertile soils or where there is an excess or deficiency in nutrients, water, and air. We know, for example, that dry soil and nitrogen deficiency prematurely "age" plants. Aging, we have learned, invariably reduces the vigor of an organism. Too much moisture or an excess of nitrogen likewise has an adverse effect, especially in making plants susceptible to fungus and bacterial diseases.

The problem of nitrogen requires special attention. Nitrogen, of course, stimulates growth and in this respect tends to have the opposite effect of potassium or phosphorus. However, rapid growth occasioned by excessive nitrogen is not like the growth resulting from balanced nutrition as supplied, for example, by manure. An excess of nitrogen leads to poor cell differentiation and thus to diminished vigor. A high level of vigor excludes one-sidedness in plant structure or development.

It is not always possible to make efficient pre-winter preparations to increase hardiness. Hence, unusual "methods of treatment" must be employed: application of phosphorus and potassium fertilizer, green manure, etc. These will not be necessary if plants are provided during their normal growth period with what they require in the way of nutrients (and in correct proportion), water, and air.

2. STRENGTHENING WINTER HARDINESS OF PLANTS BY CHANGING SOWING TIMES

Plants can be affected through the air in two ways. The first and direct way is to change the air itself and the climate; to create, for example, a more favorable microclimate by wall cultivation of fruit trees or trench cultivation of citrus, etc. The second and indirect way is to change the plants' rhythm of development, start of vegetation, time of individual phases, etc. In the latter case there is a change only in the association of individual stages and phases of development with the time of the year and, therefore, with weather conditions.

The most effective and at the same time most convenient method of strengthening the hardiness of winter annual plants is to change the sowing time. The optimal times have been worked out by experience in the individual oblasts. For example, the best time to sow winter crops in the central belt of the European part of the U.S.S.R. is the second half of August, somewhat earlier in the western oblasts, somewhat later in the eastern oblasts. It is set in accordance with weather conditions, insect invasions (especially of the fruit and Hessian flies), possible spread of rust, etc. People believe that crops should go into the winter strong, with ample foliage and a thick root system. However, there has been no scientific physiological analysis of sowing times and their significance in building hardiness. Let us try to make such an analysis in the light of the facts set forth above.

The results of field and pot experiments clearly reveal that plants in the shoot or two-leaf stage are not hardy because they do not have a sufficiently large reserve of plastic substances. In addition, they readily "heave" after alternate freezing and thawing of soil owing to their weakly developed root system. That is why it is not safe to plant winter grains and grasses too late.

Early sowing exposes plants to the danger of injury by insects and rust. High temperatures too, still insufficiently studied, are another important factor.

Four winter wheat varieties were sown near Moscow at two different times — August 26 and September 14. The former date is considered normal throughout the central belt of the U.S.S.R., the second late. Carefully selected and germinated seeds (with due regard for uniformity of growth) were planted at the same depth, each box containing all the varieties. The boxes were kept outdoors. From the end of August to almost the end of September the mean daily air temperature did not fall below +11.4°, the maximum being +20°. The weather cooled off at the end of September. The mean daily temperature for the next two weeks was +6°. It then fell quite abruptly. The comparatively high temperature at the end of August and in September naturally favored the plants sown early, which formed four nodes of leaves by the time the cool weather set in. There were only shoots in the plants sown late. Their basic leaf mass grew at relatively low temperatures. On December 15 the plants were brought into a greenhouse because of frost. Forty days later the surviving plants were counted and all the leaves on the main shoots of both living and dead plants were measured. The results are shown in Tables 32 and 33.

Length of winter wheat leaves in relation to time of sowing

Wheat variety	Time of sowing	Length of leaf, cm					
		1st node	2nd node	3rd node	4th node	5th node	6th node
Kooperatorka	26.VIII	15,8±0,38	17,3±0,34	22,1	22,7	20,5	15,3±0,37
	14.IX	5,8±0,26	7,8±0,35	8,2±0,23	7,8±0,19	—	—
Moskovskaya 2411	26.VIII	17,5±0,36	19,8±0,37	18,1	20,4	18,9	16,6±0,32
	14.IX	5,2±0,31	7,8±0,35	7,7±0,31	7,4±0,17	--	—
Gostianum 237	26.VIII	14,3±0,37	17,6±0,31	19,1	19,6	15.7	14,4±0,39
	14.IX	4,8±0,20	7,1±0,18	7,1±0,15	6,7±0,17	—	—
Lutescens 329	26.VIII	13,9±0,30	18,3±0,31	16,8	17,7	15,0	12,0±0,32
	14.IX	5,7±0,20	7,9±0,16	7,6±0,16	6,5±0,13	—	—

Table 33

Relationship of winter wheat hardiness to time of sowing

Time of sowing	Plants that overwintered, %			
	Kooperatorka	Moskovskaya 2411	Gostianum 237	Lutescens 329
26.VIII	0	27	33	30
14.IX	0	55	67	80

The plants of the August 26 sowing grew much more rapidly under identical temperature conditions in the late fall than did the plants of the September 14 sowing. Frost resistance varied with the growth. All the Kooperatorka plants of both sowings died. The three other more resistant varieties partly survived and over twice as many in each variety sown September 14 remained alive as compared with the August 26 batch. Accordingly, the more rapid growth of the August 26 plants was associated with lower frost resistance.

Again, winter wheat, variety Moskovskaya 2411, was sown outdoors in boxes at four times: August 24, September 10 and 25, and October 10. By frost time the plants of the first sowing had 6 to 7 shoots each and 6 leaves on the main shoot, the second sowing — 2 to 3 shoots per plant and 4 leaves on the main shoot; the third sowing — two-leaf phase; fourth sowing — only individual tips of the shoots. The leaves of plants sown late grew more slowly and were thus smaller. The same differences were noted in the growth of entire shoots.

Fig. 72 pictures the bases of the shoots. The length of the sheaths is interesting. It was longer in the August 24 plants than in the September 25 plants. The difference in sheath length among the individual shoots on each plant were insignificant, although they emerged at different times and developed under different conditions.

If the sheath length is taken as an indicator of growth, we may draw the following conclusion: the later the time of sowing, the slower the growth of the shoots. Thus, individual shoots have the same growth pattern as individual leaves. The rate of growth in both in the fall is determined both by the temperatures at which they develop and by the influence of the shoots and leaves already grown. All the aerial (and, apparently, the underground) parts of the plants sown early, which began to grow when the temperature was comparatively high, grow more rapidly in the fall than the plants sown later. And it is this more rapid fall growth that is the cause of their low frost resistance.

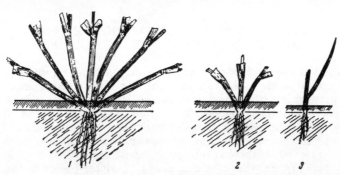

Fig. 72. Bases of shoots of winter wheat, variety Moskovskaya 2411
1 — sowing of Aug. 45; 2 — sowing of Sept. 10; 3 — sowing of
Sept. 25

In Moscow oblast winter crops sown in September go into winter in the early tillering stage and are very hardy. This does not mean, however, that they should be sown at this particular time. Given the fertile soil in Moscow oblast, plants sown even earlier — in August — come through the winter very well and produce higher yields than crops planted in September, which go into the winter rather weakly developed, at best with two or three shoots per plant.

In the colder and less snowy regions, e.g., along the Volga, frost protection of plants is a vital matter. The greater resistance of September-sown plants is decisive in determining whether winter crops can be grown at all. That is why they are planted comparatively late — the first 10 days or so of September. Late sowing is recommended by the Krasnokutsk Experiment Station, which has been successful over a number of years in obtaining very high yields of winter wheat sown in mid-September (Report of the Krasnokutsk Station, 1935).

It follows from the above that by knowing the relationship between hardiness and time of sowing we can more deliberately set about obtaining regular high yields of winter crops in each individual region. If a long-range forecast tells us that the fall is going to be long and warm, we should delay the sowing to avoid the risk of the plants going into the winter unhardened. On the other hand, if the fall promises to be short and cool, it would be well to start the sowing earlier. Moisture and other conditions, of course, likewise have to be taken into account.

There are many ways of changing the association of the individual stages of the life cycle with certain weather conditions, e.g., sowing herbaceous plants in rows from north to south, as suggested by V.I. Vitkevich (1941), so as to expose them to the direct rays of the sun, an important factor in hardening. Then there is the method of artificially shortening the day by cutting off morning and evening hours in the pre-winter period, which markedly increases the winter hardiness of many plants. It can also be effectively applied to seedlings in fruit crop and forest nurseries.

Continuous whitewashing of fruit trees in the fall and winter is likewise useful. If done carefully and at the right time, it can delay the opening of buds from three to seven days depending on the amount of sunlight to which they were previously exposed. Postponement of the plants' vital activity prevents premature loss of hardiness and combats the destructive effect of spring frosts on flower buds and blossoms (I. M. Vasil'yev, 1951).

3. STRENGTHENING WINTER HARDINESS BY DIRECT ACTION ON SEEDS AND GREEN PLANTS

There are various methods of strengthening hardiness by direct action on seeds and green plants. First of all, only the larger seeds must be sown. They have greater germinating power and will produce more vigorous plants in all respects (cf. Part II, chapter 7). A good example of how hardiness can be influenced through seeds is provided by pre-sowing hardening at about $0°$. Plants become more resistant from the appearance of shoots to the formation of two or three leaves. Light too is effective, as demonstrated by F. M. Kuperman (1949) and others who kept the seeds of winter plants in the light for several days, resulting in deeper tillering nodes. This phenomenon is caused by the so-called light aftereffect.

An ancient, sometimes very useful way of intensifying the winter hardiness of trees is pruning. The general idea is to check excessive fall growth and increase the store of reserve plastic substances while accelerating the "ripening" of young shoots. However, if unskilfully applied, pruning may have precisely the opposite effect. Done at the wrong time and without regard for the physiology of the tree, it fails to check growth, indeed, it intensifies it and thus weakens the tree's hardiness. If a rapidly growing tree is pruned too early, the dormant buds on which plastic substances have previously been expended will start to open. Moreover, the actual wounding of a tree stimulates adjacent buds and cambium to grow. This explains the conflicting results of pruning. Successful use of the technique requires a sound knowledge of plant physiology. Pruning aids hardiness only when it is understood how the tree stores plastic substances following removal of the most rapidly growing parts of the shoots.

A dual role is played by girdling, a technique frequently employed by fruit growers. It is sometimes helpful in promoting fruiting, its main purpose, and in strengthening winter hardiness. At other times, however, it may weaken hardiness. For example, V. A. Tyrina of the Far Eastern branch of the Academy of Sciences USSR girdled about ten young apple trees at different times in the spring and summer. It was discovered the following spring that the trees girdled at the earlier dates died because of sharply decreased hardiness of the parts of the trees below the cuts which failed to receive the plastic substances they needed. When girdling a tree, it is important to remember that it is done to force the tree to store plastic substances above the cuts and not to permit the parts below the cuts to starve.

Mowing winter grains sometimes helps to strengthen their hardiness. This is done if the plants are too thick or overgrown or there is a danger of heaving. Removal of part of the leaves improves the lighting and aeration of the lower leaves and thus hinders the growth of snow fungi. Mowing is permissible if sowing was done very early and the fall is long, warm, and moist. It should not be done late in the fall. The plants should not be cut too low so as to enable them to store enough plastic substances by winter.

CONCLUSION

There are many other methods currently known for strengthening the winter hardiness of plants indirectly, through measures applied to the soil and air, and directly. A full list and detailed description of the various methods is within the competence of agronomists. Attempts have been made in this connection (Mosolov, 1934, 1938, 1953) and there is no doubt that the problem will be solved in the near future.

PART III

DEVELOPMENT OF WINTER-RESISTANT
FORMS OF PLANTS

INTRODUCTION

Plant adaptation to wintering as to other adverse conditions is literally limitless. Dahurian larch, Siberian spruce, pine, birch, aspen, etc. are found in Yakutia where the temperature in winter falls to 70° below zero (Verkhoyansk, Oymyakon). Here too they grow winter rye, variety Sitnikovskaya, which under snow can tolerate temperatures as low as -30°. In the Northern Urals local amateur breeders have developed apples — Filippovka, Anisik, Zheltoye transparent, etc. — capable of safely withstanding frosts of -50°.

The lower plants provide even more striking examples of extraordinary frost resistance. Many of them survive a liquid helium temperature of -269°.

The conditions of the plants' habitat limit the degree of adaptation. The hardiest forms are always found in regions with the coldest winters, never in regions with mild winters. This applies equally to resistance to winter evaporation, "sunburn" at the end of winter and early spring, etc. There is invariably a close connection between hardiness and wintering conditions.

CHAPTER 1

WINTER HARDINESS IN CULTIVATED
AND UNCULTIVATED PLANTS

1. WINTER HARDINESS AND ECOLOGICAL CONDITIONS

There are no hardy tropical plants except those growing in high-altitude regions. No plants in moist tropical forests can become hardened and they die after the first light frost. The coffee tree, cacao, pineapple, and other typical tropical plants cannot grow outdoors even in Batum and must be kept under glass in winter. The reason is clear. There is no winter in the tropics and the temperature the year round is fairly high and almost constant (Voyeykov, 1884; Wallace, 1936).

We come across fairly hardy plants in the mountainous regions of the tropics, the degree of hardiness varying with the altitude at which they grow.

Such plants as the cacao, vanilla, cocoanut, etc. grow in the tropical countries of South America to about 1200 m above sea level. On plateaus from 1200 to 1400 m above sea level we find representatives of subtropical flora — citrus. Above 2400 m are the ordinary plants of the temperate zone — apples, pears, plums, etc. (Bukasov, 1930; Verdoorn, 1945). The mountainous tropical regions of Asia, Ceylon, Java, and elsewhere display the same pattern (Kovalevskiy, 1939).

Vertical zonality plays a major role in the hardiness of tropical plants. Any tropical plant that withstands light frosts is undoubtedly indigenous to mountain regions, e.g., the cinchona, a native of tropical South America. All of its species grow on the eastern slopes of the Cordilleras. The main species yielding cinchona bark are found at about 2000 m where the temperature is always high, and they are totally unhardy. However, other species growing in the Cordilleras at 3400 m above sea level are somewhat hardy and they can safely tolerate frost of -1° (Kreyer, 1934).

The subtropics are characterized by a fairly wide range of temperatures. In some virtually winterless regions the temperature during the winter months falls to one or two degrees below zero just for a short time, e.g., in the citrus areas of Peru and Bolivia. The subtropical zone also includes such regions as the Black Sea littoral where frosts are common, the temperature falling to -10° or lower. Thus, subtropical plants differ greatly among themselves. Depending on origin, some are very hardy, others not at all. The Indian and South Chinese forms of tea, for example, are cultivated in the U.S.S.R. in the region of Batum, whereas the more northern Chinese forms are successfully grown in the Sochi-Adler region and more recently even on the northern slopes of the Caucasus near Maykop, Goryachiy Klyuch, and in the Transcarpathian Region.

High zonality affects plant hardiness in subtropical as well as in tropical countries. Consider, for example, the potato. The potato Solanum tuberosum originated in subtropical South America (the island of Chiloe off Chile) where it still grows in the lowlands in wild form. That is why all varieties are unhardy and incapable of enduring -3 to -3.5° for any length of time. Yet there is a potato growing high up in the Andes that withstands frosts of -8°. Some forms of this hardy potato are cultivated by the local population almost along the permanent snow line (Bukasov, 1937).

The close connection between hardiness and geographic origin is also in evidence in plants of the northern and temperate zones. The popular black locust, for example, is common in Rostov oblast and in Kuban. In Moscow, however, and near Leningrad it is quite rare and park plantings are generally winterkilled unless given special protection. The Amur cork tree is frequently encountered in the southern areas of the Far East, but not in Siberia. The same thing can be said of any wild plant — it is well adapted to wintering only if the conditions parallel those of its original habitat; otherwise it loses some or all of its hardiness. According to I.V. Michurin: "When selecting hardy plants for crossing with tender foreign plants, one cannot always rely on the severe conditions of their habitat. It is also necessary to take into consideration local soil conditions and length of growing season. Otherwise, it may happen that plants safely withstanding 45° (Réaumur) in their habitat will freeze in the Soviet Union at 25°, e.g., the Nerchinskiy apricot Prunus sibirica L., which grows on mountain slopes near the city of Nerchinsk in Siberia. In Michurinsk seedlings are regularly winterkilled the very first winter. The reason is that this apricot is accustomed to a short summer and dry location on its native mountain slopes. With us, however, unless planted on a steep slope, it finishes its growth in the middle of the summer; by fall its sap begins to move again and congeals before it can be 'disposed of' " (Collected Writings, vol. 1, 1939, p. 337).

This is an instructive example of how a plant becomes less hardy when exposed to new conditions. The Nerchinskiy apricot could not retain its hardiness in Michurinsk and died of much lighter frost than it endured in its Siberian habitat. The reason is simple. Hardiness, as we know, is not a permanent characteristic. It develops continuously in close association with the conditions surrounding a plant. And when these conditions do not accord with its historically acquired demands, it will naturally fail to reveal all of its characteristic properties.

Artificial protective measures may enable cultivated plants possessing comparatively little natural hardiness to winter in regions with comparatively rigorous weather. For example, unhardy Kooperatorka winter wheat, a selection of the former Odessa Experimental Station, frequently came safely through the winter on the fields of the Institute of Grain Raising of the Far East at Saratov when snow fences were used. Lutescens 62 spring wheat sown in the fall does well near Moscow even without these fences as long as there is enough snow.

This frequently breaks the organic connection between hardiness and habit. However, in many cases it shows up quite clearly. Let us compare, for example, the hardiness of winter grains with their origin — without exception the most resistant varieties come from the coldest regions. The winter rye record holders — Omka and Vyatka — were developed by the former West Siberian Plant Breeding Station and former Vyatka, now Kirov, Plant Breeding Station. All the hardiest winter wheat varieties are the product of Volga plant breeding stations. To these should be added the world record holders for hardiness — Lutescens 329 and Lutescens 1060/10, selections of the former Saratov Plant Breeding Station. Erithrospermum 2411, a product of the former Moscow Plant Breeding Station, was much less hardy in conformity with the less rigorous wintering conditions in Moscow oblast. Ukrainka, produced by the Mironov Plant Breeding Station, is somewhat less hardy. All the varieties of the Krasnodar Plant Breeding Station, e.g., Novoukrainka, are even less hardy owing to the comparatively mild winters in Krasnodar kray. The same close relationship between hardiness and origin is to be found in every modern variety.

What we have just said applies equally to hibernation. We saw in chapter 9 that it is most marked in varieties originating in regions with a long and relatively warm fall and winter thaws. It is less significant in regions with a short fall and invariably cold winter because frost itself serves to check the development of reproductive organs. That is why all the unusually hardy Volga, Ural, and Siberian varieties, particularly of winter rye, have a less pronounced hibernation period than the varieties from Western and Northwestern Europe.

This is also the case with that major factor in the hardiness of wintering trees and shrubs — fall-winter dormancy. As pointed out in Part II, chapter 8, dormancy is especially well defined in trees from our southern regions with a relatively long and mild fall. It is shorter and less pronounced in northern trees and shrubs. Dormancy has evolved in strict conformity with the wintering conditions of the plants.

Cultural practices naturally modify hardiness. Of special interest in this connection is the hardiness of spring plants sown early in the spring. Many of them harden while green and tolerate temperatures as low as -10°, e.g., wheat, barley, oats, and spring rye. Such hardiness was developed by early sowing with normal return of frost and late ripening, notably in the northern and mountainous regions where the plants generally terminate their life cycle when night frosts set in. Spring plants imported not too long ago from warm countries — beans, cucumbers, etc. — do not possess such hardiness in the green state, but it is being developed. An example is the hardy tomato variety of A.V. Alpat'yev (1947) which can endure temperatures as low as -3 or -4°.

Cultural practices include, when necessary, various means of protection from unfavorable wintering conditions. Lemon trees in the Sochi-Adler area winter safely if shielded by gauze or other coverings or warmed by oil heaters when the temperature falls abruptly. In the more northern regions hitherto new for citrus, e.g., Odessa oblast, lemons are grown only by trench cultivation with extra protection during the winter. Ornamentals like the palm, which enhance the Black Sea health resorts, must be provided with individual shields to avert the direct rays of the sun and snow. Their broad leaves would be broken under the weight of the snow.

Protective measures are also of great value for plants of the northern and temperate zones. It is difficult to conceive at the present time of successful cultivation of winter wheat in regions of little snow without snow protection or successful raising of large-fruited apple varieties in the Maritime Territory without continuous fall-winter whitewashing of trees to reflect the direct rays of the sun which are responsible for severe "burns" in the winter and spring. Large-fruited varieties of fruit trees in Eastern Siberia could scarcely survive the winter unless they were heeled in, etc.

2. WINTER HARDINESS AND PLANT TAXONOMY

Let us now correlate winter hardiness with plant taxonomy using winter and spring grains by way of illustration. Here within the same variety, e.g., Lutescens wheat, we find Lutescens 329, a typical winter form, very hardy, and Lutescens 62, a typical spring form, quite unhardy when in the green state. The same thing holds true for Erithrospermum and other wheats. We also find winter and spring forms in rye, barley, and oats. Sometimes they are externally indistinguishable — similar in structure and color of ear, presence or absence of hairiness, and other criteria for classifying the varieties. The winter and spring forms differ in hibernation and hardiness, in which respect they are diametrically opposite. And when we seek the reasons for these biological and physiological differences, we invariably find that they are the result of cultural practices. Some have been cultivated by man since ancient times as winter crops, others as spring crops. These characteristics have been strengthened by heredity; they have made the plants biologically separate breeds. Consequently, different external conditions, in this case related to cultural practices, have contributed to the development of differing degree of hardiness regardless of the plants' inherent systematic characteristics.

We have recently witnessed changes in winter hardiness while taxonomic features are preserved in grains, with winter varieties transformed into spring varieties and vice versa. In 1936 Lysenko changed Kooperatorka winter wheat into spring wheat without modifying its external features. However, the nature of its hibernation period was modified and its hardiness sharply reduced so that it came to resemble typical spring wheat. This is by no means an isolated case. We now have tens of altered winter and spring wheats belonging to different varieties, yet taxonomically they are unchanged.

Regardless of the species or genus of the plants compared, the conclusion is the same: taxonomic position is completely unrelated to winter hardiness. There are genera, to be sure, that are wholly lacking in hardiness like the cacao and coffee trees, but this is due solely to the tropical conditions under which they grow rather than to their taxonomic position.

CONCLUSION

Winter hardiness is invariably determined by the plants' wintering conditions which have apparently become part of their nature and are fixed by heredity. Taxonomic position is of no significance in winter hardiness. Cultural practices influence inherited variability of winter hardiness as do the ecological conditions in which uncultivated plants live.

It follows from the above that in breeding more winter hardy forms of plants their wintering conditions must be changed accordingly.

CHAPTER 2

CHARACTERISTICS OF WINTER HARDINESS AND TYPES OF WINTER-HARDY PLANTS

1. ANATOMICAL AND MORPHOLOGICAL CHARACTERISTICS OF ADAPTATION TO WINTERING

The transpiration surface of wintering trees and shrubs is reduced by loss of leaves during the winter and by the development of xeromorphic structure in the leaves, e.g., pine, spruce, and fir needles. Coniferous needles have a thick cuticle impervious to air and water, very small cells, highly developed vascular bundles, etc. This type of adaptation tends to diminish winter transpiration because xeromorphism is also characteristic of trees which in summer experience no difficulty in obtaining water.

Trees and shrubs in Eastern Siberia, Transbaikalia, and in the Far East, the sunniest areas of the U.S.S.R. in winter, are well adapted to ward off the direct rays of the sun. In the birch, for example, the white bark serves this purpose. The branches of the Amur cork tree, found in the Maritime Territory along with the birch, are thickly covered with cork which prevents the heat of the sun from penetrating the living cells of the bark and thus protects them from sharp fluctuations in temperature.

A common morphological characteristic of winter hardiness, especially in herbaceous plants, is the prostrate state of the stems and leaves. Aerial parts near the ground are covered by snow and obtain warmth from the soil. The leaves of all winter grains are more nearly horizontal in the fall than spring grains sown at the same time, notably clover.

A horizontal position of shoots and even of stems is characteristic of woody plants growing in the Far North and in mountainous regions. This is well exemplified by specimens of Pamir flora — small, low-growing shrubs (Zalenskiy, 1949). Horizontal, literally decumbent trees are very common in Tien-Shan. They cannot be threatened by severe frosts or drying winds.

The decumbent pine displays an unusual form of adaptation to wintering. As described by M. Kerner (1899), the peculiar thing about it is the extraordinary resiliency of the branches which in summer rise a meter or more over the horizontal trunk but in winter are pressed to the ground by the snow. When the sun induces thawing in spring, the branches straighten up and again resume their vertical position.

The underground position of the tillering nodes and crowns is very important in winter hardiness. In herbaceous biennials (winter grains, beets, etc.) only leaves grow from the tillering nodes and collars the first year while the short stems and their apical buds remain in the soil. Thus, they derive warmth from the ground and are better able to withstand frost. The tillering nodes and crowns of nonwintering annuals are not in the ground; in corn, for example, the tillering nodes are generally above the ground.

Besides low growth and spreading quality Pamir plants are characterized by underground development of many of their shoots, hence the name "subterranean plants" (Zalenskiy, 1949) applied to some of them. This trait is also found in wintering rhizomatous plants. Couch grass, known for its extreme hardiness, readily tolerates severe frosts and snowless winters largely because most of its rhizomes are buried deep in the soil. The latter serve as reserve shoots which enable the plant to survive even if all its aerial parts are killed.

Of exceptional interest is the active "burial" of the terminal growing point of the shortened stem or, as they call it, "crown" of clover, alfalfa, and root crops. P.I. Lisitsin (1947) studied this phenomenon throughly, discovering that in clover it begins 8 to 10 days after the seeds germinate and continues throughout the first three years of the plant's life. The growing point reaches the ground by the end of the first month, 2-1/2 months later it is 1 cm below the surface and 0.5 cm lower at the end of the third month. The process slows down and gradually ceases in subsequent years. The direct cause of this unusual phenomenon is longitudinal contraction and lateral expansion of the parenchymal cells of the xylem and cortex of the roots despite the increase in turgor pressure, which is caused by the uneven thickness of the membrane along the perimeter. The remaining root cells are passive or resist the parenchymal cells so that there is tension and even rupture of tissue.

Structural peculiarities of cell walls account for another type of adaptation. Manchurian rhododendron leaves, for example, which remain green throughout the winter, curl up when they are chilled, thus substantially reducing the transpiration surface. The air inside the leaves is not exposed to the sharp fluctuations of the outside temperature. The leaves curl because dehydration following chilling causes the cells of the spongy parenchyma with their unusual walls to contract more in one direction than in another.

For a long time investigators considered small cells a sign of plant resistance not only to frost, but also to drought and other unfavorable external conditions. The biological significance of this sign was carefully studied by V.V. Kolkunov (1905, 1913) who went so far as to suggest that breeders should be guided in selecting plants for winter and drought resistance by the size of the cells, particularly those near the stomatal cells. He believed that plants have distinct "anatomical-physiological correlations" that make it possible to determine major physiological properties, including frost resistance, by the size of the cells.

Kolkunov's suggestion was not accepted and no breeder is guided by it. However, no one denies the value of cell size as a factor in plant physiology, including frost resistance; indeed, it has become the object of further research, e.g., the previously mentioned work of V.S. Iljin (Part II) and the studies of V.G. Aleksandrov (1922). Although the latter deal specifically with the water regime and drought resistance, they contain material pertinent to an understanding of winter hardiness. The main fact established by Aleksandrov is that as the cell decreases in size, there is relative enlargement of the surface and shrinkage of the vacuoles. Enlargement of the surface intensifies physiological activity while shrinkage of the vacuoles eliminates the possibility of mechanical deformation and rupture of protoplasm following dehydration and subsequent flooding as a result of freezing and thawing of the plant.

The above is far from being an exhaustive account of the anatomical and morphological characteristics of plant adaptation to wintering. Our purpose was merely to give a general idea of the various forms of winter hardiness. A closer examination of the physiological properties of wintering plants reveals even greater variety.

2. PLANT GROWTH UNDER SNOW AND OTHER PECULIARITIES OF WINTERING PLANTS

The snowdrop is a good illustration of adaptation to wintering. At first glance this appears to be an unusual phenomenon. Flowers are of course the parts of plants most sensitive to frost. If a fruit tree, for example, blossoms late in the fall, the flowers invariably die when the weather gets cold. Yet there are plants which go through the winter with flower buds and even with open flowers, i.e., our large group of snowdrops. According to Ye. I. Lapshina (1929), the wood violet, pansy, camomile, dandelion, buttercup, etc. flower through the winter near Petergof. Lapshina also found flowering blue bell and haircap alive after frosts of -16°. In the spring she found 29 species of plants that had wintered with flowers and buds.

Adaptation to this way of life is reflected in growth of the plants under snow. According to A.V. Kozhevnikov (1931, 1950), many early spring plants in our larch forests, particularly the anemone, star-of-Bethlehem, corydalis, squill, etc. investigated by the author near Moscow, do not freeze under the forest litter, but grow throughout the winter, emerging in the spring ready to blossom. As a result they have acquired the habit of winter growth, which is a major form of adaptation to their environment. They develop under snow when the woods are comparatively light — before leaves form on the trees that overshadow them — and thus normally end their life cycle by the time the trees start their growth.

The growth of the above-mentioned plants under snow may seem unusual as compared with winter grains. We pointed out in Part II, chapter 2 that the major physiological characteristic of winter crops that enables them to develop greater hardiness than spring crops is cessation of growth when the temperature is low. Precisely the opposite is the case with snowdrops. The fact that they grow under snow is the reason they can exist in a forest. The different ecological conditions of winter grains and plants growing under snow are responsible for their different growth habits during the winter.

Comparatively rapid growth at low temperatures is characteristic of many of the lower plants. The familiar phenomenon of "red snow" is caused by the algae Sphaerella nivalis, commonly found on Kol'sk Peninsula, in the Urals, and in Eastern Siberia. Large stretches are covered with "red snow" in Greenland. The algae gradually stop growing as the temperature falls below zero. But as soon as the sun melts the snow, the functions interrupted by frost are promptly resumed and Sphaerella nivalis completes its entire life cycle — nutrition, growth, and multiplication — in the water from melted snow. Frost may come upon the plant at any stage in its development. Sphaerella nivalis can even withstand the bitter frosts that are frequent during early spring nights in the north and in the mountains.

The following experiment which I conducted over a period of years at the Institute of Grain Raising in the Nonchernozem Belt near Moscow reveals the differences in hardiness existing among the individual plants. I tested winter wheat in soils of varying fertility, variety Moskovskaya 2411, and the winter wheat-wheatgrass hybrid 599, bred by N.V. Tsitsin and distinguished for its many excellent qualities. It can withstand frost but clearly does better when under snow for a long time. In other words, hybrid 599 is just a bit less hardy than Moskovskaya 2411, but is more resistant to the conditions favoring damping off due to the great reserves of plastic substances stored during the winter. These peculiarities of adaptation are responsible, as every breeder knows, for the lack of universality in the hardiness of varieties and require that the latter be chosen for the different parts of the country only after preliminary tests in each region.

3. WINTER HARDINESS, DROUGHT RESISTANCE, AND SALT TOLERANCE

The physiological characteristics of winter hardiness as compared with those of drought resistance are quite significant. Some investigators believe that winter hardiness is a special case of resistance inherent in all plants and that resistance to cold, drought, and salt has the same physiological basis (Sergeyev and Lebedev, 1936). There is some truth in this view. Frequently individual anatomical and morphological as well as physiological characteristics actually turn out at the same time to be the characteristics of drought resistance, salt tolerance, and resistance to fungus diseases, etc.

Winter grains, as we have seen, cease growth in the fall and during winter thaws so that they may store plastic substances to be expended during the winter. The same cessation of growth during periods of drought is characteristic of many drought-resistant plants, e.g., millet, corn, sorghum, sudan grass, and others. We all know that millet appears to die during drought, yet quickly revives as soon as there is rain.

Frost and drought resistance have many other properties in common.

Biochemical changes in the contents of the cell, studied in detail by N.A. Maksimov (1929), are unusually significant in this respect. Osmotic pressure of cell sap, hydrophilic nature of the colloids, water-holding capacity of cells as a whole, etc. — all these change the same way in hardening to frost as to drought. Nevertheless, this does not mean that frost and drought resistance are identical, as the following experiment of mine shows.

On July 12 I planted germinated seeds, with sprouts of identical size, of Moskovskaya 2411 winter wheat and Vyatka winter rye in different halves of the same pot. Watering was halted as soon as they had branched out somewhat in order to check growth and harden the plants to drought. They gradually exhausted the soil moisture and wilted. Fig. 73 shows the difference between rye and wheat in drought resistance. The photograph was taken 18 days after the severely wilted and partially dried out plants were watered. It is evident that Moskovskaya 2411 winter wheat suffered less from drought than Vyatka winter rye under identical circumstances. Yet the winter wheat is incomparably less hardy than the Vyatka rye. The nature of frost resistance and drought resistance in these varieties, therefore, was different.

Fig. 73. Difference in drought resistance between wheat
and rye
On the left — Vyatka winter rye; on the right — Moskovskaya
2411 winter wheat

The same holds true for other plants as well. The extraordinarily drought-resistant cactus from Arizona is capable of remaining without water for months or even years. This typical house and greenhouse plant cannot stand frost. The very drought-resistant millet, watermelon, pumpkin, and other vegetables and melons of southern origin are all heat-loving.

The above observations apply equally to salt tolerance, which under natural conditions both resembles and differs from frost resistance. An example of this is provided by the experiments of a former co-worker at the Institute of Grain Raising in the Nonchernozem Belt, I.N. Kondo (1940). He used several varieties of winter wheat differing in hardiness — Moskovskaya 2411, wheat-wheatgrass hybrid 599, Kooperatorka, perennial wheat 34085, etc. They were planted in pots and kept in a cool greenhouse early in spring. Each variety was tested in soils of different degrees of salinity. Salt was added after the lants had developed somewhat and clearly showed differences in growth normally observable at low temperatures. Several days later the varieties that grew fairly rapidly at low temperatures were clearly suffering from the salt. Their leaves were very wilted and quickly died. The varieties that grew slowly were in better condition. The relationship between rate of growth at low temperatures and, consequently, frost resistance and reaction to salt was pronounced. The result of arrested growth at low temperatures was not only greater hardiness but also greater tolerance of salt.

It is not difficult to understand the reason for this reaction of the wheat to salinity. Rapid growth is a general manifestation of considerable plant activity. Hence, more salt is taken up by the plant with the adverse effects more evident. The results of this experiment were similar to those of the experiment described in the first part of this book. The wheat varieties that grew rapidly at low temperatures suffered more from waterlogging due to oxygen deficiency of the soil than the slower growing varieties under the same conditions.

Investigators have frequently compared salt tolerance with frost resistance and drought resistance with frost resistance. Although the common features are frequently in evidence, yet there may be a greater difference between salt tolerance and frost resistance than between drought resistance and frost resistance. This difference shows up quite clearly when comparing frost resistance in the most salt-tolerant plants, e.g., those from the Sahara, with frost resistance in non-salt-tolerant plants from the central belt of the European part of the U.S.S.R. The Saharan plants are completely unhardy and they grow only in greenhouses. Such well known salt-tolerant U.S.S.R. plants as the glasswort and wormwood are likewise far from being hardy and if chilled in the summer during the period of maximum salt tolerance, they die as soon as ice forms in them.

4. TYPES OF WINTER-HARDY PLANTS

The various methods of adapting to unfavorable winter conditions do not, of course, preclude individual groups of plants from having several hardiness characteristics in common. Plants may be grouped in terms of winter hardiness. First of all, there are the herbaceous annuals. Annuals of the northern and temperate zones are definitely wintering plants. They winter in the form of dormant seeds, tubers, or bulbs. The adaptation value of dormancy was noted when we compared the postharvest ripening of seeds in winter and spring grains which, in the case of the latter, was longer (Part II, chapter 8). The value of dormant seeds is even more pronounced in uncultivated annuals, in weeds, whose seeds do not germinate for months, and in meadow grasses. The dormant period of potato tubers, a typical cultivated annual, is likewise an adaptation to wintering. Dormant tubers remaining in the ground sometimes winter successfully under the snow, even in the northern regions of the U.S.S.R., whereas tubers going into the winter with their tops on are killed by the first frost.

Herbaceous annuals in their adaptation to wintering resemble the ephemera found in arid locations. Ephemera escape drought because the rapid rate of development enables them to complete their entire life cycle before it sets in. Herbaceous annuals of the northern and temperate zones escape wintering in the green state because they too have a rapid rate of development and thus complete their life cycle in one summer, usually just before the start of frosts.

Herbaceous perennials with leaves that die off during the winter constitute a second type of wintering plants, e.g., couch grass, field sowthistle, field horsetail, lanceolate hedge nettle. These plants winter in the vegetative state in the form of rhizomes, tillering nodes, and shoot-forming roots, etc. buried in the soil. Their aerial parts are not very hardy and generally die off during the winter. Exposed to the same freezing conditions as our winter crops, many of these plants, or rather their aerial parts, are no more hardy, sometimes less so. This also applies to couch grass. I made comparative tests of hardiness for several years on several varieties of winter grains and different forms of couch grass. And in every case the green parts of the latter proved to be less frost resistant than the leaves of Vyatka rye and Lutescens 329 wheat.

The dying off of the aerial parts of couch grass and similar herbaceous perennials resembles the process in annuals. Both are unable to survive the winter in the green state. Annuals completely end their developmental cycle by winter. Perennials like couch grass continue it, but go into the winter leafless, all or almost all of their aerial parts dying off. There is a peculiar "physiological defoliation" somewhat comparable to the shedding of leaves by trees and bushes, which protects them from desiccation. This is due to the conditions prevailing in steppe regions of little or no snow. Heredity has fixed the dying off in winter of the aerial parts of plants in the Maritime Territory, Kazakhstan, and Siberia. Couch grass, wildrye, and other typical Kazakh steppe plants brought to the snowy regions of the U.S.S.R. go into the winter with dead leaves, just as in the snowless regions, and initially present a strange sight as compared with winter grains which remain green under the snow. For several years I sowed in the environs of Moscow different species of couch grass and wildrye from N.V. Tsitsin's collection from the Kazakh steppe, and in every case I found total desiccation of the aerial parts by winter time even with ridge culture, while the winter grains remained green.

A third type of wintering plants is the evergreen herbaceous perennials. These include all our winter grains, winter rape, clover, alfalfa, many weeds and wild grasses like meadow peavine, common yarrow, goutweed, and others, which have been adapted to wintering under snow. If the amount of snow is normal, they are unaffected by drought or ordinary frost so that they remain green all winter with no signs of xeromorphism. They are typical mesophytes, but they have a marked capacity to absorb the warmth of the soil by virtue of their spreading leaves and shoots and the depth at which the tillering nodes and crowns lie in the soil.

The result of wintering under snow is comparatively weak frost resistance. The hardiest representatives of this type such as winter rye are markedly inferior in this respect to the buds and young shoots of woody plants wintering above snow. The lowest temperature that the hardiest winter rye varieties — Omka and Vyatka — can tolerate is about -30°. It never gets colder than this under snow even in the coldest taiga regions of Siberia where winter rye is cultivated. Yet the buds of trees in Siberia are exposed to -50° and lower without being killed. And even in the central belt of the U.S.S.R. our ordinary garden and forest plants can safely endure temperatures as low as -40°, which are absolutely lethal for the hardiest winter crops.

212

Deciduous trees and shrubs make up the fourth type of wintering plants. The shedding of leaves, as we have seen, is a method of adaptation to wintering conditions which prevents transpiration. Deciduous trees like the birch and evergreens like the pine are common along the river banks in the coldest parts of Siberia, whereas only deciduous trees are found in the very sunny and dry permafrost regions. But desiccation is not responsible for leaf shedding in the fall, which takes place as a result of the formation at the base of the petiole of a layer of cells with suberized membranes causing the connection between leaf and branch to be broken. The connection with the system of vascular bundles is broken last. That is why the yellowed leaves shed in the fall are often turgescent.

Evergreen trees and shrubs make up the fifth type of wintering plants. Specimens of this group are found throughout the northern and temperate zones as well as in the subtropics. These include both coniferous and leafy trees like the red bilberry in the north and citrus and tea in the south. An important characteristic of these plants in the xeromorphic structure of the leaves which limits transpiration, e.g., the needles of the conifers with their comparatively small surface covered, moreover, with a thick cuticular layer. In the evergreen leafy species the leaves are always leathery, likewise with a well developed cuticle.

The leafy species, chiefly subtropical, have to contend with a comparatively mild winter and soil that freezes only on the surface. The flow of sap is more or less normal all winter and the transpiring leaves receive moisture from soil that doesn't freeze too deeply. However, they lose a good deal of water in uneconomical fashion, especially in direct sunlight. No leafy plant with tender leaves of ordinary mesophilic structure can tolerate even the very mild subtropical winter. Leafy northern species are solely shrubs which grow in forests and are frequently under snow all winter.

These are the main types of winter-hardy plants as distinguished by morphological and biological characteristics.

CONCLUSION

We have learned that plants adapt to wintering in a variety of ways. Our classification, based mainly on form, structure, and biology, is far from complete. It could have been amplified if biochemical characteristics were also used as criteria.

The partial resemblance in adaptation to wintering, summer drought, and salinity is due primarily to the fact that winter and summer have certain features in common. This is particularly true of drought which can occur in winter as well as in summer. It is natural that the adaptive mechanism functions the same way in either case. The similarity may also be accidental as, for example, in comparing frost resistance and salt tolerance among winter crops following arrested growth at low temperatures. We found that the winter wheat varieties whose growth was inhibited more, were also more resistant in this condition to frost and to salinity. The similarity here is somewhat accidental since under natural conditions plants become most tolerant of salt usually during the hottest and driest period of the year, and not in the fall when the weather is cool.

There are differences as well as resemblances among the three qualities, as can be readily seen in comparing frost resistance in plants in a state of maximum hardening to drought and salinity. Not a single one of the most drought-resistant and salt-tolerant plants displays any marked frost resistance during the summer. That is why winter hardiness cannot be equated with general "physiological hardiness". The fact that it has some features in common with drought resistance and salt tolerance does not justify our identifying it with these types of resistance.

In a preceding chapter we determined the organic relationship between winter hardiness and the wintering conditions of plants. In the present chapter we further showed that plants may differ in hardiness under the same wintering conditions. We shall now try to develop and define more concretely our views with reference to the problem of wintering of concern to us here.

CHAPTER 3

NEW FORMATION OF PROPERTIES OF WINTER HARDINESS IN RELATION TO EXTERNAL CONDITIONS

New hereditary properties and characteristics depend on changes in the external conditions of plants. They start with changes in individual development which are then transmitted by heredity and are fixed in the offspring by planned training. However, changes in plants by no means automatically follow changes in external conditions. The preceding history of the plants, nutrition, age, developmental phase, etc. are major factors in hereditary variability that must be taken into account when studying variability.

1. FIXING OF HARDINESS IN INDIVIDUAL DEVELOPMENT

Changes in the individual development of plants arising as a result of external influences differ in kind. Some disappear without a trace under new conditions while others have a more or less profound influence, revealed in the so-called phenomenon of "aftereffects". Let us examine some specific examples of aftereffects bearing on the acquisition of new properties of winter hardiness.

Experiment 1. A study was made of the aftereffect of temperature, the experimental objects being Kooperatorka winter wheat and Lutescens winter wheat seeds identical in size, germinated, and kept on ice at 0 to +2°. The same thing was done 10 days later with another batch of seeds, then with another batch, etc. Thus, two months after the start of the experiment there were sprouted seeds on ice for 60, 50, 40, 30, and 20 days as well as sprouted seeds not subjected to chilling.

All the seeds were sown at the same time, May 4, in pots, some of which were kept in a greenhouse while the others were placed outdoors at lower temperatures. The purpose of the experiment was to discover whether the high temperature of the greenhouse overcomes the aftereffect of low temperature, which always shows up when seeds of winter plants that have started growth are chilled. The results are shown in Fig. 74.

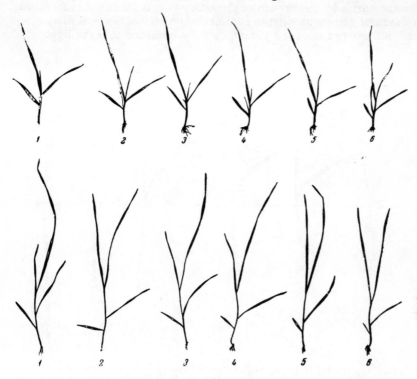

Fig. 74. Aftereffect of low temperature on the growth of Kooperatorka winter wheat
1 — plant from sprout not subjected to cooling; 2 - 6 — plants from sprouts kept on ice 20, 30, 40, 50, and 60 days, respectively. In the upper row — plants from outdoors; in the lower row — plants from a greenhouse

We find that the lowest or first leaves are the shortest, the length varying directly with the time the seeds remained on ice. This is the aftereffect of low temperature that was not overcome by the high temperature of the greenhouse during the growth period of the leaves. The leaves of the second node show a similar but not quite as distinct a picture, and their size, too, varied with the length of exposure to low temperature. Moreover, the high greenhouse temperature failed to overcome the aftereffect of low temperature. The high temperature was reflected only in the leaves of the third and fourth nodes, the sheath and blades of which were longer in the greenhouse plants, as is invariably the case with grains grown at high temperatures.

The aftereffect of light, which can be regulated by the depth at which the seeds are planted, is similar.

Experiment 2. Winter wheat, Moskovskaya 2411, was planted in a greenhouse on September 19 at depts of 2, 2.5, 4.8, 7, 8.3, and 12 cm. As is evident from Fig. 75, which shows a plant from each series one month after sowing, the deeper the sowing, the more elongated were the leaves as a result of etiolation. Note the blades of the first leaves. They were etiolated, like the sheath, in plants from the seeds sown more deeply. Yet the growth of the sheaths only started in the soil and largely proceeded above the soil whence they were borne by the growth of the epicotyl and sheath. Consequently, the aftereffect of darkness on the rudimentary cells of the leaf blades was reflected in their growth even after they fully emerged into the light.

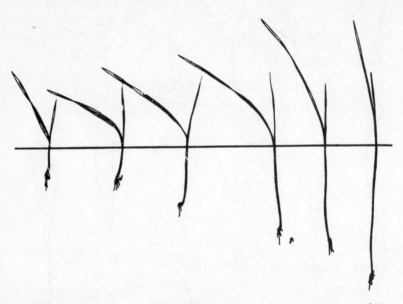

Fig. 75. Changes in the habit of Moskovskaya 2411 winter wheat in relation
to depth seeds were planted
From left to right: sowing at 2, 2.5, 4.8, 7, 8.3, and 12 cm

The aftereffect of light is manifested in still another respect. It is a well known fact that the tillering nodes form in grains as soon as the shoots appear. The first leaf becomes, so to speak, the transmitter of the light stimulation to the epicotyl cells, and they begin to differentiate in the tillering nodes after receiving a suitable light stimulus. Such a stimulus can be given to plants even as sprouts. If sprouted seeds are exposed to sunlight, the tillering nodes form more deeply (Briginets, 1940).

Among the numerous studies on aftereffects we should like to call attention to the highly significant work of P.A. Genkel' (1946) on presowing hardening of plants to drought and salinity. He found that the physiological changes undergone by sprouts largely remain during the period of vigorous growth.

2. TRANSMISSION TO OFFSPRING OF NEWLY
ACQUIRED WINTER HARDINESS

For a newly acquired characteristic to become hereditary, it is necessary that there be appropriate changes in the cells from which the offspring develop — sexual cells in sexual reproduction or vegetative cells giving rise to buds from which new plants will grow. This is well illustrated by T.D. Lysenko's modification of grains carried out by planned measures in 1936. I shall describe in brief the first experiment.

Two plants each of winter wheat, varieties Kooperatorka and Lutescens 329, were sown in a greenhouse early in March. Three plants died during the summer, only a single Kooperatorka surviving. It formed several fruit-bearing shoots in August and produced seeds in September. These seeds were immediately sown in a warm greenhouse and the new plants yielded new seeds the following March which were promptly sown, etc. In each new generation of the original winter wheat grown under the unfavorable conditions of constant high greenhouse temperatures (+15 to +20°), earing became increasingly delayed and more and more like that of a spring variety. Thus, in a comparatively short time (after three generations) a winter wheat variety was transformed into a spring variety (Lysenko, 1937).

This experiment was responsible for wholesale transformation of winter forms of grains into spring forms, e.g., winter wheat, varieties Stepnyachka, Ukrainka, Novokrymka, and several barley and rye varieties (Avakyan, 1938; Shimanskiy, 1938; Khitrinskiy, 1938). Soon the reverse process of transforming spring into winter varieties was achieved. In February 1948 I was afforded the opportunity of studying a field of winter crops produced from spring varieties at the Krasnodar Breeding Station. Many of the new forms were much closer in habit to typical winter varieites than they were to the original spring forms. The large and erect leaves characteristic of spring varieties changed into comparatively small, horizontal leaves in the course of a few generations. The change was so marked that even an expert would unhesitatingly have called them typical winter varieties (Luk'yanenko, 1948).

We now have many such winter forms, e.g., winter wheat from spring Erythrospermum 1160, winter barley from spring Pallidum 32, etc. (Shimanskiy, 1940). The new forms have also turned out to be hardy. Research conducted in the Trans-Urals and Western Siberia under the dirdction of T.D. Lysenko is highly significant. For example, according to A.T. Trukhina (1948), a spring wheat variety Mil'turum 321 sown in the fall in stubble became four years later so hardy that in strain tests it proved the equal of the most frost-resistant winter varieties.

In all these cases the new qualities of hardiness arising in the course of individual development were transmitted through appropriately changed sexual cells to the offspring. This process can also take place vegetatively through the cells from which buds originate.

Let us now consider hardy forms arising from so-called "sports", e.g., the Washington navel orange, one of the finest and hardiest orange varieties growing on our Black Sea coast. It is believed that this orange originated as a sport early in the 19th century in a Brazilian citrus grove. It was brought to the United States in 1870 and then to Russia when groves were first planted along the Black Sea. The history of this orange has been repeatedly described along with the notation that its increased hardiness emerged during the process of spontaneous deviation that produced its buds in Brazil (Webber, 1946). Actually, this is not so. The spontaneous deviation that gave rise to the Washington navel orange was simply the recondition of greater hardiness since a sport always appears as a result of a loosening of heredity. The newly acquired hardiness developed because of changed wintering conditions beginning with its importation into California, where winters are colder than in the Bahia region of Brazil, the source of the orange, and then into the Black Sea area, which has even lower winter temperatures. We are interested here in the vegetative transmission of newly acquired hardiness, for the Washington navel orange reproduces vegetatively.

Then there are the Antonovka, a 600 gram apple, and Yubileynaya cherry, both bred by I.V. Michurin. The former was a sport on a branch of a five year old Antonovka in Mogilev, the latter on a Ostgeymskaya Griot cherry. Besides producing excellent fruit both are more frost resistant than the original varieties. This achievement of Michurin was the result of planned training, including the creation of more rigorous wintering conditions for the young plants. The greater hardiness occasioned by loosened heredity was transmitted in the process of individual development of the original plant from some cells to others and through slips and buds following vegetative reproduction.

The hereditary transmission of newly acquired hardiness, therefore, is not a specific characteristic, the nature of which is the same as when new formations are transmitted from cell to cell in the process of individual development of plants. The point is that cells which received fixed new formations became the source of new organisms. The newly acquired hardiness is thus transmitted by heredity.

3. THE NATURE OF PLANTS AND ITS ROLE IN THE HEREDITARY VARIABILITY OF WINTER HARDINESS

It is a well known fact that plants and animals differ in persistence of inherited characters. This is also true of cultivated plants. Self-pollinating winter grains are quite interesting in this respect. I.F. Lyashchenko (1947) succeeded in transforming winter into spring wheat varieties by sowing them in spring. It turned out that certain varieties changed at differing rates of speed; while some were completely altered after three generations, others continued to remain more or less what they were at the beginning. We encountered the phenomenon in our own research in the field as did V.N. Stoletov (1948). The difference in persistence between plants can be seen the first spring that winter wheat is sown, particularly if large field plots are used. For example, in Lutescens 329 only individual plants reach the stem-extension stage and come into ear by the end of summer, whereas in Ukrainka there is a mass of such plants. The conservatism of Lutescens 329 also shows up in many other respects, as everyone knows who has to handle this wheat.

One of the major factors predisposing to hereditary variability is age. A young organism is always more susceptible to external influences of all kinds than an old one because of the nature of its cells and tissues. Changes in newly formed cells take place much more readily than in differentiated cells. That is why hereditary variability in differentiated cells and in differentiated organisms is incomparably weaker than in undifferentiated cells and organisms.

Likewise an organism obtained from seed and at a young stage is always more susceptible to external influences than an organism at an older stage obtained by vegetative reproduction from a slip or bud. Our older journals on fruit growing contain quite a few references to the exceptional importance of growing plants from seeds when breeding new varieties more capable of adapting to unfavorable external conditions. The so-called "grain sowing" was the basis of the success of such outstanding fruit growers as M. F. Kopylov from Syzran', A. Perevoshchikov from Urzhum, I.A. Yefremov from Blagoveshchensk, V.V. Spirin from Nikol'sk (formerly Vologodskaya province), and many others. I.V. Michurin was the founder of the scientific method of growing fruits from seeds by breeding new varieties. Unlike his contemporaries, he not only ascertained empirically the positive value of planting seeds, but also worked out the underlying theory. Therefore, the use of young plants at early stages of development to obtain new varieties is today justly associated with his name.

The preceding history of a plant is another significant factor in the variability of hardiness. The earlier external conditions do not always disappear without a trace. Indeed, they frequently continue to exert a strong influence on the offspring. Plants growing in damp or dry places invariably differ in structure, properties, and reaction to the same external factors. Plants from dry places tend, so to speak, to age prematurely so that they have little capacity for hereditary variablity. The same thing holds true of soil nutrients. Plants growing on rich soil are more capable of change then plants growing on infertile soil. The greater variability of domestic animals and plants is primarily due to more abundant food. The major factor in hereditary variability of hardiness in plants is their hybrid nature.

4. LOOSENING OF HEREDITY AND NEW ACQUISITION OF HARDINESS

The new acquisition of hardiness by plants starts with the loosening of heredity. Old properties and old environmental requirements must disappear before new properties and new environmental requirements arise.

Such common varieties of self-pollinating grains as wheat, barley, and oats are good examples of newly acquired hardiness resulting from changes in wintering conditions. The overwhelming majority of modern varieties of these plants arose as a consequence of simple selection from the populations. This is the origin of such record holders for hardiness as the selections of the former Saratov Station Lutescens 329, Lutescens 1060/10 and Gostianum 237, Dyurabl' of Ivanov Station (Sumy oblast), Erythrospermum 917 of Kharkov Station, Erythrospermum 2411 and 2453 known as Moskovskaya of the former Moscow Plant Breeding Station of Timiryazev Agricultural Academy, and others. Out of more than 120 winter wheat varieties zoned for 1947 about 100 were obtained from local populations by simple selection.

The plants acquired greater hardiness when shifted to more rigorous wintering conditions and in general when the wintering regime was changed. The history of the above-named varieties of winter wheat — Lutescens 329 and Gostianum 237 (Saratov selection) — is significant. The first volume of the Rukovodstvo po aprobatsii zernovykh kul'tur [Manual on Approval of Grain Crops] (1947) states that Lutescens 329 was bred from 1913 to 1924 by the method of individual selection from the local Sandomirka wheat variety acclimatized in Saratov oblast after importation from Poland. Gostianum 237 was bred from 1913 to 1925 the same way from a Kharkov winter wheat imported from the Ukraine to the Volga region.

We do not know when the hardy ancestors of Lutescens 329 and Gostianum 237 first appeared, but it obviously had to be before 1913, the first year of selection. Their greater hardiness attracted the attention of plant breeders. It is also obvious that the marked hardiness of the ancestors of Lutescens 329 and Gostianum 237 was acquired in Saratov oblast rather than in Poland or in the Ukraine, as proved by the fact that the well known Polish and Ukrainian varieties do not include their equals in hardiness. The increased frost resistance of the ancestors of Lutescens 329 and Gostianum 237 could only have been acquired as a result of importation to Saratov oblast and exposure to harsher wintering conditions which shattered their heredity and created the prerequisite for the development of greater hardiness.

Heredity is shattered when external changes exceed normal limits, thus breaking the previously existent organic connection between the nature of the plant and its environment. The plant is then more or less altered in accordance with the new conditions. Darwin contended that variability itself was the chief way of loosening conservative heredity. A single change in a property is enough to make the offspring of an organism more plastic in this respect. Frequent changes lead to increasing ease of variability. That is why selected cultivated plants are far more variable than wild plants.

Heredity can be shattered only by using those means which are generally not alien to the nature of the plant. A classic example is the sowing of winter varieties in the spring and vice versa. Both varieties are exposed to the required external factors, only the degree of tension being abnormal. The change in external factors shatters heredity. The plants subsequently adjust to this change.

5. THE NATURE OF NEWLY ACQUIRED WINTER HARDINESS

Modern biology rests on the undisputed fact that the life of an organism is inseparably connected with its environment. It is impossible to conceive of a living organism apart from its environment. Every living thing is in constant contact with it, is created from it, lives at the expense of it, and is part of the environment of other organisms. The organic connection between the two explains why the organism invariably changes when the environment changes.

This shows up very clearly in plant physiology. Any physiological process in the absence of limiting factors closely follows a change in external conditions. Studying, for example, the daily pattern of transpiration, we observe that very weak transpiration in the early morning hours of summer gradually increases as the temperature rises and solar radiation intensifies along with a mounting deficit of air moisture until the afternoon when the reverse gradually takes place by night. The same thing happens with photosynthesis and other processes (I. M. Vasil'yev, 1927; Zhemchuzhnikov and Skazkin, 1927).

However, deviations are not infrequent, occasioned primarily by a variety of limitations that may be imposed on the plants. For example, with inadequate soil moisture transpiration does not follow the ordinary course described above and the peak of the transpiration curve sometimes occurs much before the maximum intensity of temperature, insolation, and air moisture deficit. Here is another example. When the plastids overflow with starch, as often happens on summer days favorable for photosynthesis, the rate of photosynthesis begins to drop, even though the external conditions remain favorable. This is caused by internal factors related to the insufficient outflow of starch from the plastids where it formed as a product of photosynthesis. We see from these examples that plants do not always respond automatically to a change in external conditions.

It is also important to note how plants respond to unfavorable external conditions. Their physiology changes and they acquire increasing powers of resistance. Let us again illustrate our point with transpiration. This process, as pointed out above, closely follows the daily pattern of weather conditions if there are no limiting circumstances such as insufficient soil moisture, salinity, etc. As soon as these limitations arise, the rate of transpiration begins to slow down. One of the direct causes is the drying of the cell walls whence the water evaporates. Following intense transpiration, when the cell water balance is disturbed, water menisci penetrating the wall of the capillaries are drawn inside. As a result the pressure of the vapor on the surface of the menisci diminishes and transpiration decreases. We have here an apparently automatic transpiration-regulating mechanism which operates more vigorously under circumstances of inadequate water supply to cells the more strongly transpiration is inhibited.

This type of automatic mechanism also comes into play following a decrease of water in the cells when osmotic pressure of the cell sap mounts and the suction force as a whole increases, thereby reducing the delivery of water to the cells. This is what happens not only while the plant is very active in the summer, but also in the winter. Transpiration or freezing of water from cells is reduced in winter depending on the extent of dehydration. Dehydration activates forces capable of preventing further dehydration. This is the way the entire self-regulatory system of the plant acts, including the enzymatic apparatus. I was able to show in my research on the dynamics of carbohydrates in wheat that drought first increases the sucrose content of the leaves, which naturally raises the osmotic pressure and water-holding capacity of the cells; as drought continues, the sucrose is hydrolyzed into monosaccharides so that each osmotically active sugar particle is converted into two osmotically active particles. The result is that with the same amount of sugar in the cell its water-holding capacity is doubled (I. M. Vasil'yev, 1931b). A similar conversion of sucrose into monosaccharides in wheat leaves due to enzymes occurs in winter at low temperatures and after intense freezing of water from the cells.

Changes of this kind in plant physiology caused by adverse external influences are fixed under certain conditions in individual development. An experiment that I performed in 1928 is significant in this respect. The amount of water in wheat leaves was determined before the soil was artificially dried, then while the plants were suffering from drought, and finally after watering was resumed. It turned out that after the plants were watered the amount of water in the drought-stricken leaves was 10 to 15% more than before water was withheld and as compared with corresponding leaves on the controls. The drought was responsible for a permanent increase in the suction power of the cells so that they became capable of taking in more water than before. Similar phenomena regarding the aftereffect of low temperatures on leaf growth were described above.

The aftereffect of adverse external conditions is even more marked when reflected in structural changes in cells, e.g., thickening and lignification of the walls, cutinization, suberization, etc. These changes are inevitable after drought in arid regions. Rain generally does not reverse them. Thickened and lignified walls, cutinized and suberized integuments are retained, even though the drought that caused them is no longer present.

Any external factor, however essential for the plant, may cause pathological changes if it is extreme. The borderline between the normal and the pathological is faint and the former sometimes passes imperceptibly into the latter. For example, intensified osmotic pressure, as we have seen, has a positive effect on the water-holding capacity of cells and thus on drought and frost resistance. But beyond a certain point it affects protoplasm adversely, becoming a pathological factor. Pathological influences of this kind are frequent in hereditary variability.

What has been said above applies to so-called phenotypic variability, i.e., to variability within the individual development of an organism. However, it fully applies to hereditary variability as well. There is no difference in principle between the two types of variability. As previously noted, hereditary variability is merely phenotypic variability fixed in the offspring. Both types depend on external conditions. Heredity always changes sufficiently in accordance with changes in external conditions. This explains the organic connection between hardiness and wintering conditions that we have already discussed. Yet neither in hereditary nor phenotypic variability does the organism change automatically when external conditions change. This is due to the conservatism of heredity.

A major element in conservatism is aging. Aging is characteristic both of the organism as a whole and of each individual cell and protein molecule. The physicochemical nature of aging, according to modern data, is primarily reflected in thickening of protoplasm, in unusual protoplasmatic hysteresis. The cells as a whole and their colloidal particles increasingly lose the capacity to hold water, i.e., then become dehydrated. Dehydration is accompanied by reduced degree of dispersion and partial loss of electrical charge. Protoplasmic colloids are transformed from sols into a state closely resembling gels, and their substances, originally abounding in energy, highly mobile, and capable of different reactions, are transformed into substances poor in energy reserves, relatively stable, and almost unreactive (Rokhlina, 1936; Nagornyy, 1948; Blagoveshchenskiy, 1950).

By applying these now familiar facts of physical chemistry to "aging" of the hereditary structure we can easily account for the increasing conservatism of heredity with age. The "aging" of each protein molecule in the organism determines the growing conservatism of its hereditary structure with age, i.e., the steady fixing of changes adopted earlier and the decreasing capacity for new changes.

CONCLUSION

External conditions are a prerequisite of the acquisition of hardiness. A change in external conditions causes changes in plants. Changes in hardiness always match changes in external conditions.

All hereditary changes in hardiness begin with the so-called phenotypic changes in individual development. If they arise in young cells, they become fixed in the individual development of the organism in all its parts or in specific organs depending on what develops from these cells. If changed cells become the source of sexual or vegetative cells from which new organisms originate, the newly acquired hardiness is transmitted to the offspring.

External conditions in one form or another always affect plants. Depending on their nature, plants may be more or less susceptible to changes in their hereditary make-up and thus to changes in hardiness when exposed to certain external conditions. In one state the organism may be more susceptible to such changes, in another more conservative.

Yet no matter how conservative it may be, its heredity may be shattered and made more plastic by drastic changes in external conditions, especially by cultivation, shift to other natural or artificially created climatic or soil conditions, etc. The very fact of variability is responsible. It is sufficient to change a plant just once in a given direction to make it more prone to change in this direction, e.g., winter hardiness.

Newly acquired hardiness due to shattered heredity is not stable at first and is easily lost when the external conditions that gave rise to it change. That is why it must be fixed by training, i.e., by duplicating in several generations the conditions responsible for the change in the original organism. It is a process of transforming a plastic into a conservative hereditary make-up as far as the particular characteristic is concerned. The hereditary make-up is first shattered and made plastic in order to substitute desirable for undesirable characteristics and when this is done it is again made conservative. Therefore, conservatism in plant heredity when modifying hardiness is as necessary as plasticity.

CHAPTER 4

HYBRIDIZATION AS A FACTOR IN WINTER HARDINESS

Hybridization plays an exceptionally important part in developing new forms of plants and animals. It involves much more than recombining parental characteristics in the offspring. Hybridization is a powerful source of variability in the broad sense of the term. As a factor in developing hardier forms of plants it is active both in nature and in plant growing. Let us concentrate on hybridization in plant growing because it is easier to trace its role in the production of hardier forms than in nature.

1. SIGNIFICANCE OF HYBRIDIZATION IN SELECTING PLANTS FOR WINTER HARDINESS

I.V. Michurin's work contains the best examples to illustrate the importance of hybridization in breeding plants for hardiness. Michurin began to use his method back in 1878 and soon produced the interspecific cherry hybrid Krasa severa by crossing the Vladimirskaya early cherry with the Winckler belaya cherry. The former combines excellent fruit qualities with considerable hardiness thanks to which, Michurin wrote, "not only doesn't the tree suffer from frosts, but the blossoms themselves are capable of withstanding the chilly fall weather" (1940, vol. 2, p. 132). Besides hybridization Michurin used the "acclimatization method" recommended by Grell which involved grafting slips from mature plants of sourthern varieties onto the crown of hardier winter varieties so as to make them more stable hereditarily. After a few severe winters in Michurin's nursery all the southern varieties acclimatized by Grell's method died. This led Michurin to abandon this approach and concentrate on hybridization.

He used it extensively on apple trees. The 36 out of 45 varieties obtained by hybridization included such well known ones as Bel'fler-kitayka, Bel'fler-krasnyy, Kal'vil' anisovyy, Kandil'-kitayka, Kitayka zolotaya, Pepin shafrannyy, Shafran-kitayka, Slavyanka, and others. They all have excellent fruit as well as a high degree of frost resistance. Bel'fler-kitayka was obtained by crossing a Bel'fler zheltyy with a Chinese apple. The aim was to increase the hardiness of the Bel'fler zheltyy, which has excellent fruit but low frost resistance, by giving it the hardiness of the Chinese apple. The effort was successful and the hybrid is the equal of its mother — the Bel'fler zheltyy — in quality of fruit and all parts of the tree are highly resistant to frost, even at 58° No. Lat. in Ivanov oblast, 500 km north of Michurinsk where it was bred. Michurin also bred 6 pear varieties, including the famous Beurre zimnyaya Michurina, 1 quince variety, 5 mountain ash varieties, 12 cherry varieties, 10 plum varieties, 1 almond variety, and 1 raspberry variety. All combine good quality of fruit with considerable hardiness.

Hybridization has become tremendously important in recent years in breeding hardier varieties of field crops. Many of our common winter grains have been produced by hybridization, e.g., the wheat varieties Lesostepka 75 of the Belotserkovskaya Plant Breeding Station, Lutescens 9 and Lutescens 17 of the Verkhnyacheskaya Plant Breeding Station, Lutescens 33/266 of the Kharkov Planting Breeding Station, Novoukrainka 83 and Pervenets of the Krasnodar Plant Breeding Station, the wheat-wheatgrass hybrid 599 (Shekhurdinovka) of the Institute of Grain Culture in the Nonchernozem Belt, the rye-wheat hybrid 46/131 and Erythrospermum 118 of the former Saratov Plant Breeding Station, and others. All these varieties have been zoned and each is hardy, productive, and possessed of good baking qualities in the regions where they are cultivated. The same thing holds true for winter rye and winter barley. Among the winter rye varieties of hybrid origin is the very hardy Omka of the Siberian Institute of Grain Culture, produced by free transpollination of four rye varieties. The hybrid varieties of winter barley include Krasnodarskiy H-1918 of the Krasnodar Plant Breeding Station and Krymskiy H-30 of the Crimean Plant Breeding Station.

Many other crops could be cited by way of illustrating the significance of hybridization in selecting plants for winter hardiness. Hybridization has now become the basic modus operandi of breeders to obtain new forms of plants. This applies equally to the breeding of more winter-hardy forms.

2. PRINCIPLES GOVERNING THE INHERITANCE OF HARDINESS IN HYBRIDIZATION OF PLANTS

K.A. Timiryazev was the first to classify the forms of hereditary variability in hybridization. He distinguished cases in the hybrid offspring where "the characters of the parents are merely shuffled (mosaic heredity), or blended like the commingling of liquids, giving rise to characters in between the two, or are mutually exclusive, i.e., in the hybrids the characters of one parent displace those of the other" (Collected Writings, vol. 6, pp. 184, 185).

The basic ideas on inheritance were formulated by I.V. Michurin in 10 points in chapter 4 of his Printsipy i metody raboty [Principles and Methods of Work]. According to Michurin, the parental characters in the hybrid may or may not show up, for everything depends on external conditions and the parents' powers of hereditary transmission. The inheritance of parental characters proceeds by means of their development. Dominant in the hybrid is that which has greater force for manifestation and finds favorable conditions for development. Recessive is that which has less force for manifestation and finds less favorable conditions for development. In all cases external conditions are the decisive factor.

The works of Michurin contain many examples supporting these views. For example, hybrid seedlings obtained by crossing the Bessemyanka pear with a wild pear invariably inclined toward the Bessemyanka when growth conditions were favorable, but resembled the wild pear when conditions were unfavorable. Seedlings obtained by crossing the cultivated variety of the Vladimirskaya cherry with the Samarskaya stepnaya cherry externally resembled the Vladimirskaya when grown in soil brought from Vladimir, but looked completely different when grown in nursery soil near the town of Michurinsk. Crossing foreign winter pear varieties with local but uncultivated hardy varieties growing in Tambov oblast produced hybrids in whose fruit the characters of the local varieties were dominant owing to their greater power of hereditary transmission when growing under normal conditions. However, crossing them with the geographically remote Ussurian pear generally resulted in hybrids possessing the fruit quality of the foreign varieties. In this case the power of hereditary transmission of fruit quality in cultivated foreign pear varieties was greater than in the wild Ussurian pear which encountered in Michurinsk conditions that were very different from those of its habitat.

3. NEWLY ACQUIRED HARDINESS IN HYBRIDS

A hybrid is a plant with shattered heredity. The heredity of a hybrid is not only richer than that of either of its parents, but is also more variable. The process of new formation of characters is more rapid in the hybrid than elsewhere. This has been known a long time. All the prominent breeders of the 19th and early 20th centuries like Knight, Van Mons, Villemoraine, Burbank, Shreder, and M.V. Rytov used this peculiarity of hybrids. Michurin attached a great deal of significance to the loosening of heredity in these plants. Combining the hybrid nature of seedlings with planned training while they were young was Michurin's basic technique for obtaining new varieties of fruit trees and berry bushes.

The phenomenon of heterosis, which we encountered in connection with winter hardiness, is particularly significant in the formation of new characters in hybrid plants. Heterosis is the term usually applied to the greater vigor and capacity for growth displayed by first and succeeding generations of hybrids as compared with their parents. A typical example of it is the high-yielding corn obtained by crossing inbred lines. The greater vigor of first-generation hybrids may show up in a variety of ways, e.g., in increased hardiness of wintering plants. We may thus speak of the heterosis of winter hardiness.

Darwin cited examples of heterosis of winter hardiness. "Mr. Chondy," he wrote, "produced a great many cross breeds, planting six different cabbage varieites in a row. The characters of these crossbreeds were infinitely varied; but the most remarkable fact of all was that when the severe winter destroyed all the other cabbage and broccoli in the garden, these hybrids suffered little and were eaten when no other cabbage could be obtained" (The Variation of Animals and Plants under Domestication, 1941, p. 375*).

T.D. Lysenko's investigations embraced many instances of heterosis of winter hardiness. Owing to the absence of pure lines of wheat in nature, he used intervarietal crosses of self-pollinating plants and obtained specimens with typical manifestations of heterosis. The winter forms became more resistant in the process, e.g., Krymka, Ukrainka, Gostianum 237, etc. The heterosis of winter hardiness has also been noted in many other plants. It has been described by A.S. Yablokov (1936) in interspecific walnut hybrids, by A.S. Pyatnitskiy (1946) in hybrid oaks, and by others in a variety of plants.

Here is an example from my own research. Timofeyeva spring wheat, semiwinter wheat turgidum, and their hybrids obtained by A.P. Zhebrak were compared for hardiness. The sowing was done in pots early in September. The plants remained outdoors all fall and thus became hardened. When the weather turned cold, the plants were brought into an unheated greenhouse where they spent the winter. They were covered with a little snow to prevent desiccation. They were checked from time to time for frost injury and some of them were further chilled in a refrigerator.

The result was invariably the same. The hybrids suffered less injury and were killed by lower temperatures than plants of both parental varieties. Fig. 76 shows the plants after exposure to about -14° — a hybrid and one of its parents, Turgidum. The other parent, Timofeyeva, was killed by this temperature.

Hybridization may also produce the opposite result — weak or even completely unviable offspring, as in systematically remote crossings. Hybrids from these crossings often develop more or less normally, but their seeds have low germinating power. Moreover, as in heterosis, the hybrids display various forms of depression. The resemblance to heterosis is underscored by the fact that it shows up only in the first generation, the hybrids becoming completely normal with the fourth and fifth generations, as noted by Michurin in seed germination. We are thus entitled to include the low vitality of hybrids in the same category of phenomena as heterosis, i.e., it is heterosis with a reverse sign.

Heterosis is not always transient, for there are well known instances of prolonged heterosis, both positive and negative. This is called transgression in genetics. Here is how Michurin describes a case of this kind. "In 1888 I crossed a Winckler mazzard with a Vladimirskaya rose cherry and obtained a new variety representing an interspecific hybrid of cherry and mazzard. . . . which in Siberia, in Omsk, is capable of withstanding the Siberian frosts and yielding good fruit, whereas the simple European cherry varieties and even the semicultivated Vladimirskaya rose sour cherry are winterkilled there" (Collected Writings, vol. 1, p. 337).

The American winter wheat variety Minturki is a good example of transgression of winter hardiness. It is one of the hardy varieties in the

---

*The reference is to the Russian translation, cf. Bibliography—transl. note.

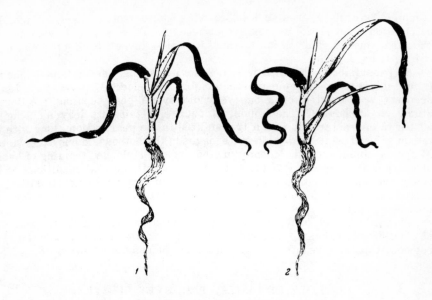

Fig. 76. Heterosis of frost resistance in wheat
1 — parental form of Turgidum semiwinter wheat; 2 — hybrid Turgidum
and Timofeyeva spring wheat

United States and Canada. It was obtained by crossing two winter wheats named Turetskaya and Odesskaya. The latter, imported some time ago from Odessa (whence it received its name), was quite hardy. However, the hybrid named Minturki surpassed its hardy parent in this respect, as proved by many comparative field experiments conducted over a number of years at experimental stations in the United States and Canada (Hayes and Aamodt, 1927). Similar cases are to be found in all branches of plant growing, particularly in viticulture where hybrid varieties, obtained by crossing northern with southern varieties, are often hardier than their parents (Negrul', 1946).

4. DEVELOPMENT AND FIXING OF HARDINESS IN HYBRIDS

Newly formed properties of hardiness in hybrids are developed and fixed in individual development and in offspring by planned training. A powerful means of planned training is grafting, which reached its culmination in the mentor method worked out by Michurin. Use of this method, especially on perennials, is inseparably connected with hybridization. Here is a passage from Michurin describing how he produced the Kandil'-kitayka apple:

"By crossing the well known Crimean apple variety Kandil' sinap with a Chinese apple I obtained seedlings insufficiently able to withstand our local frosts. So in order to increase hardiness to the necessary level, I had to insert several branches of the best seedlings in the crown of the mother tree, the Chinese apple. Knowing beforehand the fine taste of the fruit of this Chinese apple, I merely risked producing a tree with small fruit. In return I hoped to develop in the new tree considerable productivity along with

227

complete hardiness or else I would have had to destroy the seedlings. My calculation proved to be correct and the result was a hardy variety with excellent quality fruit which I named Kandil'-kitayka'' (Collected Writings, vol. 1, 1939, p. 503).

An experiment performed by P.N. Yakovlev, a close associate of Michurin, is an interesting example of the mentor influence. A one year old lemon seedling was grafted on a one year old hybrid pear seedling, the Beurre zimnyaya Michurina. The lemon, of course, retains its leaves during the winter, a characteristic that it transmitted to the pear, which along with the lemon grafted on it likewise kept its leaves in the hothouse during the winter. Michurin considered the mentor method best for planned training of hybrid seedlings. He also employed the effect of suitable external conditions on the young hybrids. Michurin attached particular importance to soil moisture. He solved the difficult problem of breeding mazzard varieties hardy in Michurinsk by growing hybrids on soil with moderate moisture.

Planned training of hybrid seedlings is an inseparable part of the selection of plants for hardiness. Without it all the work might be in vain and the richest potential for strengthened hardiness might remain undeveloped.

5. ROLE OF VEGETATIVE HYBRIDIZATION IN WINTER HARDINESS

The above-described mentor method gave rise to the study of vegetative hybridization. The scion and stock affect each other by their juices, the stronger influence being borne by whichever is younger in age and stage. A necessary condition of vegetative hybridization is the presence in either of still intact hereditary make-up. No change takes place if a cutting or bud is grafted upon the crown of a mature tree and the cutting or bud has been taken from a mature tree. This results in simple union of the grafted components instead of hybridization. It is the very poor acclimatization method of Grell which Michurin abandoned after frost killed almost all the tender European varieties acclimatized according to Grell.

The stock and scion may be altered by the actual grafting process, which sometimes has a profound effect on the structure and properties of both. For example, it is a well known fact that cultivated apple varieties grafted upon an ordinary wild apple grow very rapidly into tall trees. Grafted upon a Dusen, they grow more slowly into medium size trees. Slow growing dwarfs are produced by grafts upon a Paradizka. At the same time winter hardiness and other characteristics likewise change.

A fruitgrower named Sofronov (1902) noted that the pistachio without grafting, on its own roots, normally is winterkilled when the temperature falls to -7.5°, whereas when grafted on Pistacia terebenthus it can withstand frost of -12.5°. Pear on quince and apple on paradise apple are unable to survive in a severe climate since their hardiness is greatly reduced by grafting upon the aforementioned stocks. According to M. Nikiforov (1905), the Siberian apple as a stock gives cultivated apple varieties substantial hardiness along with early termination of growth in the fall, thus enabling them to endure Eastern Siberian winters. Such experts as R.I. Shreder (1898) and M.V. Rytov (1898) cite many examples of this kind as do modern fruitgrowers (Yenikeyev, 1946).

Changes in the hereditary foundation here are associated with changes in the nutrient and water regimes of the grafted plants. When a cultivated apple is grafted upon a wild apple the former, thanks to the thick roots of the latter, obtains much more water and nutrients than does an ungrafted cultivated apple. On the other hand, when a cultivated apple is grafted upon a Paradizka, the scion does not obtain sufficient water and nutrients. Then too the conditions of union of scion and stock are of significance. In some cases the union is complete, in others it is only partial (Krenke, 1928).

The effect on the hereditary foundation of grafted plants due to changes in the nutrient and water regimes is the same in principle as the effect of the juices of one plant on the cells of the other. The hereditary foundation may be altered in either case, the difference being merely in the name of the phenomenon. In the first case we may speak of the effect of changed external conditions, as discussed above. In the second the mentor influence is at work. If the latter is examined more deeply, it will be seen that the borderline between both phenomena is quite blurred. The juices of the mentor plant, regardless of composition, are as much an external factor as far as the cells on which they act are concerned as the juices of the soil solution. That is why we can speak in both cases more or less of the same thing — the influence of changes in external conditions. This is the basis on which to appraise the role of vegetative hybridization in winter hardiness. The role is similar to that of changes in temperature, light, nutrients in the soil solution, etc. Hardiness can be increased or decreased by external conditions. Similarly, hardiness can be increased or decreased by vegetative hybridization, as we saw in the examples cited above. Vegetative hybridization shows up only when changes in hardiness are transmitted by heredity, which is possible only when plants young in age and stage are used. If not, i.e., when the graft and stock are completely formed plants, the result is a simple graft instead of a hybrid. Should any changes in the hardiness of the grafted components arise, they would not go beyond the limits of the individual development of the plants.

6. SELECTION OF PAIRS IN HYBRIDIZATION FOR WINTER HARDINESS

To obtain his remarkable varieties of fruit trees and berry bushes Michurin was very careful in selecting the parents. He gave major consideration to the habitat of plants intended for hybridization. He crossed the finest European varieties with the hardiest wild or semicultivated forms, e.g., Nerchinskiy apricot, Amur grape, and other Siberian and Far Eastern plants. Michurin was thus the first in history to use remote hybridization, remote not in the taxonomic situation of the plants, but in ecological conditions.

Michurin also took into account the parent plants' power of hereditary transmission. His many years of experience taught him that wild plants possess greater power of hereditary transmission than cultivated plants; plants of pure species possess greater power of hereditary transmission than hybrids; own-rooted plants possess greater power of hereditary transmission than grafts; mature plants possess greater power of hereditary transmission than young plants; healthy and thriving plants possess greater power of hereditary transmission than sickly plants or plants weakened by adverse external conditions, and so on.

Michurin repeatedly called attention to the need of thorough familiarity with the pedigree of producer plants: "In selecting the combination of producer pairs, it is necessary to know not only the characters of each, but also the characters of their closest relatives. The reason is that hybrids and mongrels in most cases inherit characters not from their actual parents — father and mother — but from their grandfather and grandmother indirectly throught the material as well as paternal lines" (1939, vol. 1, p. 598).

Selection of pairs according to Michurin provides both the knowledge of the producers' characters needed by the breeder and the assurance that these characters will show up in the hybrid offspring if appropriately trained. Michurin has this knowledge to perfection and he chose pairs strictly in accordance with what was needed to solve a given problem. For example, in order to create a winter pear variety combining excellent taste of fruit with great hardiness all over the tree, he crossed the foreign Beurre royale with the wild Ussurian pear. Both producers were exposed to unfamiliar soil and climatic conditions, thus making their hereditary make-up plastic. But Michurin knew that the Ussurian pear, being a wild plant, possesses greater power of hereditary transmission than any of the cultivated pears. To weaken this power, he took a young tree the first year it flowered. The result of his efforts is the famous Beurre zimnyaya Michurina with excellent quality of fruit and exceptional frost resistance in Michurinsk.

The use of Michurin techniques in choosing plant pairs for hybridization made it possible to turn selection into a true science capable of producing varieties according to plan.

CONCLUSION

Hybridization shatters the hereditary foundation of plants and makes each character more plastic and changeable. Hybridization so to speak rejuvenates the hereditary characters, although not uniformly, and makes living matter more active and vital. It strengthens the adaptability of plants to adverse wintering conditions, etc. But just as when the hereditary foundation is shattered and variability enhanced by external factors, so does newly formed hardiness in hybrids become fixed in the offspring only by subsequent planned training. Without it the finest choice of pairs and excellence of technique would not yield the desired results and the potential of the hybrids might not be realized.

CHAPTER 5

PATHOLOGY OF HEREDITARY VARIABILITY
IN WINTER HARDINESS

Hereditary variability, as we have seen, is caused by the exposure of young plants to unusual external conditions, including those arising in hybridization. These conditions may be harmful whereupon the hereditary foundation is shattered and more or less injured. This process of injury is frequently wholly unavoidable and it is encountered both in nature and in selection work. The forms which the pathology of hereditary variability take may be quite varied. Disturbances of cell division have been studied most of all.

1. PATHOLOGICAL CHANGES IN CELLS DUE
TO CHILLING AND ANESTHESIA

About half a century ago the Moscow botanist I.I. Gerasimov discovered the following interesting phenomenon in a number of experiments on the alga Spirogyra (1890, 1892, 1896, 1900, 1901, 1904). If at the moment of division the cells are subjected to more or less severe but not lethal chilling, the normal course of division is disturbed and the resultant daughter cells are deformed in various ways. They may have large nuclei or no nuclei at all or many nuclei — with two, three, four, and a great many smaller nuclei. The number of nuclei in the daughter cells may be uniform or not. Along with an increase in the mass, the author found an increase in number of chromosomes in the nuclei, a phenomenon that was later called polyploidy. The ordinarily constant number of chromosomes may be doubled or even quadrupled as a result of chilling. The same type of abnormality was also observed when the cells were anesthetized, but only when the cells were dividing. Dormant cells withstood both chilling and anesthesia without visible changes.

After studying the physiological significance of changes in the dividing cells, Gerasimov concluded that they were absolutely harmful. The viability of such cells was invariably low. The lack of nuclei was particularly harmful. The cells lived for a while and even grew. Photosynthesis took place in the light and starch was stored, but they steadily lost viability and stopped growing. The chloroplasts became pale, photosynthesis slackened, and the cells eventually died.

'The extreme enlargement of the nuclear mass in the cells was no less harmful. The cells resembled those without nuclei in reduced viability. In time the effect of the enlarged nuclei tended to weaken.

The author also observed some other deviations that left their mark on cell viability. They are not uncommon and occur in nature as well.

Gerasimov's investigations laid the foundation for the study of cell division and the pathology of hereditary variability in plants. Unfortunately, they were ignored for a long time and many authors in surveys of polyploidy failed to mention the Russian scientist who pioneered in the field. His conclusions on the harmful effect of polyploidy were of course completely overlooked. The increase in number of chromosomes was regarded as something beneficial in the origination of new forms of plants and virtually the main element in progressive evolution. Newly acquired frost resistance was directly linked with polyploidy. This idea still finds supporters so we must set forth the facts on the basis of Gerasimov's work and elucidate the genesis of more frost-resistant plants when the process of cell division is disturbed.

2. CONCENTRATION OF POLYPLOID PLANTS IN MOUNTAINOUS AND ARCTIC REGIONS

A point of departure for studying the relationship between polyploidy and development of hardier forms of plants is the fact that polyploids of wild flora are concentrated in mountainous and arctic regions. The most extensive research in this field was carried out by the Soviet botanists A.P. Sokolovskaya and O.S. Strelkova. They began by making a detailed karyological analysis of species of bentgrass (Sokolovskaya, 1937) and meadow foxtail (Strelkova, 1938) found in the U.S.S.R. It turned out that the number of chromosomes in individual species of bentgrass varies from 14 to 56. Most of the polyploid forms are adapted to the far north and mountainous regions. According to Sokolovskaya, these forms once migrated from the Central Mediterranean area where the simplest diploid species of bentgrass are still concentrated. They turned into polyploids when they encountered the rigorous ecological conditions characteristic of the present-day territory of the U.S.S.R. The degree of polyploidy increased the farther north and the more mountainous the place in which the plants settled.

O.S. Strelkova describes in similar fashion the formation of polyploids in the meadow foxtail. The species of this grass are widespread from 30° No. Lat. to the far north. They are found up to 4500 m above sea level, particularly in alpine and subalpine meadows. The number of chromosomes varies from 14 to 98 and 105. Multichromosome species are adapted chiefly to the far north and mountainous regions. Strelkova too assumes migration from the Central Mediterranean area, the habitat of the diploid species.

In subsequent joint work Sokolovskaya and Strelkova (1938) subjected to karyological analysis the flora of the mountainous regions of the Pamirs and the Altai. In the former 150 species of different families and 200 in the latter were investigated. The overwhelming majority proved to be polyploid. They discovered the same thing when they subsequently studied the flora of high-altitude and arctic regions. Polyploids constituted 50% of all the plants in the main Caucasian range (Sokolovokaya and Strelkova, 1940), 64.5% of the arctic flora on the island of Kolguyev (Sokolovskaya and Strelkova, 1941).

The data of Sokolovskaya and Strelkova and other investigators (Flovick,

1940) show convincingly that under severe wintering conditions in mountainous regions and the far north polyploid plants are actually represented by a substantial number of species and races. This is readily understandable in the light of Gerasimov's research. Abrupt changes in temperature and unusual chilling during the period of fruiting disturb the process of sexual cell division and result in the origin of polyploid forms. These conditions are very common in the mountains and in the north. R.L. Perlova (1939a, b), for example, quickly succeeded in obtaining in the Pamirs a naturally formed hexaploid from a triploid Solanum vallis Mexici Juz.

3. MORPHOLOGICOANATOMICAL AND PHYSIOLOGICAL PROPERTIES OF POLYPLOIDS

A necessary consequence of polyploidy is an increase of chromatin in the nucleus and, consequently, an increase in size of the nucleus. The cytoplasmic mass grows at the same time, but not in direct proportion to the nucleus. As a result the cells of the polyploids are always larger but "not balanced" with respect to the individual constituents. These changes alter the entire appearance and properties of the plants. Polyploids very frequently differ from ordinary diploid plants in having larger and thicker leaves along with bigger flowers and fruits. Their vegetation period is generally longer, and occasionally typical annuals become biennials. However, there are examples of the opposite when the leaves, flowers, and fruits of polyploids are small and clearly look as though they were depressed.

The reasons for the different manifestations of polyploidy lie in the changed relation of chromatin to the other constituents of the nucleus and of the nuclear mass to the cytoplasmic mass, as pointed out by Gerasimov. The greater the degree of polyploidy, the larger the nuclear mass with respect to the cytoplasm. This hypertrophy of the nucleus has an adverse effect on the physiology of the cell and beyond certain limits becomes clearly harmful. Proof is found in the sharply depressed condition of plants with a marked increase in number of chromosomes.

Polyploidy also has an adverse effect on the physiology of plants in which there are no visible signs of depression, e.g., in the reduced rate of cell division in the growth zones. In determining the growth rate of the protonema of moss, Wettstein (1924) found the following number of formed cells after the same time and under the same conditions: in normal diploid plants — 49; in triploids with a set and a half of chromosomes — 32; in tetraploids with a double set of chromosomes — 13. With greater degree of polyploidy the growth rate of the protonema steadily dropped. The triploids grew one and a half times more slowly than the diploids while the tetraploids grew more than twice as slowly as the triploids.

The low rate of cell division caused by polyploidy is to some extent the cause of slow development of plants. This is illustrated by Oenothera lamarkiana gigas bred in 1895 from Oenothera lamarkiana by De Vries (1906). According to the author, it differed from the maternal form in having larger leaves and flowers, a thicker stem, a much slower growth, and a tendency to act like a biennial. Subsequent cytological investigation showed that Oenothera lamarkiana gigas was a tetraploid with twice as many chromosomes as the maternal form (Gates, 1915). A similar case in the triploid Crepis capillaris arising in the experiments of M.S. Navashin (1929). It too differed from the diploid form in developing more slowly and blooming a month later.

Polyploidy has a very adverse effect on fruit bearing. The process is always inhibited in polyploids and they have fewer but larger seeds.

An important characteristic of polyploids noted by several investigators is low osmotic pressure in the cells. Becker (1932), for example, comparing the protonema of two moss species, found that osmotic pressure decreased as the number of chromosomes increased. This may be partially correlated with another frequent if not invariable characteristic of polyploids, i.e., increased water content of cells and decreased content of organic matter and ash (Pirschle, 1942).

These properties of polyploids, it should be noted, are not necessarily permanent and in the course of time they may become lost. Even the large cells and nuclei frequently disappear, only the increased number of chromosomes remaining, usually smaller in size. Moreover, older polyploids always differ in important respects from recent polyploids. An example of the restoration of normal properties in polyploids is Rumex, a native of Sweden. Comparing the form, structure, and physiology of the various species, Löve (1944) found that in size of flowers and fruits and in size of cells and nuclei they present an unusual gamut of variations in which the increase is greater as one proceeds from the diploid to the octoploid species. Physiologically the polyploids have already changed, acquiring properties suitable to their habitat. Osmotic pressure (in moles of sucrose) in the cells of plants grown side by side rose in proportion to the number of chromosomes.

If Löve's findings are compared with Becker's, it will be seen that these authors contradicted each other on the relationship between osmotic pressure and polyploidy. Becker found that osmotic pressure in cells fell as the number of chromosomes increased. Löve, on the other hand, found that osmotic pressure rose as the number of chromosomes increased. The reason lay in the different times of genesis and growth conditions of the polyploids. Becker dealt with polyploids of recent origin obtained artificially, whereas Löve studied species arising naturally and completely adapted to their babitat. As Löve himself pointed out in a preliminary report (1942), he studied plants differing not only in chromosome numbers, but also in geographical origin, the species with the greater numbers coming from the more northerly regions.

4. WINTER HARDINESS IN POLYPLOIDS

The morphological, anatomical, and physiological characteristics of polyploid plants set forth above provide a partial basis for appraising their hardiness. Low osmotic pressure and content of dry matter in the sap together with the depressed state of the plants immediately after they are formed are by no means favorable to the development of hardiness. This has been confirmed by direct observations and experimentation.

On the tetraploid Oenothera lamarkiana gigas bred by De Vries, Gates (1915) reported that in diploids and tetraploids growing side by side frost killed the flowers of the latter first. In more extensive research on the problem, Schlösser (1936) studied artificially obtained polyploids and diploids of two species of tomato, fodder turnip, and winter rape. The polyploid plants, especially the turnip and rape, looked more full grown with much larger leaves, greater water content, and smaller content of ash and organic matter. Their osmotic pressure was lower. These things were responsible for their low hardiness. When the plants were subjected to frost in the fall, the polyploid forms were more severely affected than the diploid forms.

My experimental findings were similar. The design of the experiment was as follows. Seeds of diploid and tetraploid tomatoes, ground cherry, and polygonum* were sown in pots outdoors in mid-summer. The seeds of all the tetraploids were larger than those of the diploids. No external differences in growth were noted between the diploid and tetraploid forms of the ground cherry. The leaves of the tetraploid polygonum were bigger at first, but the difference faded in time. The tetraploid tomato plants looked depressed throughout. In the fall all the plants were subjected to natural frost, the temperature falling the first night to -3° and thereafter to -4°. The ground cherry and polygonum diploids and tetraploids suffered equally, with no marked differences in hardiness. The tetraploid tomatoes proved to be less hardy and all died the first frosty night, whereas the diploids survived at first, succumbing only after the temperature fell to -4°.

These data, isolated though they may be, nevertheless leave no doubt that polyploidy does not strengthen hardiness, as has been asserted many times on the basis of a priori considerations. The picture is different only in the case of those polyploids which have already changed and adapted to their environment. Löve's studies mentioned above are significant in this respect. A comparative test for hardiness was carried out on diploid, tetraploid, and hexaploid species of Rumex growing naturally in Sweden along with a determination of osmotic pressure. The test was run over several winters at the Svalgf Plant Breeding Station under field conditions. After the exceptionally cold winter of 1941-1942 all the diploids died, but 90% of the tetraploids and all of the hexaploids survived. Here polyploidy as an expression of pathological mitosis had no adverse effect on the hardiness of the plants.

Thus, like other physiological properties, the hardiness of polyploids is restored in time and the plants may even be hardier than diploids, depending on the ecological conditions. However, the reason for this lies not in polyploidy but in the plants' ability to adapt to more rigorous environmental factors.

CONCLUSION

The commonest cause of unusual manifestations of hereditary variability is interference with the process of cell division leading to a disparity in newly formed cells between cytoplasmic mass and nucleus and to a change in number of chromosomes. This type of interference is the result, on the one hand, of abrupt changes in environmental conditions and, on the other, of hybridization of normally very different plants.

Pathological cell division is followed by various modifications in the form, structure, and properties of plants formed from these cells. The consequence of all these changes is a low level of winter hardiness. There can be no heterosis of hardiness in polyploids due to the very phenomenon of polyploidy. Heterosis of hardiness is possible in allopolyploids as a result of hybridization, not of polyploidy.

---

*The seeds were kindly supplied by V. V. Sakharov.

Reduced viability and hardiness in plants with impaired cell division, especially in polyploids, may become normal in time. This is one of the consequences of the general principle of plant adaptation to altered external and internal conditions, including disruption in the ratio of individual constituents of cell contents. A beneficial effect of abnormal cell division is a shattering of the hereditary foundation of plants and increased variability. Thus, polyploids at the time of formation, despite their sickly state, are more variable and adapt more quickly to adverse external factors under suitable conditions. Herein lies the explanation of the concentration of hardy polyploids in mountainous and arctic regions.

CHAPTER 6

THE ROLE OF SELECTION IN PRODUCING HARDIER FORMS OF PLANTS

1. NATURAL SELECTION OF PLANTS FOR WINTER HARDINESS

Modern breeders make extensive use of the results of natural selection to produce hardier forms of plants. All wintering wild forms have acquired inherent hardiness through natural selection. The ancestors of modern cultivated plants were also wild and the hardiness that they transmitted to their cultivated descendants evolved as a result of natural selection. This property subsequently changed, becoming intensified or weakened when the plants were cultivated. Natural selection, therefore, was the invariable precursor of artificial cultivation. Both, however, may take place simultaneously.

Natural selection for hardiness tends to strengthen this property. The probability of hardier forms developing is increased when plants migrate to regions with more rigorous winters.

Natural selection rarely produces forms wholly and immediately useful to man. It merely aids plants in biologically adapting to particular ecological conditions. Yet man must have plants which are not only well adapted to specific soil and climatic conditions but are also capable of producing high yields of excellent quality. Thus, the very hardy forms of wild fruit trees, for example, which evolved after prolonged natural selection, are usually not suitable for man because the fruits are very small and of poor quality. They are useful only as parent material for breeding.

2. ARTIFICIAL SELECTION OF PLANTS
FOR WINTER HARDINESS

Artificial selection today supplies the first and last links in a complex process. The breeder deliberately chooses pairs with properties he wishes the hybrid offspring to possess. When hybridization is over, the offspring grown and given appropriate training, he selects the best specimens embodying the desired qualities. Nothing in the way of skilled selection and training can do away with the need of keeping the most valuable specimens and discarding the rest. On this point Michurin wrote: "It is impossible to make an infallible forecast of the results of crossing this or that pair of plants since atavism with wholly unexpected results may suddenly occur whether the plants involved are cultivated fruit varieties of hybrid origin or are pure species." (Collected Writings, vol. 1, 1939, p. 337).

Selection is also needed because every variety must satisfy many requirements. Frost-resistant varieties must also be able to resist diseases and pests common in a given region, have a suitably long growing period, etc. It is no easy matter to combine all the desired properties in a single variety. Sometimes only a few plants are left for propagation out of many thousands of hybrids. Michurin was ruthless in making discards, but not in the same way as his contemporaries, for example, Luther Burbank. Burbank more or less unscientifically produced masses of hybrids solely on the probability that he would find among them individuals with the qualities he was seeking. He was a master only of the art of selection. Michurin, on the other hand, planned the process from beginning to end. He chose pairs carefully and controlled the training of the hybrid offspring, relying on established principles rather than on chance. This systematic approach made his work incomparably effective and enabled him to transform selection from an art into a science.

Artificial selection is essential in selection, but it supplements rather than replaces the basic stages in the process — crossing and controlled training.

3. SELECTION FOR WINTER HARDINESS IN RELATION
TO OTHER PROPERTIES

Changes in winter hardiness are always accompanied by other changes. Wintering plants grow and develop during the warm period of the year. At this time they are exposed to external factors affecting their hereditary make-up. The result is a conglomerate of changes that may or may not be beneficial to the organism at other times of the year. Selection is by no means invariably successful in fixing a high degree of winter hardiness in plants.

Take the case of Lutescens 329, a winter wheat variety. We have frequently pointed out that this wheat is one of the hardiest varieties known, yet its distribution in cold regions is very limited. The main reason is that it ripens so late that in arid regions it suffers much more from drought than early ripening varieties do.

Another and somewhat contradictory example is provided by Ukrainka, the commonest winter wheat variety in the Ukraine. It has many rivals which surpass it in hardiness, but it continues to be grown in certain places because of its outstanding milling and baking qualities. The low hardiness of Ukrainka is thus compensated for by another economically important characteristic —

excellent quality of flour. In both cases we are dealing with cultivated plants. Economic considerations have dictated where they are to be grown.

The same thing may happen in nature. Let us recall Michurin's example of the Nerchinskiy apricot wintering in Michurinsk. This apricot is potentially highly frost-resistant, yet in Michurin's garden it suffered severely from frost because it ended fall growth late and the shoots failed to ripen completely before winter. Thus, the inability of the Nerchinskiy apricot to adapt to wintering conditions in Michurinsk and its long growth period nullified its potential hardiness.

Hardiness induced by external conditions, therefore, does not always guarantee that plants will be able to survive in very cold regions. Other properties must not conflict with newly acquired adaptation.

CONCLUSION

Hardy forms of plants, it seems to us, are the result of a process consisting of three main stages. The first stage is a shattering of the hereditary foundation. Before a plant can acquire winter hardiness it must first lose its relatively stable hereditary foundation and become plastic. The second stage is fixing of the new property in the plant. In the absence of old and familiar conditions it involuntarily adapts to the new in which it has become placed. This adaptation becomes a hereditary part of the plant's make-up. The third and final stage is testing of newly acquired hardiness in combination with other properties. Each newly acquired property by itself is positive only in respect to the conditions that produced it. As far as other conditions are concerned — time of year, weather, etc. — and to the plant as a whole it may even be harmful at times. Such plants are kept only if the new together with the other properties are biologically or economically useful.

CHAPTER 7

TESTING PLANTS FOR WINTER HARDINESS

Selection for winter hardiness also incudes testing plants under appropriate conditions. In modern practice artificial conditions are ordinarily used to supplement natural conditions. The breeder tests his new plants in the field under the natural wintering conditions of the particular year. At the same time he also creates artificially unfavorable wintering conditions such as might occur during any given year. This "provocation method" markedly accelerates the testing process and evaluation of candidates for varieties. Without it one might have to wait several years for unfavorable conditions to occur so that the varieties could be adapted to them.

1. FIELD TESTING OF PLANTS FOR WINTER HARDINESS

The final testing of plants is always done in the field. For winter grains it begins with tests at a plant breeding station (where the new forms have been bred and propagated) and ends on state testing plots under divers soil and climatic conditions. Here the future variety is given a definitive appraisal and its regional suitability determined.

Winter hardiness is usually determined in selection sowings and on testing plots by counting the plants on a definite portion of ground late in the fall, before it snows, and early in the spring, after the snow melts and as soon as growth starts. The difference between the number of plants entering the winter and those alive in the spring indicates the degree of hardiness of the form being tested. In addition, samples are frequently obtained during the winter for "resuscitation" or, more correctly, for aftergrowth, to determine hardiness dynamically. Such samples make it possible to find out roughly when and from what unfavorable conditions the plants suffered or died.

In making field tests one must always bear in mind the fact that circumstances may complicate and distort the results, e.g., differences in soil and agricultural practices. To create identical conditions on field plots for all the plants is virtually impossible. Even after the most careful selection of land, cultivation, use of fertilizers, method of sowing, etc., as is the case at breeding stations, one can always see patches of more developed and dark green plants along with patches of less developed and pale plants. Close scrutiny of the plot reveals still greater differences. Plants in the same row, even within a single meter, are never completely uniform in habit, height, bushiness, coloring, etc. The conditions of the individual plants, thanks to minor variations in soil composition, fertilizer, position in row, light, moisture, etc. are always somewhat different. All this affects overall growth before the winter and the hardiness of the plants.

The results are further complicated by pests and diseases. Wire worms and midges tend to attack plants selectively so that healthy plants are always found alongside ailing ones, thus distorting the picture of hardiness.

These shortcomings in ordinary field tests of plants for hardiness have long led breeders to seek a better method to assure maximally uniform conditions. Thus, pots and boxes came into use (Yur'yev and others, 1950). Another technique involves open, unfertilized coldframes set in the ground with sifted soil uniformly distributed. I shall now describe the method which I used in my own field tests of certain forms and varieties for hardiness.

The first step is to select a completely level plot of ground that would prevent water from standing and allow snow to lie evenly. The soil and subsoil should also be similar. The ground is first smoothed down and then a pit with steep sides dug about 0.5 m deep, depending on the soil, 1-1.5 m wide, and 10-20 m long, depending on the number of plants to be tested. The soil is piled up in one place and immediately screened. It is then mixed, about a quarter of a cubic meter at a time, with organic and mineral fertilizers and sifted two or three times for better mixing. The soil is now returned in 5-10 cm layers and tamped down each time with wooden hammers taking care to keep the entire area level. The tamping is done four or five times, depending on the depth of the bed. The soil might subside without it after the first rain, but it would be covered with cracks when it dried out and thus become useless.

The result of the distribution throughout the bed of soil that is uniform in composition and structure is what might be considered a gigantic pot except that the plants are exposed to a natural heat regime prevailing throughout the fall and winter. In ordinary metal, wooden, or earthen pots left outdoors for the winter the temperature frequently differs from the natural temperature and thus does not always satisfy testing requirements. The advantage of filled beds over regular field plots is that they assure uniformity of growing and wintering conditions for all the plants and freedom from such destructive pests as wire worms, at least for the first year. These beds, in addition to accuracy, make it possible to limit the number of plants in each form to be tested, a matter of considerable importance early in the selection process. Once prepared beds last several years. Maintenance consists in preventing uneven packing, removal of wire worms that may creep in, loosening the surface, etc.

The combined pot and field method is sometimes of value in testing plants for hardiness. I used it in the following way. Plants are set out in the fall in enamelled or clay pots. When the weather turns cold and growth ceases, the plants are placed in the ground where they spend the winter. This operation is fairly simple. A level plot is marked off which resembles a bed in shape and size, but the soil is not treated. Holes of the shape and size of pots are then dug and the plants inserted after they are removed with soil from the pots. The pots are lightly rapped on the sides and bottom. The soil clinging to the roots is not disturbed. After the plants are transferred into the already prepared holes, soil is added to fill up the spaces and prevent cracks. This method combines the advantage of pots in permitting uniformity of growth before the winter with the advantage of a bed in approximating natural conditions.

A variation of the above is to bury pots in the soil. The method is simpler, but it entails some deviation from the normal heat regime of the soil, especially if metal pots are used, because the rims of the pots come over the soil and being better heat conductors tend to affect it.

In making a differential determination of hardiness by taking samples during the winter one must work only when the weather is comparatively warm in order to prevent the plants from becoming frozen while they are being dug out of the ground. This can easily happen because they are immediately deprived of the protection of snow and the warmth of the soil in the bed. Aftergrowth of the plants following transfer to a warm place is quite significant. The plants must first be thawed in a cool place and great care taken to prevent serious damage. If the temperature is too high, the transpiring plants quickly lose water from the intercellular spaces as well as water left in the cells. The more injured plants become as a result of impaired permeability of protoplasm, the more easily and irreversibly is water lost in transpiration. Rapid thawing at high temperature may kill plants that are potentially still viable.

High temperatures during the aftergrowth period are also harmful, particularly in view of the weak light normally obtaining in winter. Plants at this time tend to suffer from inadequate photosynthesis if the place is not properly equipped. Hence, it is necessary to provide as much natural light as possible by setting the plants close to the windows or keeping them in a greenhouse. The temperature should not exceed +15° in rooms where wintering plants are kept. The higher the temperature, the more rapid the growth. The plants become exhausted more quickly from intensified respiration if photosynthesis is weak.

The so-called method of monoliths involves growing the plants in boxes of soil after being dug from the frozen ground with balls of earth. However, they can also be successfully grown without soil. Plants are brought into a cool room where the soil is washed off. They are then placed in glasses or deep dishes of water in such a manner that the roots are completely submerged while the green parts remain above the water. The water must be changed daily with a little fresh soil added. Plants can grow in water for many weeks. The degree of injury in the preceding wintering period is ascertained from the number of dead plants and leaves as well as from the number of new shoots, leaves, and rootlets which differ from the old in having a lighter color and less branchiness. The hydroponic method of growing plants in winter has the undoubted advantage of not requiring much space and permitting a more differential appraisal of degree of injury with due regard for both the aerial and underground parts of the plants. However, the plants require more careful handling and more skilled observers. The method cannot be successfully employed unless the personnel are properly trained.

2. PROVOCATION METHODS OF TESTING PLANTS FOR WINTER HARDINESS

Provocation methods can be used both in field trails and in pot experiments. Since plants can be most easily stimulated into developing resistance to frost, we shall dwell on this type of provocation. The simplest way of testing plants is to leave them in pots outdoors throughout the winter. They become frozen all over at the same time. The effect is particularly pronounced when the pots are kept in racks above the soil and snow. All the parts are thus equally frozen to the lowest degree of air temperature; moreover, they are exposed to sharp changes in temperature. This method requires that the plants be covered with some snow to prevent desiccation. After observing the temperature of the air and soil in the pots with the help of a Savinov thermometer inserted in one of the pots in the fall and bringing some to them into a warm room after every new and sharper frost, it is easy to determine the temperature at which the plants were injured or killed and their characteristic degree of hardiness.

Provocation is also possible in the field. Here is how I proceeded in my own work. Stakes were driven into the ground along the edges and in the center of a bed until the tops were 10-15 cm above the ground. After the first heavy snowfall the stakes indicated the level to which the snow had to be cleared away. Thereafter all excess snow was removed to the top of the stakes at the earliest possible opportunity. A Savinov thermometer stuck into the ground in the fall made it possible to check the soil temperature daily at the desired depth. The 10-15 cm of snow on the plants prevented desiccation.

The best of the provocation methods of testing plants for hardiness is artificial freezing in a refrigerator. It is coming into increasing use at our plant breeding stations. Freezing apparatus specially designed for plants is now available in the All-Union Institute of Plant Growth, the Saratov Institute of Grain Culture, T.D. Lysenko Odessa Institute of Genetics and Selection, Sukhumi branch of the Institute of Tea and Subtropical Plants, and elsewhere. This method yields useful data only if the plants are hardened properly by those who understand the physiology of the process. Testing plants before they have fully attained their normal hardiness results in a distorted picture. The reason is that individual forms become hardened at different times so that those plants in which the process is incomplete before testing starts may be adjudged less hardy than they really are.

The simplest and yet safest method of hardening is to keep the plants before the tests under conditions as close as possible to those of field plants in the fall and early winter. The plants are usually grown in wooden boxes where they are subsequently hardened, chilled, and allowed to grow again. Before the test they are placed in a refrigerator, chilled at a designated temperature usually for 24 hours, gradually thawed in a cool room, and then brought into a warm greenhouse. All the other steps are as described below.

Field plants may be tested the same way. They are dug from the frozen earth with a small ball of soil and without thawing placed in a refrigerator. The following operations are the same as those involved in taking samples for aftergrowth. An even simpler method is to pull out field plants with their roots, not too long before the soil freezes and store them in a refrigerator before freezing. Bundles of plants are wrapped in paper to check transpiration. Plants are best kept in a place where they are exposed to natural frost of the same intensity as plants left in the field under snow. They can then be conveniently taken at any time and placed in a refrigerator for freezing. Aftergrowth takes place in glasses or dishes of water.

Provocation methods are not widely used by breeders to test resistance to other unfavorable wintering conditions, e.g., excessive soil moisture, winter-spring drought, etc. They are valuable chiefly for studying the physiology of plant hardiness. The underlying principle is the same. To test plants for waterlogging, water is artificially allowed to stagnate in fall and spring. To test plants for damping off, they are infected with snow mold in the fall, covered with considerable amounts of snow, and allowed to thaw over a long period of time. The practical effect of this type of provocation was discussed in connection with the examples cited in the first part of this book.

3. INDIRECT METHODS OF APPRAISING WINTER HARDINESS

These methods involve assessment of certain physiological properties and morphological and anatomical characteristics of frost-resistant plants. They are not always accurate, but are useful for a hasty approximation. Michurin used them extensively to judge cultivated fruit seedlings.

The simplest of these physiological methods is to determine the refractive index of juice squeezed from killed plants. A refractometer is very convenient for this purpose since a single drop of juice suffices. The refractive index depends on the concentration of juice, which is believed to be higher in hardy plants. This is frequently true of plants that are genetically close. An example of such determination in several winter wheat varieties differing in hardiness was described in the second part of this book.

The technique of refractometric determination is essentially as follows. Leaves, other soft parts, tillering nodes, collars, etc. weighing 10 grams or more are wrapped in moist gauze and stuffed into a wide-mouthed test tube which is immediately immersed up to the cork in boiling water for 10 minutes to kill the cells. The material is then removed in such a way as to collect with the gauze all the water on the sides of the test tube. The juice is then squeezed out under a press and used to determine the refractive index. It takes just a few minutes to determine this index along with the percentage of dry matter in a single sample. Hundreds of samples can be analyzed in a day if the work is properly organized.

Similar results can be obtained by determining the osmotic pressure of cell sap after using a cryoscope to determine the freezing point. The preparations involved are the same as for the refractive index, but much more juice is necessary — at least 15-20 cm^3 — and about 5 cm^3 if a microcryoscope is used. This method is more laborious since a single determination takes one to two hours.

The most familiar of the indirect methods of appraising hardiness is to determine the sugar content. I described it in detail in an article on the dynamics of carbohydrates in wheat varieties (I.M. Vasil'yev, 1931). It is even more time-consuming and less reliable than the determination of osmotic pressure.

Other indirect methods include a determination of bound water in tissues using a dilatometer (Novikov, 1928; Lebedintseva, 1930), determination of electrical conductivity of water extracts (S.M. Ivanov, 1931) and of electrical conductivity of tissues (Nizen'kov, 1939, 1940), determination of depth of dormancy in tissues and cells (Genkel' and Oknina, 1952). There are still other methods, but they are scarcely used by breeders since they are of value only in physiological investigations.

In selecting plants for hardiness breeders are frequently guided by the spreading form of the plant in winter grains. However, this feature is not always associated with hardiness. I have often seen plants with unusually spreading form, especially among wheat-wheatgrass hybrids, which were not particularly hardy. A more reliable indicator of hardiness in herbaceous plants is arrested growth in the fall as manifested by smaller leaves and shoots. But there are exceptions, due to the plants' having naturally small leaves, which are not directly related to hardiness.

There are many criteria employed by experienced breeders in selecting plants for winter hardiness and other economically important characteristics. Every breeder has his own tested criteria. Michurin wrote that "they can be used only by men of considerable practical experience with plants. It is impossible to describe them adequately either individually or in their various combinations" (Collected Writings, vol. 1, 1939, p. 368).

CONCLUSION

Testing plants for hardiness is an essential stage in breeding more frost-resistant varieties. Modern selection adds artificially created conditions to natural conditions along with a variety of "provocations" to hasten the testing process. Natural conditions alone over a few years may not necessarily include that combination of adverse external factors which may appear with differing degrees of intensity any given year in some particular region and to which the plants have to adapt.

Various physiological and anatomicomorphological indicators are quite useful for quick and tentative appraisals of hardiness in newly developed forms. Direct methods must be used for definitive judgments.

CHAPTER 8

THE PROBLEM OF PLANT WINTERING IN THE U.S.S.R.

(General Conclusion)

The following are some general observations on the problem of plant wintering in the U.S.S.R.

1. THE SIGNIFICANCE OF PLANT WINTERING IN THE NATIONAL ECONOMY

Almost all of our vast territory from west to east and from north to south lies in the temperate and cold zones. Only a relatively small expanse on the Black Sea and Caspian shores and in Tajikistan is subtropical and even here frosts are common in the winter. Our subtropics are the coldest in the world. We have absolutely no frostless regions. Yet every year agriculture moves steadily northward and further into the mountains. The Pechora, Igarka, Kolyma, and Pamirs until recently knew nothing of plant growing, but potatoes and other vegetables and even grains (in the Pamirs) are now cultivated there. Thus, we have to face everywhere the problem of protecting plants from frost and strengthening their resistance.

The problem also exists during warm weather, e.g., in Eastern Siberia and the Transbaikalia because night frosts occur even in summer. Frosts, of course, are particularly harmful during the wintering period of plants. Rigorous winters with little snow limit the cultivation of winter crops, notably wheat, in the eastern regions of the European part of the U.S.S.R., Siberia, and the Far East. Fruit growing here is poorly developed for the same reason. Winter frosts create difficulties in the way of extending the planting of citrus, tea, and other essential subtropical and tropical plants. Rubber, cinchona, cacao, and coffee trees do not grow even in the warmest parts of the subtropics. A few are found only in greenhouses. Many other adverse wintering conditions are usually associated with frosts.

The deleterious effect of all these conditions on our agriculture is even more evident when we realize that even in regions where wintering plants have long been cultivated they are not necessarily hardy, for they are frequently injured or killed during the winter. The winter of 1928 was memorable for the vast amount of winter crops destroyed in the Ukraine, Northern Caucasus, and Volga region. And in 1939 an unusually bitter frost lasting for several days in mid-winter killed almost all the fruit orchards in the central belt of the European part of the U.S.S.R. The year 1949 was significant for citrus for the same reason.

Injury to and death of plants every winter inflicts huge losses on the national economy so a successful solution of the wintering problem is of paramount importance.

2. SCIENTIFIC PROGRESS IN THE FIELD OF PLANT WINTERING IN THE U.S.S.R.

Our knowledge of plant wintering can be briefly summed up as follows. Hardiness varies with external conditions. It grows during the fall and early winter and drops as spring approaches, being influenced primarily by the temperature cycle. A temperature drop in the fall and early winter hardens plants and thus makes them more resistant, whereas a rise in temperature in the spring and during winter thaws makes them less resistant. Extremely low temperatures and abrupt transitions from thaw to frost injure and kill plants.

Among other conditions promoting the development of hardiness we must first mention excellent agricultural conditions — availability of all essential soil nutrients, water, and air (including irrigation, drainage, and other meliorative measures when needed) — as well as protection from pests and diseases. Fertile soil is a prerequisite not only of rapid plant growth and storage of dry substance during warm weather but also of hardiness during winter. It does incomparably more to increase hardiness than special farming practices (use of superphosphate or potassium fertilizers alone, grassing of orchards, etc.). These techniques are justified only as "means of treatment", but it is better to prevent the need of treatment than to use it.

Direct sunlight in the fall is of great significance in the development of hardiness. Our eastern regions are in a very favorable position in this respect. The weather is good for hardening wintering plants. A rich soil would be conducive to strengthening their hardiness and permit crops and varieties still uncultivated here to come through the winter safely.

Plants must also be protected from unfavorable wintering conditions. Economic considerations demand that essential crops and varieties be grown in those regions where natural conditions are very severe. Special measures will therefore have to be devised. As a matter of fact, protection from winter sun, wind, sharp fluctuations in temperature, extreme frosts, insects, and diseases is necessary for the successful cultivation of wintering plants even in regions where the winters are fairly mild. It is impossible to conceive of successful fruit growing at the present time without windbreaks around orchards or cultivation of winter crops in steppe and forest-steppe regions without snow fences, etc.

However, in protecting plants we must be careful not to coddle them. Hardening is a prerequisite of safe wintering. Hardening takes place as the weather gradually turns colder in the fall and early winter. To mitigate the effect of the low temperatures that are normal at this time would seriously undermine the ability of the plants to withstand the rigors of winter. The purpose of protective measures is simply to prevent the injury that may be inflicted by bitter frosts in winter and early spring or after thaws.

We must be unflagging in our efforts to alter the nature of plants in an economically useful direction. Soviet biology has great achievements to its credit in this field. Michurin's principles governing the modification of winter hardiness open up tremendous possibilities in selection work. The task of Soviet breeders is to master and expand these principles so as to alter the nature of wintering plants in accordance with the requirements of our socialist horticulture.

3. THE SOCIALIST SYSTEM — A GUARANTEE OF SUCCESS IN SOLVING THE PROBLEM OF PLANT WINTERING IN THE U.S.S.R.

The socialist system has created extraordinary opportunities for the development of science in our country. At the same time it has made possible the practical application of scientific achievements that was simply inconceivable in Tsarist Russia.

It is not inappropriate here to cite several illustrations of recent practical solutions of problems related to plant wintering. Not too long ago grapes were considered a southern crop, and now they are grown around Moscow. At one time Sverdlovsk oblast had no commercial orchards because of bitter frosts, but these days thousands of hectares of land are given over to the growing of fruit. In prerevolutionary times tea was cultivated only in a small area around Batum, whereas now it is common along the Black Sea coast from Batum to Tuapse and beyond to the northern slopes of the Caucasus and even in more northerly regions. Citrus groves before the revolution were very meager and were cultivated mostly by amateurs. Citrus is now grown on an industrial scale not only in the subtropics but in the more northerly regions, e.g., Odessa oblast. It was once virtually impossible to grow winter wheat in the steppe zone of Siberia. Now, however, it is gradually being extended into more and more regions where the yield is heavy and stable if sound agronomic principles are followed, etc.

The success of socialist plant growing is due to our scientific achievements and, above all, to socialist practice.

*   *   *

Every Soviet citizen lives with one thought — to be useful to his motherland. This is also true of the author of this book. If the many years of effort summarized in the book contributes in some small measure to our socialist agriculture and to the theoretical training of the youth, the author will consider that his labor was not in vain.

BIBLIOGRAPHY*

Anon. 1838. Correct care of plants. Zhurn. sadovodstva, No. 1, 39–40.
Anon. 1838a. Spring care of winter grains. Ibid., No. 3, 105–7.
Anon. 1841. Effect of cold on plants and prevention. Ibid., No. 1, 41–60.
Anon. 1841a. Magic ring. Ibid., No. 6, 62.
Anon. 1848. Common diseases of fruit trees and their origin. Ibid., No. 3, 42–55.
Anon. 1851. Effect of frost and cold on plants. Ibid., No. 3, 35–54.
Anon. 1852. A means of preventing the freezing of blossoms on fruit trees. Tr. Vol'n. ekon. ob-va, No. 1, 16–17.
Anon. 1853. Overwintering of orange trees outdoors in Southern Russia. Zhurn. sadovodstva, No. 5, 34–5.
Anon. 1857. Life of plants. Ibid., No. 3, 289–90.
Anon. 1860. Review of Becquerel's report at the sessions of January 16 and February 13, 1860 in the Paris Academy of Sciences on his studies of plant warming and cooling. Vestn. Ross. ob-va sadovodstva, No. 4.
Anon. 1861. A method of protecting fruit tree blossoms from the destructive effect of late frosts. Zhurn. sadovodstva, No. 1, 43–5.
Anon. 1862. Winterkilling of winter crops. Tr. Vol'n. ekon. ob-va, No. 2, 7–8.
Anon. 1864. On what is important in winter sowings and how they may be improved, No. 1, 181–91.
Anon. 1865. Diseases of roots in fruit trees. Ibid., 175–6.
Anon. 1866. Effect of snow on cultivated plants. Ibid., No. 4, 197–205.
Anon. 1866. Effect of snow on vegetation. Ibid., 197–205.
Anon. 1871. Effect of snow on plants according to Goppert. Ibid., No. 1, 174–8.
Anon. 1878. Dormancy in plants. Ibid., 30–5.
Anon. 1880. Selection of tolerant plants. Ibid., No. 8, 403–9.
Anon. 1889. Freezing of plants. Ibid., 123–6.
Anon. 1889. Is it useful to graze cattle on winter grains? Vestn. russk. sel'sk. khoz-va, No. 15, 1287.
Anon. 1892. Winter — the coldframe and its value in cultivating plants. Ibid., No. 5, 117–21.
Anon. 1893. Winterkilling of winter crops. Pravitel'stv vestnik, 279.
Anon. 1893. Various types of frost injury. Plodovodstvo, No. 9, 573–4.
Anon. 1896. How can we protect fruit trees from frost? Sad i ogorod, No. 8, 121–3; No. 22, 375–8.
Anon. 1898. Gangrene of fruit trees. Ibid., No. 11.

---

*Includes works not mentioned in the text.

Anon. 1898. Care of fruit trees. Ibid., No. 24, 372-3.

Abramov, M. 1896. Darkness and chaos in our horticulture. Vestn. Russk. sel'sk. khoz-va, No. 7, 124-5, 146-7, 168-9.

Absalyamova, R.A. 1948. Hardiness of young winter wheat shoots exposed to low temperatures. Dokl. VASKhNIL, No. 4, 36-40.

Aginyan, A.A. 1950. Vernalization of seeds in relation to their embryonal development. Agrobiologiya, No. 3, 57-66.

Aleksandrov, A.D. 1936. Sheltered ground as a means of combatting frosts. Sov. subtropiki, No. 9, 24-41.

Aleksandrov, A.D. 1937. To protect citrus and tung trees from frosts. Ibid. No. 10 (38), 6-14.

Aleksandrov, A.D. 1947. Cultivation of the lemon in the U.S.S.R. Moscow, Sel'khozgiz, 250 pp.

Aleksandrov, F.A. 1948. Role of buds in the resumption of activity of apple trees injured by frost. Dokl. AN SSSR 59, No. 5, 981-2.

Aleksandrov, V.G. 1922. Water regime of mesophyte foliage. Vestn. Tifl. bot. sada, seriya 2, No. 1, 1-16.

Aleksandrov, V.G. 1949. A contribution to the biology of protoplasm and the nucleus of plant cells and on Rozanov crystals. Tr. In-ta fiziol. rast. im. K.A. Timiryazeva AN SSSR 6, No. 2, 23-29.

Aleksandrov, V.G. 1950. A contribution to the biology of the cell nucleus in plant organisms. Sov. botannika 5, 14-21.

Aleksandrov, V.G. 1954. Plant anatomy. Moscow, Izd-vo Sov. nauka, 499 pp.

Aleksandrov, V.G., and O.G. Aleksandrova. 1929. Is lignification a reversible process or not? Izv. Glavn. bot. sada AN SSSR 28, 535-42.

Aleksandrov, V.G., and M.I. Savchenko. 1950. A contribution to the biology of green plastids in plants. Kokl. AN SSSR, No. 6, 1069-72.

Aleksandrov, V.G., and M.I. Savchenko. 1950. Condition of green plastids in the bark of trees during winter. Tr. Bot. in-ta im. Komarova AN SSSR, SERIYA VII, No. 1.

Aleksandrov, V.G., M.S. Yakovlev, and A.V. Klimochkina. 1947. Specificity and tendency of plastids in plants. Bot. zhurn. SSSR 32, No. 4, 135-61.

Alekseyev, A.M. 1948. Water regime of plants and effect of drought on it. Kazan'. Tatgosizdat, 355 pp.

Alekseyev, I.F. 1929. Effect of mowing and cattle grazing on clover hardiness. Leningr. obl. s-kh. op. stantsiya, No. 2, 1-8.

Alekseyev, M.B. 1951. Effect of removing dry husks on seed yield and obtaining a second yield of onions. Agrobiologiya, No. 5, 67-73.

Alisov, M.S. 1950. Windbreaks — an important means of increasing crop yield. Sad i ogorod, No. 11, 49-56.

Alpat'yev, A.V. 1947. Hardy tomatoes. Agrobiologiya, No. 2, 143-52.

Avakyan, A.A. 1948. Individual development of plants. Agrobiologiya, No. 2, 10-21.

Avakyan, A.A. 1948a. Inheritance of acquired characteristics. Ibid., No. 6, 13-49.

Avakyan, A.A. 1948b. Stage processes and so-called florigens. Ibid., No. 1, 44-77.

Avakyan, A.A. 1950. Flowering of biennials the first year. Ibid., No. 2, 12-22.

Avakyan, A.A., and N.I. Feyginson. 1947. Results of many years' experimentation on interspecific free transpollination of winter rye. Tr. In-ta gen. AN SSSR, No. 14, 138-91.

Ayzenshtat, Ya. S. 1950. Changes in dominance due to a short day. Kokl.

AN SSSR 70, No. 1, 97-100.

Babadzhanyan, G.A. 1949. Notes on the phenomena of the sexual mentor in plants. Izv. AN SSSR, seriya biol., No. 4, 455-69.

Bakh, A.N. 1936. Biochemical and technological significance of enzymic processes. Izv. AN SSSR, No. 4, 627-38.

Balabanov, M. 1898. Value of copper sulfate and lime in orchards. Plodovodstvo, No. 5, 408-10.

Baranetskiy, O.V. 1883. Proceedings of the Seventh Congress of Russian Natural Scientists and Physicians in Odessa. Zased. bot. sektsii 24 avgusta.

Baranov, P.A. 1938. Plant growing under the rigorous conditions of Pamir mountain deserts. Yarovizatsiya, No. 4-5.

Baranov, P.A. 1939. On "aftereffects." Sbornik AN SSSR, posv, akad. V.L. Komarovu, 154-66.

Baranov, P.A. 1939a. Formative role of the environment. Yarovizatsiya, No. 5-6.

Barinova, R.A. 1937. Dynamics of the carbohydrate-colloidal complex as a factor in drought resistance of the sugar beet. Izv. AN SSSR, No. 1, 225-70.

Batalin. 1892. Artificial creation of snow drifts on fields. Vestn. russk. sel'sk. khoz-va, No. 6, 156.

Bedro, I.P. 1914. Apropos of an article by A.F. Perevoshchikov, "Acclimatization of trees and shrubs and propagation of new varieties from seeds." Plodovodstvo, No. 12, 854-6.

Belikov, P.S. 1947. Effect of heteroauxin on accelerating growth and frost resistance in the kok sagyz. Dokl. AN SSSR 58, No. 1, 143-5.

Belikova, V. 1936. Wintering of citrus in Chakva. Sov. subtropiki, No. 1(17), 114.

Belin, I. 1861. Notes on horticulture in Vladimir province. Zhurn. sadovodstva, No. 1, 291-9.

Belokhonov, I.V. 1950. Fruit growing. Moscow, Sel'khozgiz, 504 pp.

Belozerova, N.A. 1947. Stubble sowings of winter wheat. Agrobiologiya, No. 2.

Belozerova, N.A. 1949. Experiments with winter wheat in Omsk oblast. Ibid., No. 3, 142-59.

Belyayev, A.A. 1912. Initial stages in the development of cereals. In the publication: Iz rezul'tatov vegetatsionnykh opytov i laboratornykh rabot za 1910 [Among the results of pot experiments and laboratory work for 1910], vol. VII, 193-8.

Berg, 1891. Winterkilling of cereals. Vestn. russk. sel'sk. khoz-va, pt. 168, 70-7.

Blagoveshchenskiy, A.V. 1938. Factors in plant hardiness. Sov. subtropiki 1, 76-9.

Blagoveshchenskiy, A.V. 1945. Biochemical factors in natural selection of plants. Zhurn. obshch. biol. 6, No. 4, 217-34.

Blagoveshchenskiy, A.V. 1949. Types of activation of enzymes. Tr. In-ta fiziol. rast. im. K.A. Timiryazeva AN SSSR 6, No. 2, 70-7.

Blagoveshchenskiy, A.V. 1950. Biochemical foundations of the evolutionary process in plants. Moscow, Izd-vo AN SSSR, 269 pp.

Blagoveshchenskiy, A.V., and A. Yu. Kologrivova. 1945a. Activation of catalase by biogenic stimulants. Dokl. AN SSSR 48, No. 8, 599-602.

Blagoveshchenskiy, A.V., and A. Yu. Kologrivova. 1945b. Stimulation of root growth by certain organic acids. Ibid., No. 6, 467-70.

Bluvshteyn, I.N. 1950. Effect of whitewash on the hardiness of grape buds. Sad i ogorod, No. 10, 56-7.

Bobko, Ye. V., and R.A. Popova. 1929. Materials on drought resistance and hardiness of plants. Communication 1. Hardiness and bound water in several winter wheat varieties. Reprint of Tr. Sib. in-ta sel'sk. khoz-va i lesovodstva 12, 13.

Bogdan, A.V. 1935. Renewed activity of cambium injured by frost. Sov. botanika, No. 4, 72-6.

Bogdanov, P.L. 1946. Poplar vegetative hybrids. Kokl. AN SSSR 54, No. 4, 361-3.

Bokunov, M.A. 1949. Meteorological conditions of sowing and overwintering of winter rye in the southern part of the Maritime Territory. Tr. Tsentr. in-ta prognozov, No. 18(45), 65-71.

Bolotov, A.T. 1952. Selected writings on agronomy, fruit growing, forestry, and botany. Izd. Mosk. ob-va ispyt. prirody, 523 pp.

Bondartsev, A.S. 1931. Diseases of cultivated plants and control measures. 3rd ed., Moscow, Sel'khozgiz, 600 pp.

Borodin, I.P. 1876. Physiological research on respiration of leaf-bearing shoots. St. Petersburg, 114 pp.

Boyakov, M.D. 1949. Causes of death of winter wheat in the Cis-Ural region. Sov. agronomiya, No. 12, 61-8.

Briginets, N.L. 1940. Deepening the tillering node of winter and spring wheat by the method of pre-sowing treatment of seeds. Tezisy dokl. soveshch. po fiziol. rast. Izd. AN SSSR, 120-1.

Brilliant, V.A., and V.A. Mirimanyan. 1937. Seasonal changes in photosynthesis in the lemon as a result of winter coverings. Sov. botanika, No. 3, 54-63.

Brovtsina, V.L. 1937. A laboratory method of diagnosing hardiness in wheat sprouts. Tr. In-ta fiziol. rast. 1, No. 2, 81-92.

Brokert, N.G. 1932. Physiology of plant hardiness. "Tr. Vseukr. selekts. korpor." Kharkiv.

Bugaevs'kiy, M.F. 1933. How to determine the condition of winter crops. Kharkiv, 64 pp.

Bugaevs'kiy, M., and A. Lododa. 1936. The impaired nutrition of winter grain crops. "Zbirnik zobit 2 agrofiziologii." Vol. 1, No. 1, Kiiv-kharkiv, 173-184.

Bugayevskiy, M.F. 1939. Dynamics of plant cell destruction by low temperatures. Dokl. AN SSSR 22, No. 3, 132-5.

Bugayevskiy, M.F. 1939a. Causes of death of root crops from low temperatures. Ibid. 25, No. 6, 529-32.

Bugayevskiy, M.F. 1947. Freezing of parenchymal tissues of plants. Ibid. 58, No. 6, 1195-6.

Bukasov, S.M. 1930. Cultivated plants of Mexico, Guatemala, and Colombia. Appendix No. 47 to Tr. po prikl. bot., gen. i sel., 553 pp.

Bukasov, S.M. 1932. Hardiness in the potato. Ibid., seriya 2, 3, 287-97.

Bukasov, S.M. 1937. Potato selection. Teoret. osnovy sel. rast. Moscow, Sel'khozgiz 3, 3-76.

Bukin, V.N., and Stupak. 1938. Transformation of vitamin C in cabbage varieties during storage. Biokhimiya, No. 1, 13.

Bulgakova, Z.P. 1937. Effect of length of day on opening of buds on woody plants. Bot. zhurn. SSSR 22, No. 5, 413-9.

Burygin, V.A. 1936. Agrotechnology in the struggle against winterkilling of China grass in Central Asia. Sov. subtropiki, No. 10(26), 36-9.

Burygin, V.A., and N.N. Karaul'shchikova. 1937. Wintering of ramie on the Vaksh. Ibid. No. 10(38), 28-32.

Butyagin, P.V. 1909. Effect of low temperatures on bacterial viability. Izv. Tomsk. un-ta, book 35, 1-55.

Bystrikov, F.V. 1931. Effect of soil reaction on the hardiness of winter rye and wheat. Tr. po prikl. bot., gen. i sel. 25, No. 3, 128-51.

B-n, V.A. 1899. Winter crops and the Hessian fly. Vestn. russk. sel'sk. khoz-va, No. 18, 1533-4.

Chaylakhyan, M. Kh. 1933. Vernalization. 1. Formation of chlorophyll in the leaves of spring and winter grains. Sov. botanika 5, 11-33.

Chaylakhyan, M. Kh. 1935. Permeability of protoplasm in the leaves of spring and winter wheat. Dokl. AN SSSR 2, No. 2, 154-8.

Chelyadinova, A.I. 1947. Nature of dormancy in the potato. Tr. In-ta gen. AN. SSSR, No. 14, 309-22.

Chelyadinova, A.I., and N.A. Svyatelik. 1951. Ways of strengthening hardiness in mint. Agrobiologiya, No. 1, 34-9.

Chendler, U. Kh. Chandler, W.H. . 1935. Fruit growing. Trans. from the English. Moscow-Leningrad, Sel'khozgiz, 608 pp.

Chereteli, L. Ya., and N.N. Chinturiya. 1937. Control of rot in citrus while in storage. Sov. subtropiki, No. 10(38), 92-3.

Chernenko, S.F. 1950. A new apple variety — suvorovets. Sad i ogorod, No. 6, 20-3.

Chernetskiy, A.I. 1935. Top dressing of winter wheat in the spring. Khimizats. sots. zeml., No. 4, 29-33.

Chernetskiy, A.I. 1937. Times of adding mineral fertilizers to winter wheat in the spring. Ibid., No. 1, 67-79.

Chernobrivenko, S.I. 1940. A search for possible biennial winter grains. Selektsiya i semenovodstvo, No. 11-12.

Chernyayev, I.P. 1951. Strengthening the hardiness of fruit trees by crown grafts. Agrobiologiya, No. 5, 151-5.

Chernyshev, N. 1904. What can be seen in the garden in winter? Plodovodstvo, No. 1, 30-7.

Cherobayev, G. 1899. Mounding of fruit trees with snow. Plodovodstvo, No. 2, 205-6.

Cherobayev, G. 1901. What can be seen in the garden in winter? Ibid., No. 1, 30-7.

Chirvinskiy, P.N. 1932. Snow and snow fences. Izd. Severnyy Kavkaz, Rostov-on-Don, 420 pp.

Chistik, A.A. 1948. Why there are no hardy clover varieties. Sel. i semenovodstvo, No. 3, 30-33.

Chkheidze, I. 1940. Tea in the southern regions of Krasnodar kray. Sov. subtropiki, No. 4, 49-51.

Chkheidze, I.I., and L.I. Kotenko. 1950. Overwintering of tea in the Trans-Carpathian region. Byull. Vsesoyuzn. n.-i. in-ta chaya i subtrop. kul't., No. 1, 104-6.

Chvilev, I.M. 1930. Mass destruction of fruit trees. Voronezh, izd-vo Kommuna, 67 pp.

Dadykin, V.P. 1950. Water regime and plant nutrition on cold soils. Dokl. AN SSSR 70, No. 6, 1073-6.

Dadykin, V.P. 1950. Biological characteristics of plants from cold soils. Priroda, No. 5, 21-9.

Danilov, M.D. 1946. Winter transpiration of annual shoots of English oak trees (Q. robur L.) of different ages. Dokl. AN SSSR 52, No. 5, 445-8.

Danilov, M.D. Causes of differences in winter transpiration of annual shoots of English oak trees (Q. robur L.). Ibid. 58, No. 8, 1805-7.

Dan'shin, T. Ye. Developmental stages of wheat in the north. Moscow, Sel'khozgiz, 77 pp.

Danzhar, P. 1950. Cytology of plants and general cytology. Transl. from the French, Leningrad-Moscow, IL, 652 pp.

Darwin, C. 1941. The Variation of Animals and Plants under Domestication. Moscow-Leningrad, Sel'Khozgiz, 375 pp.

Derevitskiy, N.F. 1941. Sowing periods in evaluating winter wheat varieties. Dokl. VASKhNIL, No. 6.

Doich, K.A. 1914. Osmotic pressure as a factor determining the degree of plant hardiness. Khozyaystvo, pts. 2, 3, 4, 5.

Dolidze, Sh. 1937. Is it necessary to pinch tung plantings? Sov. subtropiki, No. 12(40), 51.

Drachev, S.I. 1924. Mound planting as a means of combatting the winterkilling of winter plants. Vestn. sel'sk. khoz-va, No. 9.

Dragintsev, A.P. 1937. Growing figs in the north. Ibid., No. 5(33), 40-6.

Dubenskiy, N. 1853. Gardening in Vladimir province. Tr. Vol'n. ekon. ob-va, Nos. 6, 7, 10.

Dubovikh, M. 1938. Frost resistant varieties of Dahlias, "Sod ta grod", No. 11-12, 33.

Dumanskiy, A.V. 1948. Theory of colloids. 3rd ed., Moscow-Leningrad, Goskhimizdat, 416 pp.

Dylevskiy, G.A. 1939. Decumbent forms in fruit growing. Sov. subtropiki, No. 1 (53), 43-5.

Ed, P. 1861. A method of protecting apple blossoms from late frosts. Zhurn. sadovodstva, No. 1, 43-5.

Ekleben, G. Ya. 1760. The Siberian acacia and its great value. Tr. Vol'n. ekon, ob-va, No. 1, 60-73.

El'port, S.G., and Z.N. Ladariya. 1950. Changes in protoplasmic permeability of citrus tissues caused by frost. Dokl. AN SSSR, No. 5, 913-6.

Enke, K.O. 1865. A few words on the importance of propagating fruit trees. Shurn. sadovodstva, No. 5, 218-21.

Enke, K.O. 1885. Acclimatization and naturalization of plants. Sad i ogorod, No. 5, 37-9.

Famintsin, A.S. 1883. Metabolism and transformation of energy in plants. Izd. Ross. AN, St. Petersburg, 819 pp.

Fedin, A. Kh. 1938. Effect of winter shelters on the dynamics of carbohydrates, ash, and nitrogen in lemon leaves. Sov. botanika, No. 3, 108-14.

Fedin, A. Kh. 1938a. Effect of soil moisture on the dynamics of carbohydrates in lemon leaves. Ibid., No. 4-5, 166-8.

Fedorenko, I.P. 1936. Horticultural experience in Kemerovo. Sb. Opyt sibirskikh michurintsev. Zap.-Sib. krayev, izd-vo, 45-9.

Fedorovskiy, M.T. 1936. Combatting spring waterlogging. Khimizats. sots. zeml., No. 4, 91-5.

Filipchenko, A. 1894. Causes of death of winter grains in the winter. Sel'sk. khoz-vo i lesovodstvo, yanvar', 85-96.

Filipenko, I.A. 1937. Formation of bios in vernalized embryos of winter wheat. Dokl. AN SSSR 17, No. 6, 325-8.

Filipenko, I.A., E. Kh. Gerber. 1938. Photosynthesis in citrus. Sov.

subtropiki, No. 3(34), 50–3.

Filippovich, V.A. 1939. Sowing of winter wheat in shallow drills. Dokl. VAShNIL, No. 12.

Frey-Wyssling, A. 1950. Submicroscopic structure of protoplasm and its derivatives. Transl. from the English, 1948, Moscow-Leningrad, 364 pp.

Frolov. 1931. Hardiness of red clover. Semenovodstvo, No. 11–12.

Galashinskiy, G.I. 1939. On climate improvement. Sov. subtropiki, No. 12, 27–8.

Garskova, K.I., and N.P. Sokolova. 1949. Agrometeorological evaluation of conditions of overwintering, growth, and development of winter wheat sown in stubble and on clean fallow. Tr. Tsentr. in-ta progn., No. 18(45), 18–35.

Gashkova, O.A. 1939. Effect of abrupt fluctuations of temperature on the physiology of the lemon and mandarin. Sov. subtropiki, No. 11, 33–4.

Gashkova, O.A. 1939. Response of plants to abrupt changes in temperature. Dokl. AN SSSR 24, No. 5, 498–501.

Gavrilova, L.G. 1924. Effect of temperature on water intake by roots of higher plants. Kzv. Glavn. sada 23, No. 1, 20–40 and 25; No. 2, 177–96.

Genkel', P.A. 1946. Resistance of plants to drought and methods of strengthening it. Tr. In-ta fiziol. rast. im. K.A. Timiryazeva AN SSSR 5, No. 1, 1–237.

Genkel', P.A., and S.S. Kolotova. 1940. Pre-sowing strengthening of salt tolerance. Izv. AN SSSR, No. 4, 474–483.

Genkel', P.A., and L.S. Litvinov. 1930. Seasonal changes in the photosynthetic capacity of certain plants. Izv. Biol. n.-i. in-ta i biol. stantsii pri Permskom un-te 7, No. 3, 133–46.

Genkel', P.A., and K.P. Margolina. 1949. Causes of plant death at low temperatures. Tr. In-ta fiziol. rast. im. K.A. Timiryazeva AN SSSR 6, No. 2, 91–5.

Genkel', P.A., and Ye. Z. Oknina. 1945. Changes in the condition of protoplasm in plant cells during dormancy. Referaty nauchn.-issl. rabot za 1944 g. Otd. biol. nauk AN SSSR.

Genkel', P.A., and Ye. Z. Oknina. 1952. A study of depth of dormancy in trees to determine their hardiness. Izd-vo AN SSSR, 28 pp.

Genkel', P.A., and O. A. Sitnikova. 1953. Dormancy and hardiness in plants. Tr. In-ta fiziol. rast. 8, No. 1, 276–88.

Genko, N.K. 1901. Statistics of forests in European Russia. Plodovodstvo, No. 6, 511–2.

Gerasimov, I.I. 1890. Functions of the cell nucleus. Byull. Mosk. ob-va ispyt. prirody, No. 4, 548–91 (in German).

Gerasimov, I.I. 1892. Non-nuclear cells in certain conjugates. Ibid., No. 1 (109–31) (in German).

Gerasimov, I.I. 1896. Obtaining non-nuclear cells (a contribution to cellular physiology). Ibid., No. 3, 477–80 (in German).

Gerasimov, I.I. 1904. Cellular physiology. Ibid., No. 18, 1–134 (in German).

German, V. 1896. In defense of Sukhum. Plodovodstvo, No. 11, 747–8. Death of winter cereals and methods of preventing it. 1929. Appendix No. 34 to Tr. po prikl. bot., gen. i sel. Leningrad, 412 pp.

Gigiberiya, Sh. S. 1947. Effect of organic fertilizers on citrus hardiness. Agrobiologiya, No. 2, 135–42.

Ginsburg, A.S., and N.K. Yurashevskiy. 1934. Growing the cacao in the greenhouse of the Leningrad Botanical Garden. Sov. botanika, No. 1.

Girnik, D.V. 1953. Water regime of trees in winter and winter drought. Author's summary of dissertation for candidacy in biological sciences. Forestry Institute, Academy of Sciences USSR, Moscow.

Glinyanyy, N.I. 1951. Experiments on hereditary change of spring wheat into winter wheat. Agrobiologiya, No. 3, 19–29.

Glushchenko, I. Ye. 1947. Significance of vegetative hybridization for regenerative processes in plants. Tr. In-ta gen. AN SSSR 14, 45–81.

Glushchenko, I. Ye. 1948. Vegetative hybridization and heterosis. Ibid. 15, 41–57.

Glushchenko, I. Ye., V.R. Bazavluk, and G.B. Medvedeva. 1948. Plant chimeras as a form of vegetative hybridization. Ibid. 58–97.

Gocholashvili, M.M. 1931. Testing hardiness in certain tea varieties. Tr. po prikl. bot., gen. i sel. 25, No. 3, 110–27.

Gocholashvili, M.M. 1937. Hardening of subtropical plants to low temperatures. Izv. Batumsk. subtr. bot. sada 3, 3–34.

Gocholashvili, M.M. 1940a. Effect of fertilizers on hardiness of the lemon. Sov. subtropiki, pt. 4, 8–14.

Gocholashvili, M.M. 1940b. Hardiness of subtropical plants. Izv. AN SSSR, No. 4, 525–35.

Gocholashvili, M.M. 1949. Mineral nutrition and hardiness in the lemon. Byull. In-ta chaya i subtr. kul't., No. 3, 21–41.

Gocholashvili, M.M., and Sh. G. Zoldatanishvili. 1937. Hardiness in different forms of citrus, tung, and avocado trees. Izv. Batumsk, subtr. bot. sada 3, 35–47.

Gocholashvili, M.M., and T.S. Sulukadze. 1937. Hardiness in the main subtropical plants. Batumsk. subtr. bot. sada, 28 pp.

Gol'din, I.L. 1950. Introduction of exotics into the center of European U.S.S.R. Lesnoye khoz-vo, No. 9, 81–3.

Golodkovskiy, V.L. 1934. Winter hardiness of pea varieties. Tashkent, 40 pp.

Golonti, M.D., and Ye. Yu. Sobatin. 1952. Results of overwintering of subtropical plants in the Batum Botanical Garden. Byull. Glavn. bot. sada AN SSSR, No. 12, 53–60.

Golovlev, A. 1949. Introduction of winter wheat into Siberia. Sov. agronomiya, No. 9, 17–29.

Golovyanko, Z.S. 1949. Causes of desiccation of pine plantings. Izd-vo AN Ukrainskoy SSR, Kiev, 43 pp.

Golubinskiy, I.N. 1949. Variability of the karyotype and the conception of genetic heterogeneity of tissues. Usp. sovr. biol. 27, No. 2, 151–76.

Golush, B.M. 1937a. Effect of temperature on permeability of plasma. Tr. In-ta fiziol. rast. im. K.A. Timiryazeva AN SSSR 1, No. 2, 111–40.

Golush, B.M. 1937b. Effect of supercooling on permeability of plasma. Ibid., 141–7.

Golush, B.M. 1938. Permeability of protoplasm as a factor in hardiness. Dokl. AN SSSR 18, No. 6, 363–6.

Golush, B.M., and N.A. Sharina. 1940. Physicochemical changes in plasma upon freezing. Izv. AN SSSR, No. 4, 536–45.

Goncharov, P. 1907. Coating fruit trees with lime. Plodovodstvo, No. 3, 229–31.

Gordinskiy, A. 1894. Notes of an old landowner. Zemledel'ch. gazeta, No. 22, 473–4.

Gordyagin, A. Ya. 1925. Winter transpiration of certain trees. Tr. Ob-va yestestvoispyt. pri Kaz. gos. un-te 50, No. 5, 1–57.

Gordyagin, A. Ya. 1930. Rate of transpiration of annual shoots of a linden specimen during winters of different years. Reprint from the jubilee collection of Prof. B.A. Keller, 1-11. Voronezh.

Gorodkov, B.N. 1938. An investigation of Soviet Arctic vegetation during the past 20 years. Sov. botanika, No. 1, 143-59.

Gorodkov, B.N. 1946. Attempt at classifying Arctic vegetation. Ibid., 5-18.

Gorshkov, I.S. 1927. Mass death of fruit trees in Tambov province. Sad i ogorod, No. 11, 30-4.

Govorov, L.I. 1922-1923. Nature of the differences between winter and spring forms of cereals in relation to the winter hardiness of winter crops. Tr. po prikl. bot., gen. i sel. 13, No. 1, 525-59.

Grabovskiy, I.S. 1935. Use of agrotechnical methods of controlling winter-killing in winter wheat. Tr. Sev. Kavk. in-ta zern. khoz-va, seriya 2, No. 4, 1-86.

Grammatikati, O.G. 1948. Change in plasmic viscosity in leaf cells of the sugar beet in relation to mineral nutrition. Dokl. AN SSSR 61, No. 3, 549-52.

Grayevskiy, E. Ya. 1948. Living matter and low temperatures. Priroda, 5.

Grayevskiy, E. Ya. 1948. Vitreous state of protoplasm during deep freezing. Usp. sovr. biol. 25, No. 2, 185-202.

Grayevskiy, E. Ya., and Yu. A. Medvedeva. 1948. Causes of protoplasm injury in deep freezing. Zhurn. obshch. biol. 9, No. 6, 455-60.

Grebinskiy, S.O. 1914a. Carbohydrate metabolism in high-altitude cereals in connection with the problem of adaptation. Ibid. 31, No. 3, 279-82.

Grebinskiy, S.O. 1941b. Vitamin C and oxidizing enzymes in high-altitude plants. Biokhimiya 6, No. 3, 253-60.

Grebinskiy, S.O. 1941c. Basic features of nitrogen metabolism in high-altitude plants. Ibid., No. 4, 411-7.

Grebinitskiy, A.S. 1884. Starch as a reserve material in our trees. Tr. Spb. ob-va yestestvoispyt. 15, 691-737.

Grebnitskiy, A.S. 1893. Manual on orchard care. St. Petersburg, 218 pp.

Grebnitskiy, A.S. 1910. Causes of death of fruit buds of Vladimir cherries. Plodovodstvo, No. 5, 508-10.

Gruzdev, S.A. 1946. Winter cereals in the southern regions of Chelyabinsk oblast. Sov. agronomiya, No. 7, 91-2.

Gutiyev, G.T. 1939. Agroecological principles for setting out citrus. Sov. subtropiki, No. 1 (53), 19-24.

Gutiyev, G.T. 1940. Attempt at controlling the growth and hardiness of the lemon, mandarin, and tung. Ibid, No. 4, 46-8.

Gutiyev, G.T. 1950. Hardiness in the tung tree. Dokl VAShNIL, No. 1, 22-5.

Gutiyev, G.T. 1950. Decumbent culture in growing subtropical plants. Byull. Vsesoyuzn. n.-i. in-ta chaya i subtr. kul'tur, No. 4, 53-66.

Ibragimov, B.B. 1930. Causes of plant death from winterkilling and the nature of hardiness in wheat seeds. Tr. biol. fak. Tomsk. gos, un-ta 1, No. 1, 71-96.

Il'yashenko, K. 1936. Winter pruning of citrus. Sov. subtropiki, No. 6, 53-8.

Imshenetskiy, Ya. K. 1894. Winterkilling of winter crops. Khozyain, No. 22, 436-7.

Isayev, S.I. 1949. Michurin's method of growing southern plants further north. Moscow, 29 pp.

Ivanov, L.A. 1925. Water regime of trees in the winter. Izv. Leningr. lesn. in-ta 32, 3-38.

Ivanov, L.A. 1934. Effect of wind on tree growth. Bot. zhurn. 19, No. 3, 211-9.

Ivanov, L.A. 1936. Plant physiology. Leningrad. Goslestekhbumizdat.

Ivanov, L.A. 1941. Changes in transpiration capacity of trees during the year in relation to temperature. Bot. zhurn. SSSR 26, No. 2-3, 97-109.

Ivanov, L.A. 1944. Light and moisture in the life of our trees. Dokl. na 5-m yezhegodnom Timiryazevskom chtenii. Moscow-Leningrad, Izd-vo AN SSSR, 60 pp.

Ivanov, L.A., and N.L. Kossovich. 1932. Function of the assimilation apparatus in trees. 2. Bot. zhurn. SSSR 17, No. 1, 3-71.

Ivanov, L.A., and L.M. Orlova. 1931. Winter photosynthesis of our conifers. Zhurn. Russk. bot. ob-va 16, No. 2-3, 139-56.

Ivanov, P.K. 1936. Diagnosis of hardiness and drought resistance in plants from seeds. Izv. AN SSSR, seriya biol., No. 1, 89-110.

Ivanov, P.K. 1946. Hardiness of winter rye at different phases of development. Selektsiya i semenovodstvo, No. 4-5, 43-9.

Ivanov, S.L. 1931. Evolution of the plant world from the biochemical point of view. Byull. Mosk. ob-va yestestvoispyt. prirody 155, No. 6, 404-9.

Ivanov, S.L. 1937. Climatic variability in the chemical composition of plants. Izv. AN SSSR, No. 6, 1789-1800.

Ivanov, S.L. 1940. Intermediate substances in biochemistry in the light of the theory of evolution. Sov. botanika, No. 5-6, 81-92.

Ivanov, S.L. 1941. Formation and storage phases in the development of fruits and seeds and control thereof. Sov. botanika, No. 4, 3-13.

Ivanov, S.M. 1931. Determination of plant hardiness from changes in electrical conductivity of sap following frost injury. Tr. po prikl. bot., gen. i sel. 27, No. 5, 283-307.

Ivanov, S.M. 1932. Determination of the condition of winter plants from electrical conductivity of tissue. Sots. rasteniyevodstvo, No. 7, 49-60.

Ivanov, S.M. 1933. Effect of autumn frosts on the development of flax in relation to sowing times. Tr. po prikl. bot., gen. i sel., seriya 3, No. 3 (5), 17-29.

Ivanov, S.M. 1935. Response of spring crops to autumn frosts. Ibid., No. 6, 199-200.

Ivanov, S.M. 1935. Response of spring crops to low temperatures. Ibid., 163-98.

Ivanov, S.M. 1939a. Activity of growth processes — a basic factor in the hardiness of citrus. Dokl. AN SSSR 22, No. 5, 281-5.

Ivanov, S.M. 1939b. Effect of intensity of light on the hardening of citrus. Ibid. 25, No. 5, 445-7.

Ivanov, S.M. 1939c. Significance of temperature in hardening citrus to frost. Ibid., 440-4.

Ivanov, S.M. 1939. Sources of hardiness in plants. Sov. subtropiki, pt. 12, 38-9.

Ivanov, S.M. 1940. Effect of photoperiodism on hardiness in citrus. Dokl. AN SSSR 23, No. 8, 737-9.

Ivanov, S.M. 1945. Investigation of hardiness in citrus. Tr. In-ta fiziol. rast. im. K.A. Timiryazeva 4, No. 2, 116-23.

Ivanov, V.V. 1941. Effect of potassium and superphosphate fertilizers on the hardiness of spring plants. Sov. botanika, No. 5-6, 84-6.

Ivanovskaya, T.L. 1947. Nature of dormancy in farm crops. Tr. In-ta gen. AN SSSR 14, 287-308.

Ivanovskiy, L. 1900. Control of mice and rabbits. Plodovodstvo, No. 3, 198-201.

Ivashchenko, A.I. 1951. Hardy eucalyptus forms. Agrobiologiya, No. 3, 47-51.

Iversen, V. 1867. Fruit growing in Russia. Tr. Vol'n. ekon. ob-va, No. 2, 274-80.

Kalabukhov, N.I. 1946. Conservation of the energy balance of the organism as a basis of adaptation. Zhurn. obshch. biol. 7, No. 6, 417-34.

Kalichova, A.D. 1950. Decumbent lemons in Zugdidi. Byull. Vsesoyuzn. n.-i. in-ta chaya i subtr. kul't., No. 4, 67-71.

Kalitin, N.N. 1938. Actinometry. Moscow, Gidrometerorologicheskoye izd-vo, 324 pp.

Kamarinskiy, A.M. 1949. Can coffee be grown in the U.S.S.R.? Ibid., 59-73.

Kamenskiy, M. 1901. Natural and artificial mounding of trees with snow. Plodovodstvo, No. 12, 931-3.

Karapetyan, V.K. 1950. Conversion of hard wheat into soft wheat. Selektsiya i semenovodstvo, No. 6, 8-13.

Kasatkin, I. 1893. Water cycle in treeless and forest-steppe countries. Meteorol. vestn., 277-93.

Kashin, P. 1912. Results of research on fruit growing in South Ussurian kray. Plodovodstvo, No. 10, 881-90.

Kashin, P. 1913. Results of research on fruit growing in South Ussurian kray. Ibid., No. 9-10, 633-42.

Kasparova, S.A. 1942. Causes of death of winter crops and control measures. Syktyvkar, 28 pp.

Kasparova, S.A. 1948. Role of biochemical processes in determining clover hardiness in the polar region. Biokhimiya 13, No. 5, 441-8.

Kasparova, S.A., and S.M. Vartapetyan. 1947. Effect of photoperiodic conditions on clover hardiness. Referaty nauchn.-issled. rabot za 1945 g. Otd. biol. nauk AN SSSR, 82-3.

Kasparova, S.A., and T.A. Proskurnikova. 1944. Role of carbohydrates in determining clover hardiness beyond the Arctic circle. Dokl. AN SSSR, novaya seriya 57, No. 8, 369-73.

Kasparova, S.A., and T.A. Proskurnikova. 1947. Effect of ammonia and nitrate nutrition on red clover hardiness. Referaty nauchn.-issled. rabot za 1945 g. Otd. biol. nauk AN SSSR, 84-5.

Kasparyan, T.G. 1940. Aftereffect of winter shelter. Sov. subtropiki, No. 1 (65), 34-8.

Kazenas, L.D. 1948. Methods of controlling fruit tree gangrene. Sad i ogorod, No. 7, 33-5.

Keller, E.F. 1936. Fluctuations in osmotic pressure of cell sap in plants from the moist subtropics by seasons. Sov. botanika, No. 2, 48-53.

Keller, E.F. 1936a. Changes in starch content and carbohydrate dynamics in the leaves of certain evergreens. Ibid., 54-62.

Keller, E.F. 1936b. Osmotic pressure in Soviet subtropical plants during summer. Ibid., 40-8.

Kerner, M.A. 1899. Life of plants. St. Petersburg, izd-vo Prosveshcheniye.

Keta, G.S. 1936. Carbohydrate dynamics and ash content of leaves in citrus plants of different ages. Sov. botanika, No. 2, 62-70.

Khitrinskiy, V.F. 1950. Changing the heredity of spring rye into winter rye. Agrobiologiya, No. 2, 117-30.

Khlebnikova, N.A. 1937. Chemical nature of the resistance of plants to temperature. Tr. In-ta fiziol. rast. im. K.A. Timiryazeva AN SSSR 1,

No. 2, 93–110.

Kholodnyy, N.G., and I. Ye. Kocherzhenko. 1948. Control of developmental processes in the lemon by means of growth substances. Dokl. AN SSSR 61, No. 2, 391–4.

Khoroshilov, I.I. 1947. Principles of cultivating grain crops in Rostov oblast. Rostov, 1–160.

Khoroshkov, A.A., and P.S. Chernobrivtsev. 1925. Increased variation in the characteristics of flowering plants in unfavorable environmental conditions. Byull. Mosk. ob-va ispty. prirody 38, 3–4.

Kirichenko, F.G. 1947. Depth of tillering nodes in winter wheat. Agrobiologiya, No. 2, 130–4.

Kirsanova, V.A. 1944. Content of vitamin C and carotene in alfalfa in the Uzbek SSSR 9, No. 2–3, 113–8.

Kishkovskiy, T.N. 1950. Ecological conditions of plants at the upper limit of their occurrence in the Eastern Pamirs. Bot. zhurn. 35, No. 6, 657–66.

Kishkovskiy, T.N., and Z.T. Artyushenko. 1951. Biology of high-altitude plants in the Pamirs. Ibid. 36, No. 5, 523–7.

Kizel', A.R. 1940. Chemistry of protoplasm. Moscow-Leningrad, Izd-vo AN SSSR, 624 pp.

Kizyurin, A.D. 1930. Latent forms of "frost clefts" and experiments in chilling apple trees at the root. Sad i ogorod, No. 4, 13–6.

Kizyurin, A.D. 1937. A creeping orchard. Moscow, Sel'khozgiz, seriya Novoye v sel'sk. khoz-ve, No. 3, 44 pp.

Kizyurin, A.D. 1950. Protection of fruit trees from winter warming. Sad i ogorod, No. 10, 19–23.

Klebs, G. 1903. Spontaneous change in plant forms. Transl. from the German. K.A. Timiryazev, Soch. 6, 293–454.

Kley, K. 1848. Observations on allowing cattle to graze on winter crops. Zhurn. sel'sk. khoz-va i ovtsevodstva, No. 5, 39–41.

Klimenko, K.T. 1937. Red-meat oranges of Ajaria. Sov. subtropiki, No. 12 (40) 33–6.

Klimenko, G.A., and Z.M. Kozlova. 1947. Heat regime of wintering of clover and alfalfa in regions of irregular snow in the Maritime Territory. Tr. Dal'nevost. Gornotayezhnoy op. stantsii im akad. V. L. Komarova 5, 201–16.

Kling, Ye. G. 1931. Protein enzymes of winter grains and hardiness. Zhurn. opytn. agr. Yugo-Vostoka 9, No. 1, 123–41.

Klunnyy, G.M. 1935. Heaving of plants. Khimizats. sots. zeml., No. 2, 72–82.

Kocherzhenko, I. Ye., and D.P. Snegirev. 1946. Effect of growth inhibitors on hardiness of the lemon. Byull. po kul't. vlazhn. subtr., No. 14–5, 42–60.

Koldayev, B.M. 1934. Glutathione and enzymes. Priroda, No. 12, 13–9.

Koldayev, B.M. 1935. Glutathione, its characteristics and role in physiology and pathology, Kiiv, 82 pp.

Koldurov, I. 1901. Time of harvesting fruits. Plodovodstvo, No. 8, 681–2.

Kolkunov, V.V. 1905. Breeding of drought-tolerant races of plants. 1. Anatomicophysiological research on degree of xeromorphism of certain grasses. Izv. Kievskogo politekhn. in-ta 5, 1–82.

Kolkunov, V.V. 1931. Correlation of anatomical coefficients and physiological properties of plants. Zhurn. opytn. agronomii 14, 321–40.

Kolomiyets, I.A. 1948. Conditions of formation of reproductive organs in the apple. Agrobiologiya, No. 2, 22–9.

Kolomytsev, G.G. 1936. Winter hardiness and early ripening of wheat. Dokl.

AN SSSR 3, No. 7, 351-6.

Kol'tsova, Z.A. 1950. Changes in the heredity of spring wheat, variety Mil'-turum 321. Agrobiologiya, No. 2, 130-2.

Komarov, V.L. 1938. Origin of cultivated plants. 2nd ed., Moscow-Leningrad, Sel'khozgiz, 240 pp.

Komarov, V.L. 1945. Selected writings, 1, Izd-vo AN SSSR, 668 pp.

Komissarov, P. 1913. Progress in fruit growing in Siberia. Plodovodstvo, No. 4, 273-7.

Kondo, I.N. 1940. Frost and winter resistance of grape species and varieties in Uzbekistan. Tezisy dokl. soveshch. po fiziol. rast., 134-5, Izd-vo AN SSSR.

Kononenko, M.V. 1940. Effect of times of sowing winter wheat on seed properties. Dokl. VASKhNIL, No. 3.

Konstantinov, N.N. 1945. Length of day as a factor determining whether a species can exist. Dokl. AN SSSR 47, No. 9, 688-90.

Konstantinovich, M. 1899. Mounding. Plodovodstvo, No. 2, 203-4.

Konstantinovich, M. 1901. More on mounding trees with snow. Ibid., 144-5.

Kopylov, M. 1902. Attempts at breeding new varieties from seeds for northern Russia. Ibid., No. 5, 356-66.

Koryunayev, S.I., and Ye. I. Vinogradova. 1950. Duration of vernalization of winter wheat seeds in relation to times of harvesting of seeds. Agrobiologiya, No. 3, 67-9.

Kossovich, P.S. 1906. Effect of plant development at low soil temperature during initial growth on transpiration capacity. Zhurn. opytn. agron. 7, No. 1, 1-9.

Kostyuchenko, I.A. 1938. Effect of seed vernalization during ripening on hardiness. Dokl. AN SSSR 18, No. 8, 589-92.

Kostyuchenko, I.A. 1938. Relationship between winter wheat and winter rye hardiness and ripening conditions of plants. Selektsiya i semenovodstvo, No. 2.

Kostyuchenko, I.A. 1947. Wintering conditions of winter wheat in Siberia. Agrobiologiya, No. 2, 110-20.

Kostyuchenko, I.A., and T. Ya. Zarubaylo. 1937. Possibilities of passing through the vernalization stage in ripening seeds. Tr. In-ta gen., Nov. 11, 33-47.

Kotko, I. 1900. Bush form of the apple. Plodovodstvo, No. 11, 780-4.

Kott, S.A. 1944. Some developmental characteristics of Siberian weeds. Sov. botanika, No. 4-5, 81-4.

Kott, S.A. 1949. Overwintering of perennial weeds in sowings of fodder grasses. Byull. Mosk. ob-va ispytat. prirody, otd. biol. 54, No. 4, 83-8.

Kovalev, N. Ye. 1934. Effect of low temperatures on swollen seeds and sprouts of wheat and sunflower (in connection with sowing just before winter). Tr. Sarat. selekts. stantsii 2, 42-62.

Kovalevskiy, G.V. 1939. Theory and method of investigating vertical agro-ecological zones. Sov. botanika, pt. 4, 34-46.

Kozhevnikov, A.V. 1931. Overwintering and rhythm of development of spring plants in a linden forest. Byull. Mosk. ob-va ispyt. prirody. Otd. biol 40, No. 1-2, 79-108.

Kozhevnikov, A.V. 1937. Investigations of duration of winter dormancy in certain West Caucasian plants. Tr. Bot. sada Mosk. gos. un-ta, No. 1, 5-24.

Kozhevnikov, A.V. 1950. Spring and fall in the life of plants. 2nd ed. Mosk.

ob-va ispyt. prirody, seriya Sredi prirody, 240 pp.

Kozhevnikova, L.M. 1947. Causes of death of winter crops in certain regions. Dokl. AN SSSR 55, No. 1, 61-3.

Kozlov, V.M. 1933. Fruit bearing of the cacao in greenhouses. Sov. botanika, No. 3-4, 198-203.

Koz'mina, N.P., and M.S. Reznichenko. 1937. Wheat and barley enzyme disintegrating proteins. Biokhimiya 11, No. 4, 630-6.

Krasavin, A. 1937. Heating of citrus for the winter. Sov. subtropiki, No. 11 (27) 72.

Krasheninnikov, N., and Ageyev. 1939. Hardiness in the guayule and agrotechnical tasks. Sov. subtropiki, No. 12, 26-31.

Krasovskaya, I.V., and M.A. Krotkina. 1933. Effect of transplantation and sowing times on development of the aerial parts and roots of winter and spring cereals. Tr. po prikl. bot., gen. i sel., seriya 3, No. 3(5), 31-2.

Krasovskaya, I.V. 1940. Physiological characteristics of hardiness in winter wheat in Gor'kovskaya oblast. Tezisy dokl. soveshch. po fiziol. rast., Izd-vo AN SSSR, 135-7.

Krasovskaya, I.V. 1946. Physiological basis of hardiness in winter wheat in Gor'kovskaya oblast. Tr. In-ta fiziol. rast. im. K.A. Timiryazeva AN SSSR 4, No. 1, 112-9.

Krayevoy, S. Ya., and Ye. Z. Oknina. 1954. Hardiness in young oaks. Dokl. AN SSSR 95, No. 3, 677-80.

Krayevoy, S. Ya., Ye. Z. Oknina, and V.M. Ipekdzhiyan. 1954. Effect of low temperatures on oak seedlings. Dokl. AN SSSR 96, No. 4, 841-4.

Krenke, N.P. 1928. Plant surgery. Izd. Novaya derevnya, 657 pp.

Krenke, N.P. 1940. Theory of cyclical aging and rejuvenescence of plants and its practical application. Moscow, Sel'khozgiz, 135 pp.

Kretovich, V.L. 1941. Causes of low germination in freshly harvested wheat. Dokl. AN SSSR 33, No. 2, 151-3.

Kreyer, G.K. 1934. Ways of growing the cinchona in the U.S.S.R. Sots. rasteniyevodstvo, seriya A, No. 13, 75-86.

Kreyer, G.K. 1936. Problem of natural quinine in the U.S.S.R. Sov. subtropiki, No. 3(19), 60-6.

Kreyer, G.K. 1938. Agrotechnics of the cinchona in the U.S.S.R. Ibid., No. 3(42), 5-11.

Krivchenko, A.M. 1939. Causes of large-scale winterkilling of strawberries. Sadovodstvo, No. 8, 45.

Krivolapov, M.I. 1940. Let us boldly expand the planting of winter crops in Krasnoyar kray. Sel. i semenovodstvo, No. 2.

Krutikhovskiy, V.P. 1949. Summer planting of winter wheat. Selektsiya i semenovodstvo, No. 5, 64-7.

Krylov, M.M. 1936. Hydrothermal protection of plants from frosts. Dokl. VASKhNIL, No. 3, 113-21.

Kryukov, F.A. 1950. Plum varieties for Leningrad. Sad i ogorod, No. 6, 23-7.

Kuksa, I.N. 1936. Use of fertilizers to combat winterkilling of spring wheat. Sots. rekonstr. sel'sk khoz-va, No. 12, 179-203.

Kuksa, I.N. 1937. Effect of mineral nutrition on winter wheat hardiness and yield. In the book: [Agrotekhnika Agricultural practices]. Moscow-Leningrad, 5-54.

Kuksa, I.N. 1938. Effect of fertilizers on strengthening winter wheat hardiness and yield. Sots. rekonstr. sel'sk. khoz-va, No. 7-8, 140-7.

Kuksa, I.N. 1939. Effect of mineral nutrition on winter wheat hardiness and yield. Khimizats. sots. zeml., No. 1, 70-9.

Kuksa, I.N. 1939. For high yield of winter grains in Siberia. Sots. sel'sk. khoz⁴-vo, No. 1, 98-109.

Kuksa, I.N. 1939. Effectiveness of spring fertilization of winter wheat. Khimizats. sots. zeml., No. 4, 22-5.

Kuksa, I.N. 1940. Combatting destruction and raising the yield of winter grain crops. Za ustoychivyy urozhay na Yugo-Vostoke, No. 3, 9-14.

Kuksa, I.N. 1940. Strengthening the hardiness of winter crops by means of fertilizers. Tezisy dokl. soveshch. po fiziol. rast., 141-2, Izd-vo AN SSSR.

Kuksa, I.N. 1940. Working out methods of increasing hardiness and yield of winter grain crops. Khimizats. sots. zeml., No. 4, 75-80.

Kulakov, P. 1902. Combatting spring frosts. Plodovodstvo, No. 2, 114-23.

Kul'chitskaya, Z.A. 1945. Role of subzero temperatures in plant development. Dokl. AN SSSR 47, No. 5, 377-80.

Kuperman, F.M. 1935. Wheat hardiness in the light of the theory of plant evolution. Yarovizatsiya, No. 2, 43-76.

Kuperman, F.M. 1940. Agrotechnics of seed nurseries of winter wheat. Zelektsiya i semenobodstvo, No. 2.

Kuperman, F.M. 1941. The multistage arrangement of winter grain tillering nodes. Sots. zern. khoz-vo, No. 3, 60-9.

Kuperman, F.M. 1941. Yield of winter wheat and seed quality under the conditions of vertical zonality in Kabardino-Balkaria. Dokl. VASKhNIL, No. 7.

Kuperman, F.M. 1948. "Imaginary aftergrowth" of winter crops. Ibid., No. 5, 14-8.

Kuperman, F.M. 1949. Agrobiological developmental characteristics of winter wheat tillering nods. Vestn. Mosk. gos, un-ta, No. 8, 110-28.

Kuperman, F.M. 1950. Biological foundation of wheat culture. Pt. I. Biological developmental characteristics of wheat early in life. Izd. Mosk. gos. un-ta. 200 pp.

Kuperman, F.M., and A.I. Zadontsev. 1934. Protection of winter crops from winter injury. Moscow-Leningrad., Gosizdat, 35 pp.

Kuperman, F.M., and A.I. Zadontsev. 1935. Analysis of the causes of the death of winter crops in the Ukraine during the winters of 1931/1932 and 1933/1934. Tr. po prikl. bot., gen. i sel., seriya 3, No. 6, 97-120.

Kuperman, F.M., and A.I. Zadontsev. 1936. How to determine the condition of winter grains during the fall, winter, and spring. Vsesoyuzn. nauchn.-tekhn. ob-vo, Moscow, 1-32.

Kuperman, F.M., and M.I. Kucheryavaya. 1932. Sugar method of renewal. Sots. zern. khoz-vo, 9-10, Saratov.

Kuperman, F.M., and A.M. Shul'gin. 1943. Protection of winter crops from winterkilling. Opyty Barnaul'skoy gos. sel. stantsii. Sel'so, 280.

Kuprevich, V.F. 1947. Physiology of sick plants in connection with general problems of parasitism. Moscow-Leningrad, Izd-vo AN SSSR, 300 pp.

Kursanov, A.L. 1936. Reversible action of enzymes in living cells. Izv. AN SSSR, seriya biol., 669-78.

Kursanov, A.L. 1936. Reversible action of invertase in living plant cells and the role of structural formations in protoplasm. Biokhimiya 1, No. 4, 411-24.

Kursanov, A.L. 1940a. Action of enzymes in the living cell. In the book: Fermenty [Enzymes]. Izd-vo AN SSSR, 203-26.

Kursanov, A.L. 1940b. Reversible action of enzymes in the living plant cell.

Izd-vo AN SSSR, 234 pp.

Kursanov, A.L., and K.A. Bryushkova. 1940a. Biokhimiya 5, No. 6, 521-7.

Kursanov, A.L., and K.A. Bryushkova. 1940b. Action of enzymes in ripening wheat seeds. Biokhimiya 5, No. 6, 681-6.

Kursanov, A.L., N.N. Kryukova, and A. Morozov. 1938. Effect of temperature on the reversible action of invertase in plants in relation to their cold and heat resistance. Izv. AN SSSR, seriya biol., No. 1, 51-66.

Kursanov, A.L., and N.N. Kryukova. 1939. Enzymic indicators of hardiness in the cinchona. Biokhimiya 4, No. 5, 562-5.

Kushner, Kh. F. 1941. Physiological nature of heterosis. Dokl. AN SSSR 30, No. 2, 175-7.

Kuz'min, N. 1902. From the northern limit of fruit growing. Plodovodstvo, No. 1, 44-7.

Kuz'minskiy, V. 1861. Cultivation of peaches, apricots, and other southern fruit trees in soil. Zhurn. sadovodstva, No. 1, 156-61, 183-6.

Kvaratskheliya, T.K. 1937. Agrotechnics to protect citrus and tung from frost. Sov. subtropiki, No. 9 (37) 48-53.

Kvasnikov, B.V. 1937. Vegetative reproduction of chicory through regeneration as a method of hastening selection. Izv. AN SSSR, No. 2, 333-92.

Kyun, K. 1908. Overwintering of the sweet cherry near Peterburg. Plodovodstvo, No. 4, 321-2.

Lange, K.P. 1949. Protection of fruit tree bark from frost injury. Sad i ogorod, No. 1, 20-2.

Lapchenko, G.D. 1946. Winter wheat-wheatgrass hybrids in the nonchernozem zone. Tr. Zon. in-ta zern. khoz-va nechern. polosy SSSR, No. 13, 50-61.

Lapin, M.M. 1940. Care of winter plants on seed plots. Selektsiya i semeno-vodstvo, No. 1.

Lapin, M.M. 1948. Water-air conditions of the soil and overwintering of winter crops. Sov. agronomiya, No. 2, 17-29.

Lapin, N. 1893. Cancer of fruit trees. Plodovodstvo, No. 3, 177-81.

Lapin, P.I. 1939. Planting trees in the polar regions. Zel. stroit., No. 3/4, 71-3.

Lapin, V.K. 1938. Hybridization of citrus. Sov. subtropiki, No. 7(47), 34-7.

Lapshina, Ye. I. 1929. Overwintering of higher plants. Priroda, No. 2, 145-52.

Lavrent'yev, S. 1853. Harmful effect of loose chernozem soil on winter crops. Tr. Vol'n. ekon. ob-va, No. 7, 39-40.

Lavrent'yev, S. 1857. Cultivating winter rye near Yelizavetgrad. Ibid., No. 1, 165-88.

Lavrent'yev. S. 1867. Sketches of a farm in Khersonskaya province. Ibid., No. 3, 271-94.

Lavrent'yev. S. 1890. Pre-sowing condition of winter fields. S.-kh. listok, No. 6, 61-2.

Lavrent'yev, S. 1890a. Early and late sowings of winter grain. Ibid., No. 7, 51-3.

Lavrent'yev, S. 1892. Prevention of damping off and winterkilling of winter crops. Vestn. russk. sel'sk. khoz-va, 1-4.

Lavriychuk, I.I. 1936. Effectiveness of open heating of citrus groves. Ibid., No. 10(26), 65-9.

Lavriychuk, I.I. 1936. Espalier cultivation of citrus. Ibid., No. 3(19), 69-72.

Lavriychuk, I.I. 1937. New forms of lemon culture. Ibid., No. 10(38), 55-63.

Lavriychuk, I.I. 1939. Wall-decumbent lemon culture. Ibid., 23-30.

Lavriychuk, I.I. 1949. Decumbent lemon culture. Sad i ogorod., No. 2, 44-50.

Ladygan, I. Ya. 1946. Heating of winter cereals. Sov. agronomiya, No. 11-2, 63-6.

Lavriychuk, V.S. 1936. Artificial fog to protect citrus from frost. Sov. subtropiki, No. 9, 42-8.

Lebedev, A.F., and Ye. V. Talalayev. 1928. Hydrological and climatological conditions responsible for the destruction of wheat in 1927-1928 and possible cultural methods of controlling the death of winter crops. Donskaya selektsionnaya stantsiya, No. 2, 1-21. Rostov-on-Don.

Lebedintseva, Ye. V. 1930. Investigation of water-holding capacity of plants in relation to their drought and frost resistance. Tr. po prikl. bot., gen. i sel. 23, No. 2, 1-30.

Lesser. 1898. How to prevent cancer in fruit trees. Sad i ogorod, No. 1, 4-7.

Levkovich, L.I. 1948. Effect of chemical substances on the organism at different external temperatures. Usp. sovr. biol. 26, No. 3(6), 608-18.

Leysle, F.F. 1948. Ecological and physiological characteristics of leaves of evergreens from the Soviet moist subtropics. Eksp. botanika, No. 6, 147-99.

Lindley. 1845. Theory of gardening. Trans. from the English by I. Shikhovskiy. St. Petersburg, 417 pp.

Linneus, K. 1800. Philosophy of botany. Izd-vo AN SSSR, 195 pp.

Lisavenko, M.A. 1948. State and problems of gardening in the Altai. In the collection: Sadovodstvo Altaya [Gardening in the Altai.] Izd. Altayskaya pravda, 5-19.

Lisavenko, M.A. 1949. I.V. Michurin's teachings — a guide to the action of Michurinists of Siberia. Agrobiologiya, No. 3, 132-41.

Lisitsin, P.I. 1947. Problems in the biology of red clover. Moscow, Sel'-khozgiz, 343 pp.

Litovchenko, A.G. 1947. Significance of large size of winter wheat grains in formation of reserve tillering nodes and overwintering of the plants. Dokl. AN SSSR 55, No. 2, 165-8.

Litvinov, L.S. 1940. Several ways of strengthening the frost resistance of plants. Tezisy dokl. soveshch. po fiziol. rast., 144-6. Izd-vo AN SSSR.

Lobanov, A.A. 1938. Citrus in protected soil. Sov. subtropiki, No. 2(41), 49-50.

Lobanov, G.A. 1950. Effect of different amounts of pollen on fertilization. Agrobiologiya, No. 3, 78-86.

Lozino-Lozinskiy, L.K. 1948. Effect of salts on hardiness of infusorians and causes of death upon chilling. Zhurn. obshch. biol. 9, No. 6, 441-53.

Lukhmenskiy, V. 1915. How to increase the yield of orchards. Plodovodstvo, No. 11, 620-7.

Luk'yanenko, P.P. 1948. Changes in the nature of winter and spring wheat varieties by changing the conditions affecting the vernalization stage. Agrobiologiya, No. 2, 40-50.

Luss, A.I. 1947. Citrus crops in the U.S.S.R. Sel'khozgiz, 132 pp.

L'vov, S.D. 1950. Main trends in the historical development of the theory of respiration in plants. Timiryazevskiye chteniya, VIII. Izd-vo AN SSSR, 87 pp.

L'vova, P.F. 1947. Frost resistance of pea varieties. Selektsiya i semenovodstvo, No. 2, 45 pp.

Lyashchenko, I.F. 1947. Mutations of winter wheat. Dokl. AN SSSR 58,

No. 7, 1501–4.

Lysenko, T.D. 1928. Effect of the thermal factor on duration of the developmental phases of plants. Experiments with grasses and cotton. Tr. Azerb. tsentr. opytn. sel. stantsii im. Ordzhonikidze v g. Grandzhe, pt. 3, Baku, 1–168.

Lysenko, T.D. 1932. Main results from vernalization of crops. Byull. yarovisatsii, No. 4, 3–57.

Lysenko, T.D. 1935a. Theoretical principles of vernalization. Moscow, Sel'khozgiz.

Lysenko, T.D. 1936. Intravarietal crossing of inbred plants. Sots. rekonstr. sel'sk. khoz-va, No. 10, Moscow.

Lysenko, T.D. 1936. Physiology of plant development and hardiness in winter grains. Sel'sk. khoz-vo SSSR, Moscow, Sel-khozgiz.

Lysenko, T.D. 1937. Modifying the nature of plants. Moscow, Sel'khozgiz.

Lysenko, T.D. 1937. Collective farm hut laboratories and agricultural science. Yarovizatsiya, No. 5(14).

Lysenko, T.D. 1941. How a new hardy wheat variety is created for Siberia. Pravda of October 3.

Lysenko, T.D. 1942. Ways of increasing the germination rate of grain seeds. Omskaya pravda of April 17.

Lysenko, T.D. 1943. To increase the field germination rate of grain seeds. Dokl. VASKhNIL, No. 2.

Lysenko, T.D. 1944. Essence of our proposal to sow winter crops in the stubble on the Siberian steppes. Sovkhoznoye proizvodstvo, No. 4, Moscow.

Lysenko, T.D. 1944. Cultivation of winter crops on the Siberian steppes. Ibid., No. 10–11.

Lysenko, T.D. 1945. Cultivation of winter crops on the Siberian steppes. Moscow, Sel'khozgiz.

Lysenko, T.D. 1946. Spatial isolation of variety plantings. Sovkhoznaya gazeta of January 17.

Lysenko, T.D. 1949. For regular heavy yields from the Volga fields. Agrobiologiya, No. 2, 3–9.

Lysenko, T.D. 1949. Agrobiology. Papers on problems in genetics, selection, and seed production. Izd. 5, 1–687.

Lysenko, T.D., and D.A. Dolgushin. 1929. Nature of winter crops. Tr. Vsesoyuzn. s''yezda po gen., sel., semenovodstvu i plem. zhivotnovodstvu v Leningrade, III.

Lyubimenko, V.N. 1926. Physiological role of starch deposited in the green parenchyma of leaves (prelim. communic.). Izv. Glavn. bot. sada SSSR 25, No. 2, 101–10.

Lyudogovskiy, A. 1863. Harmful effect of frost on plants. Tr. Vol'n. ekon. ob-va, No. 3, 244–5.

Makarov, P.V. 1953. Principles of cytology. Moscow, Izd-vo Sov. nauka, 531 pp.

Makarov, V. 1896. Cultivation of pineapples in Voronezh province. Plodovodstvo, No. 11, 814–20.

Makhov, P. 1885. Water lack as the main cause of destruction in Crimean orchards. Sad i ogorod, No. 16.

Maksimov, N.A. 1908. Plant respiration at subzero temperatures. Tr. SPb. ob-va yestestvoispyt. Otd. bot. 37, 23.

Maksimov, N.A. 1908a. Winterkilling of plants. Ibid., 32–46.

Maksimov, N.A. 1913. Winterkilling and hardiness of plants. Experimental and critical investigations. Izv. SPb. lesn. in-ta 25, 1–330.

Maksimov, N.A. 1929. Internal factors in plant resistance to frost and drought. Tr. po prikl. bot., gen. i sel. 22, No. 1, 3–41.

Maksimov, N.A. 1938. Increased permeability of protoplasm after wilting of plants. Dokl. AN SSSR 21, No. 4, 182–5.

Maksimov, N.A. 1939. Suppression of growth processes as a basic factor in lowered crop yield after drought. Usp. sovr. biol. 11, No. 1, 124–36.

Maksimov, N.A., and N.G. Vasil'yeva. 1948. Effect of second wilting on colloid chemical properties of protoplasm. Tr. In-ta fiziol. rast. im. K.A. Timiryazeva AN SSSR 6, No. 2, 150–61.

Maksimov, N.A., and T.A. Krasnosel'skaya-Maksimova. 1917. Annual variations in osmotic pressure and sugar content of wintering leaves. Tr. Tifl. bot. sada 19, 213–22.

Maksimov, N.A., and L.V. Mozhayeva. 1944a, b. Growth changes in the colloid chemical properties of plant cells. Dokl. AN SSSR 42, No. 5, 236–40; No. 6, 291–4.

Markevich, N.P. 1939. Overwintering and vulnerability of ecotypes of winter wheat to snow mold. Vestn. zashchity rast., No. 1(20), 119–21.

Martens, 1860. Warming of soil in mountains. Vestn. Ross. ob-va sadovodov No. 5, 40–2.

Matskov, F.F. 1936. A rapid new method of diagnosing living, dead, and injured tissues of green plants. Dokl. AN SSSR 1, No. 6(83), 255–6.

Matyukov, A. 1911. Need of tilling the soil in orchards and treating trees injured by frost. Plodovodstvo, No. 3, 241–3.

Mchaloblishvili, S.V. 1951. Results of testing individual shelters for lemon trees in Anaseul. Byull. Vsesoyuzn. n.-i. in-ta chayn. prom. i subtr. kul't., No. 1, 28–45.

Mchaloblishvili, S.V., and G.T. Gutiyev. 1950. Wintering of citrus in trenches in the Ukraine. Ibid., No. 4, 45–52.

Mednis, Ya. A., and Ya. M. Kishnelis. 1935. Burns as a cause of winter-spring death of winter crops. Semenovodstvo, No. 4, 25–8.

Medvedeva, G.B. 1948. Cytological investigation of vegetative tomato hybrids. Tr. In-ta gen. AN SSSR 15, 108–18.

Medvedeva, G.B. 1948. Effect of developmental conditions on the formation of hybrids. Ibid., 163.

Medvedev, G.M. 1938. Method of selecting pairs of winter wheat in hybridization for frost resistance. Selektsiya i semenovodstvo, No. 6.

Mendeleyev, D.I. 1872. Experiments of the Volny Economics Society on the action of fertilizers. Tr. Vol'n. ekon. ob-va, No. 1, 407–39.

Merklin, 1860. Internal structure and life of plants. Ibid., No. 1, 2, 3, 4, and 5.

Metlitskiy, Z. 1949. The apple. Izd-vo Moskovskiy rabochiy, 2nd ed., 167 pp.

Metlitskiy, Z.A. 1949. Fruit nursery. Moscow, Sel'khozgiz, 543 pp.

Michurin, I.V. 1939–1940. Writings, I-IV, Moscow, Sel'khozgiz.

Michurin, I.V. 1888. Acclimatization of pears in Kozlov. Soch., I, 107–13.

Michurin, I.V. 1888. Effect of variety of wilding on the quality of cherry fruit. Ibid., 113–5.

Michurin, I.V. 1905. How can plants be acclimatized? Ibid., 115–7.

Michurin, I.V. 1905. My experiments in breeding new plum varieties in austere regions. Ibid., 117–22.

Michurin, I.V. 1905. What is acclimatization of fruit trees? Ibid., 122–9.

Michurin, I.V. 1906. My experiments in breeding new fruit varieties. Ibid.,

129–41.

Michurin, I.V. 1907. In reference to certain answers and articles in a periodical. Ibid., 142-3.

Michurin, I.V. 1908. Obtaining excellent cultivated varieties of fruit trees and berry bushes from seeds. Ibid., 144-50.

Michurin, I.V. 1911. Breeding new cultivated varieties of fruit trees and bushes from seeds. Ibid., 151-214.

Michurin, I.V. 1913. First steps in improving assortments of fruit trees and bushes in our gardens by selection through breeding new varieties. Ibid., 215-8.

Michurin, I.V. 1913. Hybridization is helpful in producing a better method of acclimatization. Ibid., 220-4.

Michurin, I.V. 1913. Effect of the Chinese apple when crossed with cultivated apple varieties on the size, beautiful color, and taste of the fruits of hybrid apple varieties. Ibid., 224-7.

Michurin, I.V. 1915. Life and preservation of seeds until sowing. Ibid., 230-9.

Michurin, I.V. 1917. Materials for the compilation of rules for training hybrid seedlings in breeding new fruit varieties. Ibid., 240-70.

Michurin, I.V. 1919. Usefulness of the Chinese apple and harm done by the Siberian apple in Central Russian orchards. Ibid., 270-3.

Michurin, I.V. 1923. Summary of the results of the practical work of an originator of new fruit varieties, I.V. Michurin in Kozlov. Ibid., 279-92.

Michurin, I.V. 1925. Results of 47 years of work in hybridizing fruits. Ibid., 297-309.

Michurin, I.V. 1928. How to grow fruit trees in the Urals. Ibid., 309-12.

Michurin, I.V. 1929. To horticulturists in the Central industrial oblast. Ibid., 315-7.

Michurin, I.V. 1929. Principles and methods of work. Ibid., 318-89.

Michurin, I.V. 1932. Genotypic changes in intergeneric crossings. Ibid., 410-3.

Michurin, I.V. 1934. Results of 60 years of work and the outlook. Ibid., 427-33.

Michurin, I.V. 1934. Intergeneric hybridization of fruits., Ibid., 434-40.

Michurin, I.V. 1934. Several questions of method. Ibid., 448-72.

Michurin, I.V. 1936. Pollination with mixed pollen. Ibid., 481-2.

Michurin, I.V. 1937. Rules for training hybrids. Ibid., 484-8.

Michurin, I.V. 1939. Use of mentors in training hybrid seedlings and examples of sharp changes in fruit tree varieties due to different alien factors. Ibid., 495-513.

Michurin, I.V. 1939. Changing hybrid properties by grafting on some stock. Ibid., 516-26.

Middendorf, A. 1860. Travels in Northern and Eastern Siberia, pt. I, St. Petersburg, 1-314.

Mikhaylova, L.V. 1936. Vernalization of cabbage. Izv. AN SSR, No. 1, 171-91.

Mikhaylova, Ye. N., and N.V. Shipchinskiy. 1951. Effect of temperature on the viability of the cacao. Byull. Glavn. bot. sada AN SSSR, No. 10, 28-30.

Mikhaylovskiy, A.G. 1948. Effect of arranging plants in rows on the development and yield of grain crops. Sov. agronomiya, No. 7, 72-6.

Mikhin, S.D. 1928. Winter drought in trees. Tr. Sib. in-ta sel'sk. khoz-va i lesovodstva, pt. 1-6, 123-54.

Minina, Ye. G. 1950. Shifting of sex in plants by environmental factors. Moscow-Leningrad, Izd-vo AN SSSR, 198 pp.

Mininberg, S. Ya. 1948. Frost resistance of grape roots. Navkovi Zapiski KDU.

Mininberg, S. Ya. 1949. Intensity of regeneration in various frost-resistant varieties of grapes. Naukovi zapiski KDU, 8, No. 5, 191-194.

Mirimanyan, V.A. 1950. Biological characteristics of the lemon and mandarin responsible for the differences in frost resistance. Dokl. AN SSSR 84, No. 5, 1029-32.

Moiseyev, I. 1903. Effect of climatic conditions on fruits in the Trans-Caspian region. Plodovodstvo, No. 6, 501-3.

Moroz, Ye. S. 1939. Determination of frost resistance of citrus by a direct method. Sov. subtropiki, No. 12, 34-7.

Moroz, Ye. S. 1940. Effect of low temperatures on the growth and development of woody plants. Sov. botanika, No. 5-6, 233.

Moroz, Ye. S. 1948. Experimental ecological research on dormancy in woody plants. Eksp. botanika, No. 6, 295-331.

Moroz, Ye. S., and M.V. Kotlyarova. 1939. Determination of frost resistance of citrus by indirect methods. Sov. botanika, No. 5, 107-12.

Moshkov, B.S. 1929-1930. Photoperiodism in certain trees. Tr. po prikl. bot., gen. i sel. 23, 479-510.

Moshkov, B.S. 1935. Photoperiodism and frost resistance in perennials. Tr. po prikl. bot., gen. i sel., seriya 3, No. 6, 235-61.

Moshkov, B.S. 1934. Frost resistance and photoperiodism. Sov. subtropiki, No. 2, 53-4.

Mosolov, V.P. 1934-1938-1953. Agrotechnics in the struggle against destruction of winter crops. Tatgosizdat, Kazan (1st ed. 1934; 2nd ed. 1938; 3rd ed. in Soch., II, Moscow, Sel'khozgiz).

Mosolov, V.P. 1946. Early winter sowing of winter wheat. Dokl. VASKhNIL, No. 11-12, 3-16.

Murri, N.M. 1946. Selection of lemons for frost resistance. Byull. Vsesoyuzn. n.-i. in-ta chayn. prom. i subtr. kul't., No. 2, 20-35.

Myatkovskiy, O.N. 1947. Altai fruit and berry experimental station. Byull. Alt. plod.-yagodn. op. stantsii 1, 1-90.

Nabokikh, A.I. 1905. Temporary anaerobiosis of higher plants. Experim. investig., pt. 1, Observations on growth processes in an oxygen-free medium. St. Petersburg, 1-192.

Nadaraya, G.B. 1937. Individual protection of citrus from frost. Sov. subtropiki, No. 10(38), 19-26.

Nadaraya, G.B. 1938. Water-heat regime of soil and hardiness of the lemon. Ibid., No. 2(41) 21-5.

Nadaraya, G.B. 1939a. Individual heaters for lemon trees under cloth shelters. Ibid., No. 12, 21-24.

Nadaraya, G.B. 1939b. Results of testing individual shelters for lemon trees. Ibid., No. 10, 10-6.

Nadaraya, G.B. 1948. Strengthening the lemon's hardiness by action on the water-heat regime of the soil. Agrobiologiya, No. 5, 93-109.

Nagornyy, A.V. 1948. Ageing and prolongation of life. Moscow, Izd-vo Sov. kniga, 214 pp.

Nalivkin, A.A. 1941. Direction of rows in planting as a factor in increasing the yield of field crops. Sov. agronomiya, No. 1.

Nasonov, D.N., and V. Ya. Aleksandrov. 1940. Reaction of living matter to external influences. The denaturation theory of injury and irritation. Izd-vo AN SSSR.

Negrul', A.M. 1946. Origin and classification of the cultivated grape. Ampelografiya SSSR, I, 159-216.

Nemen, Ya. 1897. North American apples. Plodovodstvo, No. 2, 102-11.

Nikiforov, V.P. 1939. Latest developments in individual protection of citrus from frost. Sov. subtropiki, No. 10, 17-22.

Nikiforov, M. 1897. Gardening in Yenisey province. Plodovodstvo, No. 1, 21-5.

Nikiforov, M. 1903. Experience in fruit growing in Yenisey province. Ibid., No. 9, 748-53.

Nikiforov, M. 1905. Dwarf stock for apples in northern latitudes. Ibid., No. 10, 803-8.

Nikiforov, M. 1906. Observations on an experimental fruit nursery on "Blagodatnyy" farm in Minusinsk district, Yenisey province. Ibid., No. 3, 207-27.

Nikitin, K.G. 1949. Effect of winter whitewashing on frost resistance of apricot buds. Sad i ogorod, No. 11, 20-1.

Nikol'skiy, D.L. 1951. Waterlogging. Lesn. khoz-vo, No. 5, 96.

Nizen'kov, N.P. 1939. Electrometrical method of determining frost resistance and drought resistance of farm crops. Dokl. VASKhNIL, No. 4, 11-18.

Nizen'kov, N.P. 1940. A new method.of determining the frost resistance of winter crops. Ibid., No. 1.

Nosatovskiy, A.I. 1946. Theoretical basis of the optimum sowing time of winter wheat. Dokl. VASKhNIL, No. 11-12, 17-20.

Nosatovskiy, A.I. 1946a. Sowing times of winter wheat. Sov. agronomiya, No. 10, 28-39.

Nosatovskiy, A.I. 1950. Wheat. Moscow, Sel'khozgiz, 407 pp.

Novikov, V.A. 1928. Research on plant hardiness. Zhurn. opytn. agronomii Yugo-Vostoka 6, No. 1, 1-30.

Novikov, V.A. 1931. Relation of spring sowings to spring frosts. Ibid., 9, No. 2, 73-9.

Novikov, V.A. 1934. Hardiness of regrowth of alfalfa varieties. Dokl. AN SSSR 4, No. 8-9, 480-6.

Novikov, V.A. 1945. Germination of snakeweed seeds. Ibid. 46, No. 5, 223-5.

Novikov, V.A., and M.L. Mokhova. 1936. Effect of wilting on alfalfa hardiness. Sb. statey sel. stantsii SoyuzNIKhI, 149-52.

Novikov, V.A., and M.L. Mokhova. 1936. Effect of phosphorus on alfalfa hardiness. Ibid., 129-48.

Olenichenko, A.I. 1936. My studies on acclimatization of fruit trees and berry patches. Sb. Opyt sibirskikh michurintsev. Zap.-Sib. krayevoye idz-vo, 34-41.

Oleynikova, T.V. 1939. Peculiarities in the phasic development of different forms of barley. Sov. botanika, No. 5, 31-49.

Oparin, A.I. 1937. The enzyme system as the basis of physiological characteristics of plants. Izv. AN SSSR, seriya biol., No. 6, 1733-51.

Oparin, A.I., and V.A. Zenchenko. 1949. Direction of action of enzymes and effect on vernalization. Sb. Probl. biokhimii v michurinsk. biol., I, 81-91.

Orekhovich, V.N. 1950. Rate of renewal of proteins in various organs and tissues. Dokl. AN SSSR 71, No. 1, 105-7.

Ostapovich, M.F. 1948. Water content and water deficit in the shoots of woody plants in winter in the Pamir Botanical Garden. Soobshch. Tadkh. filiala AN SSSR, pt. 7, 14-7.

Ozol, A.M. 1949. Method of strengthening the hardiness of the Persian walnut. Sad i ogorod, No. 10, 26-28.

Ozol, A.M. 1951. Reorganization and adaptation of the Persian walnut to new environmental conditions. Zhurn. obshch. biol. 12, No. 1, 34-9.

Palladin, V.I. 1886. Significance of oxygen for plants. Moscow, 1-94.

Pal'tsov, P. 1873. Physical properties of soil. Tr. Vol'n. ekon. ob-va, No. 2, 178-98.

Perevoshchikov, A. 1913. Acclimatization of fruit trees and bushes and breeding of new varieties from seeds. Plodovodstvo, No. 7, 450-8.

Perevoshchikov, A. 1915. The "Dundik" apple and other innovations of M.F. Kopulov. Ibid., 5, 288-98.

Periturin, F.T. 1912. Location of tillering nodes in grasses. Izv. Mosk. s.-kh. in-ta, 18, No. 2, 199-211.

Perlova, R.L. 1939b. Obtaining the autohexaploid Solanum vallis Mexici Juz. by cultivating it in the Pamirs. Dokl. AN SSSR 25, No. 5, 415-8.

Petrakhilev, I.M. 1950. Michurin fruit varieties in Krasnoyar kray. Agro-biologiya, No. 3, 52-6.

Petrakhilev, I.M. 1950. Michurin varieties in Krasnodar kray. Sad i ogorod, No. 6, 15-9.

Petrov, A.I. 1939. Attempt at protecting heat-loving woody plants in winter at the All-Union Agricultural Exhibit in Moscow. Zelenoye stroitel'stvo, No. 3-4, 65-71.

Petrovich, D. 1901. Investigation of the causes of death of apple trees in the village of Kuntsevka, Samarskiy district. Plodovodstvo, No. 7, 713-25.

Petunin, I.M. 1949. Winterkilling of winter wheat and rye. Tr. Tsentr. in-ta progn., No. 18(45), 36-57.

Pilipenko, F.S. 1951. Training hardy eucalyptus species. Agrobiologiya, No. 6, 80-91.

Pisarev, B. Ye., and M.D. Zhilkina. 1950. Direction of changes in Moskovka seed dormancy. Selektsiya i semenobodstvo, No. 3, 14-20.

Podufalyy, T.I. 1949. Methods of holding water and fertilizers in gardens. Sad i ogorod, No. 8, 9-10.

Pokrovskiy, V.N., and S.G. Merabyan. 1936. Photoperiodism and vegetation of the tea plant. Sov. subtropiki, No. 12(40), 37-55.

Polishchuk, L.K. 1950. Dynamics of chlorophyll in gourds at low temperatures. Dokl. AN SSSR, No. 3, 529-32.

Polosukhin, A. 1910. An old orchard. Plodovodstvo, No. 6, 510-22.

Ponomarev, I. 1852. A glance at gardening in Perm province. Tr. Vol'n. ekon. ob-va, No. 2, 101-11.

Popov, V.P. 1937. Role of bound water in winter wheat hardiness. Dokl. AN SSSR 14, No. 1, 49-52.

Potapenko, G.I. 1932. Winter of 1928/29 and mass destruction of woody plantings in Odessa. Bot. zhurn. 17, No. 5-6, 530-47.

Poyarkova, A.I. 1924. Correlation between depth of winter dormancy, conversion of reserve substances, and cold resistance in woody plants. Tr. Leningr. ob-va yestestvoisp. 54, pt. 3, 91-108.

Prokof'yev, S.P. 1949. Forest belts on berry plantations. Sad i ogorod, No. 8, 14.

Prokoshev, S.M. 1934. Physiological significance of glutathione. Sots. rasteniyevodstvo, seriya A, No. 11, 41-53.

Prokoshev, S.M., and Ye. I. Danchev. 1947. Protein metabolism in injured potato tubers. Biokhimiya, No. 4, 356-64.

Protsenko, D.F. 1939. Effect of low temperatures on open buds and flowers of certain fruits. Sov. botanika, No. 1, 61-8.

Protsenko, D.F. 1948. Effect of high and low temperatures on the fermentative capacity of certain races of yeast. Naukovi zapiski KDU 7, No. 6, 115-30.

Protsenko, D.F., T.M. Dubinskaya, and Ye. F. Yadrintseva. 1949. Effect of training conditions on the hardiness of winter crops. Ibid. Izd. Kievsk. gos. un-ta 8, No. 5, 91-116.

Protsenko, D.F., and L.K. Polishchuk. 1947. Heat-producing capacity as a supplementary method of determining the hardiness of fruits. Dokl. AN SSSR 55, No. 8, 781-4.

Protsenko, D.F., and L.K. Polishchuk. 1948. Effect of low temperatures on physiological processes in certain greenhouse plants. Naukovi zapiski KDY 7, No. 6, 147-62.

Protsenko, D.F., and L.K. Polishchuk. 1948. Physiological and biochemical characteristics of hardiness in fruits. Izd. Kievsk. gos. un-ta im. T.G. Shevchenko, 118 pp.

Pruss, A. 1938. Pomegranates of Surkhan-Dar'inskiy district. Sov. subtropiki, No. 3(43), 27-37.

Prutzkova, M.G. 1947. Winter wheat in the Central Chernozem Zone. Sov. agronomiya, No. 7, 9-14.

Pryanishnikov, D.N. 1891. Connection between the anatomical structure of the beetroot and its sugar content and tendency to produce beet-seed stalks. Vestn. russk. sel'sk. khoz-va, No. 7, 449-53.

Pryanishnikov, D.N., and I.V. Yakushkin. 1938. Field crops (plant production). 10th ed. Moscow, Sel'khozgiz.

Psarev, G.M. 1938. Effect of properties acquired from photoperiodic action on the behavior of soy offspring. Sov. botanika, No. 4-5, 11-20.

Puriyevich, K. 1893. Formation and decomposition of organic acids in higher plants. Kiev.

Puriyevich, K. 1899. Physiological investigations of plant respiration. Zap. Kiyevsk. ob-va yestestvoispyt. 17, 1-57.

Pyatnikskiy, S.S. 1946. Experimental formation of interspecific hybrids in the genus Quercus. Dokl. AN SSSR 52, No. 4, 345-7.

Rabinovich, A. 1909. Conditions governing the tolerance by fruit trees of frosts. Plodovodstvo, No. 6, 557-9.

Rabinovich. A. 1910. One of the causes of apple failures. Ibid., No. 4, 345-7.

Rabinovich, A. 1911. Effect of quality of soil on degree of tolerance of fruit trees. Ibid., No. 2, 139-41.

Radchenko, S.I. 1949. New data on the morphogenesis of winter grains. Tr. In-ta fiziol. rast. im. K.A. Timiryazeva AN SSSR 6, No. 2, 210-3.

Rakitin, Yu. V., F. Bulatov, and A. Stolyarov. 1935. Action of different factors accelerating the ripening of fruits. Izv. AN SSSR, No. 9, 1123-8.

Raskatov, P.B. 1939. Investigation of the water regime of trees and shrubs in winter in the forest-steppes of European U.S.S.R. Sov. botanika, No. 3, 55-65.

Razumov, V.I. 1935. Hardiness in certain potato species. Tr. po prikh. bot., gen. i sel., seriya 3, No. 6, 221-6.

Razumov, V.I. 1948. Some of our postwar work in the field of plant physiology. Yarovizatsiya, No. 3, 19-28.

Regel', E. 1860. Acclimatization of plants. Vestn. Ross. ob-va sadovodstva, No. 3, 28-40.

Rego, 1853. Professor Rego's report on travels in the central provinces of Russia to inspect horticulture. Zhurn. sadovodstva, 3-5.

Reva, I. 1890. Winterkilling of young crops. S.-kh. listok, No. 24, 222-4.

Reva, I. 1890. Preservation of young crops from cold injury. Ibid., No. 37, 362-3.

Reymers, F.E. 1939. Effect of length of day on the formation of flower shoots of the table beet planted at various times during the winter. Dokl. VASKhNIL, No. 2-3.

Rikhter, A.A. 1927. Investigations of hardiness in plants. 1. Dynamics of soluble carbohydrates in wheat and rye during the winter. Zhurn. opytn. agronomii Yugo-Vostoka 4, No. 2, 326-46.

Rikhter, A.A., and A.I. Grechyshnikov. 1932. Physiological processes underlying the death of winter grains from "damping off" or "suffocation" under ice. Izv. otd. matem. i yestestv. nauk (OMEN) AN SSSR 3, 391-408.

Rikhter, A.A., and T.A. Krasnosel'skaya. 1945. Arousal of buds of woody plants from winter dormancy. Dokl. AN SSSR 31, No. 6, 608-11.

Rodionov, V. 1936. Protection of citrus from frosts in the Sochi region. Sov. subtropiki, No. 9, 72-5.

Rokhlin, E. Ya. 1936. Age characteristics of yeast cells. Izv. AN SSSR, No. 4, 827-35.

Romanov, A.A. 1950. Vulnerability of tree trunks in forest belts. Priroda, No. 5, 52-4.

Rozhalin, L.V. 1945. Conditions for accelerated termination of dormancy in newly harvested potato tubers. Dokl. VASKhNIL, No. 7-8, 9-15.

Rozen'feld, L.M. 1949. Effect of processes of crystallization of water in soil on the overwintering of plants. Agrobiologiya, No. 5, 70-9.

Rubin, B.A. 1936a. Biochemical preservation of vegetables. Ibid., 777-90.

Rubin, B.A. 1936b. Correlation between synthetic and hydrolytic action of sucrose as a characteristic of the onion. Biokhimiya 1, No. 4, 467-78.

Rubin, B.A., and Ye. V. Artsikhovskaya. 1948. Biochemistry of plant resistance to microorganisms. Usp. sovr, biol. 25, No. 1, 27-48.

Rubin, B.A., Ye. V. Artsikhovskaya, and V.M. Ivanova. 1948. Significance of oxidation processes in citrus hardiness. Dokl. AN SSSR 60, No. 6, 1009-12.

Rubin, B.A., and N.M. Sisakyan. 1949. Enzymic systems of Michurin apple varieties. Sb. Problemy biokhimiya v michurinskoy biologii 1, 49-80.

Rubin, B.A., and V. Ye. 1949. Role of the enzymic apparatus in adaptive responses to the environment. Dokl. AN SSSR 64, No. 3, 377-80.

Rubin, B.A., and Spirodonova, N.S. 1941. Significance of oxidative activity of plant tissue in the synthesis of ascorbic acid. Dokl. AN SSSR 31, No. 6, 608-11.

Rubin, S. 1937. Preparing for the winter. Sov. subtropiki 10(38), 3-5.

Rubinshteyn, D.L. 1947. General physiology. Moscow, Medgiz, 647 pp.

Rudoy, A.I. 1951. Salt tolerance and winter hardiness of certain Azov salt marshes. Bot. zhurn. 36, No. 1, 66-7.

Rusanov, N.M. 1950. Fruit growing in Karaganda oblast. Agrobiologiya, No. 1, 108-15.

Ryadnova, I.M. 1947. Ways of strengthening the cold hardiness of the peach in Krasnodar. Sad i ogorod, No. 10, 70-1.

Ryadnova, I.M. 1950. Dormancy of fruit buds and nature of pear fruiting. Agrobiologiya, No. 1, 130-4.

Ryadnova, I.M. 1951. Development of fruit buds in the fall-winter period and their winter hardiness.

Ryazantsev, A.V. 1930. Seasonal changes in the assimilation apparatus of certain evergreens. Izv. Biol. in-ta pri Permskom un-te 7, No. 3, 105-32.

Ryazantsev, A.V. 1934. Winter transpiration of trees and its significance in their geographical distribution. Izv. Permsk. biol. in-ta 9, No. 1-3, 71-86.

Ryazantsev, A.V. 1937. Movement of the transpiration flow in tree branches in the winter. Sb. nauchn.-issled. rabot Permskogo s.-kh, in-ta, No. 6, 133-55.

Ryazantsev, A.V. 1937a. Involvement of individual elements of the surface of tree branches in winter transpiration. Ibid., 157-67.

Ryazantsev, A.V. 1949. Intake of water through the root system of trees in cold weather. Tr. In-ta fiziol. rast. im. K.A. Timiryazeva AN SSSR 6, No. 2, 214-24.

Ryazantsev, A.V. 1950. Problems related to the water regime of trees. Avtoref. diss. d-r biol. nauk Molotovsk. s.-kh. in-ta. Molotov.

Ryndin, N.V. 1937. A new solution of the lemon problem. Sov. subtropiki, No. 11(27), 56-9.

Ryndin, N.V. 1947. Relative hardiness of citrus plants. Dokl. VASKhNIL, No. 3, 25-7.

Rytov, M.V. 1890. Seed fruit trees. Plodovodstvo, No. 11, 486-88.

Rytov, M.V. 1897. Our fruit growing. Ibid., No. 2, 112-9.

Rytov, M.V. 1898. Changes in the Antonovka apple induced by a wilding. Ibid., No. 10, 803-4.

Rytov, M.V. 1901. Russian cucumbers. Ibid., No. 1, 2-28.

Sabinin, D.A. 1940. Mineral nutrition of plants. Moscow-Leningrad, Izd-vo AN SSSR, 307 pp.

Sabinin, D.A. 1949. Significance of the root system in the vital activity of plants. 9-e timiryazevskoye chteniye. Izd-vo AN SSSR, 48 pp.

Sablinskaya-Ivanova, B.I. 1935. Effect of mineral fertilizers on the winter hardiness of winter wheat. Sots. rasteniyevodstvo, seriay A, No. 16, 37-53.

Safoterov, N.K. 1937. Role of radiant energy of oil heaters to warm citrus. Sov. subtropiki, No. 10(38), 14-8.

Safoterov, N.K., and G.B. Nadaraya. 1936. Winter shields for lemon trees. Ibid., No. 9, 8-23.

Sakharov, N.L., D.A. Ponomarenko, and O.A. Pilyugina. 1934. Sowing times of spring and winter wheat and harmful insects. Sots. zern. khoz-vo 3, No. 1, 23-34.

Saks, A.I. 1934. Methods of diagnosing winter grains during the wintering period. Sots. rasteniyevodstvo, No. 12, 127-40.

Saks, A.I. 1948. An investigation of winter wheat varieties for resistance to frost and to soil dryness. Izv. AN SSSR, No. 5-6, 1187-1215.

Saltykovskiy, M.I. 1928. Spring dying off of winter grains. Zhurn. opytn. agronomii Yugo-Vostoka 6, No. 2, 1-24.

Saltykovskiy, M.I. 1929. Winter hardiness in winter grains. Ibid. 7, No. 2, 1-88.

Saltykovskiy, M.I. 1934. Methods of studying and testing the hardiness of winter grains in the field. Tr. po sel. Sarat. sel.-gen. stantsii 1, 57-81.

Saltykovskiy, M.I. 1934a. Summer death or sterility of winter grains. Ibid., 33-56.

Saltykovskiy, M.I. 1935. Determination of cold hardiness of winter grains.

Dokl. AN SSSR 3(8), No. 7, 321-4.

Saltykovskiy, M.I. 1936. Waterlogging of winter wheat. Sots. zern. khoz-vo, No. 4, 13-20.

Saltykovskiy, M.I. 1937. Causes of intermediate cold hardiness of first-generation wheat hybrids. Dokl. AN SSSR 14, No. 4, 235-40.

Saltykovskiy, M.I. 1939. Cold hardiness of first-generation wheat-wheatgrass hybrids. Dokl. VASKhNIL, No. 2-3.

Saltykovskiy, M.I. 1940. Methods of preventing death of and injury to winter crops during the wintering period. Selektsiya i semenovodstvo, No. 8-9.

Saltykovskiy, M.I., and Ye. S. Saprygina. 1935. Hardiness of winter grains at various stages of development. Dokl. AN SSSR 4(9), No. 1, 92-6.

Saltykovskiy, M.I., and Ye. S. Saprygina. 1940. A method of determining the hardiness of winter grains. Ibid. 26, No. 6, 544-7.

Saltykovskiy, M.I., and Ye. S. Saprygina. 1944. Strengthening the hardiness of wheat. Ibid. 45, No. 8-369-72.

Saltykovskiy, M.I., and Ye. S. Saprygina. 1946. Strengthening the hibernation of wheat. Ibid. 52, No. 3, 265-8.

Saltykovskiy, M.I., and Ye. S. Saprygina. 1953. Effect of winter drought on winter crops. Tr. In-ta fiziol. rast. 8, No. 1, 380-6.

Sambuk, F.V. 1937. Limit of forests on Taimyr. Bot. zhurn. SSSR 22, No. 2, 209-24.

Samofal, S.A. 1936. Winter-spring drought in forests and control measures. Nauchn. zap. Voronezhsk. s.-kh. in-ta i Voronezhsk. lesokul't. in-ta 4(19), 95-101.

Samoylov, T.P. 1948. Longevity of fruit crops in Primorskiy kray. Mater. k izuch. prirodnykh resursov Dal'n. Vost. Dal'nevost. n.-i. baza im. V.L. Komarova, No. 1, 21-4.

Sannikov, V.S. 1949. Increasing the hardiness of fruit trees. Sad i ogorod, No. 1, 17.

Sapozhnikova, S.A. 1950. Microclimate and local climate. Gidromet. izd., 1-240.

Saprygina, Ye. S. 1935. Hardiness of spring wheat. Dokl. AN SSSR 3, No. 7, 325-8.

Saprygina, Ye. S. 1940. Use of natural cold in selection of winter grains. Selektsiya i semenovodstvo, No. 8-9.

Saprygina, Ye. S. 1941. Hardiness of wheat hybrids in relation to the phasic characteristics of the parents. Dokl. AN SSSR 30, No. 9, 835-8.

Savel'yev, N.M. 1940. Effect of close-furrow sowing and subsequent hilling on yield. Dokl. VASKhNIL, No. 11.

Selyaninov, G.T. 1932. Methods of combatting frosts. Sots. rasteniyevodstvo, No. 2, 86-107.

Selyaninov, G.T. 1934. Climatic basis for zoning the Soviet moist tropics. Sov. subtropiki, No. 1, 13-30.

Selyaninov, G.T. 1936. Combatting frosts in the Soviet subtropics. Ibid., No. 10(26), 9-17.

Selyaninov, G.T. 1941. Status of studies on climatic conditions of overwintering plants in the U.S.S.R. Opytn. agronomiya, No. 4.

Semakin, K.S. 1940. Effect of mineral fertilizers on the hardiness of greenhouse plants at low temperatures. Sov. botanika, No. 5-6, 189-201.

Semakin, K.S., and L.A. Znamenskaya. 1939. Effect of differences in soil moisture on the lemon's hardiness. Ibid., 95-8.

Semakin, K.S., and Ye. S. Moroz. 1940. Effect of mineral fertilizers on citrus hardiness. Eksp. botanika, No. 5, 198-219.

Semakin, K.S., Ye. S. Moroz, and V.K. Abashkin. 1937. Effect of potassium fertilizers on citrus hardiness. Sov. subtropiki, No. 12(40), 71-4.

Serbinov, I.L. 1912. Bacterial cancer of fruit trees, berry bushes, and other horticultural and agricultural plants. Plodovodstvo, No. 9, 787-95.

Serbinov, I.L. 1916. A new bacterial disease of fruit trees in Russia. Ibid., No. 4-5, 167-73.

Sergeyev, L.I. 1936. Resistance of plants to low temperatures. Izv. AN SSSR, No. 4, 791-802.

Sergeyev, L.I., and A.M. Lebedev. 1936. A theory of physiological hardiness in cultivated grasses. Bot. zhurn. SSSR 21, No. 2, 131-52.

Sergeyev, L.I., A.M. Lebedev, and L.A. Akif'yeva. 1935. Correlation of cold hardiness with tolerance of soil salinity. Dokl. AN SSSR 4, No. 3, 149-52.

Sergeyev, L.I., and K.A. Sergeyeva. 1949. Physiological variability in olive and feijoa leaves. Tr. In-ta fiziol. rast. 6, 2, 239-48.

Sergeyeva, K.A. 1948. Age changes in the leaf structure of the olive family. Dokl. AN SSSR 61, No. 4, 745-7.

Shan-Girey, 1892. What is acclimatization? Plodovodstvo, No. 1, 4-9.

Shaposhnikova, Z.P. 1935. Injury to the tillering nodes of winter wheat by low temperatures. Tr. po prikl. bot., gen. i sel., seriya 3, No. 6, 121-44.

Shapoval, A.G. 1948. Cultivation of winter crops. Moscow, Sel'khozgiz, 96 pp.

Sharapov, N.I. 1938. Production of reserve forms of oil and protein in plants in relation to the climate. Sov. botanika, 65-92.

Sharapov, N.I. 1941. Production of starch and sugars in plants. Ibid., Nos. 5-6, 49-67.

Shcherbakov, A.P. 1938. Effect of potassium on the water-holding capacity of plant tissues and carbohydrate metabolism in leaves. Tr. konferentsii po pochvoved. i fiziol. kul't. rasteniy 2, 249-60.

Shestakov, M.A. 1890. Thoughts on Siberian fruit growing. Plodovodstvo, No. 8-9, 414-8.

Shestakov, M.A. 1891. Acclimatization. Ibid., No. 1, 37-8.

Shestakov, V. Ye. 1936. Frost resistance of rye-wheat hybrids in relation to stages of development. Selektsiya i semenovodstvo, No. 1, 14-6.

Shestakov, V. Ye. 1936a. Frost resistance of winter crops at the light stage of development. Dokl. AN SSSR 3, No. 8, 395-8.

Shestakov, V. Ye., and A.D. Smirnova. 1936. Hardening temperature and differentiation of the ear embryo in winter wheat while passing through the light stage of development. Ibid., 399-403.

Shestakov, V. Ye., and L.I. Sergeyev. 1936. Changes in permeability of protoplasm and dynamics of frost resistance in winter grains in relation to passage through the light stage. Ibid. 4, No. 1, 27-9.

Shestakov, V. Ye., and L. I. Sergeyev. 1937. Changes in frost resistance and properties of protoplasm in winter wheat while passing through the light stage. Bot. zhurn. SSSR 22, No. 4, 351-63.

Sheyerman, A. 1903. Observations on fruit growing in Yekaterinoslav province. Plodovodstvo, No. 6, 503-8.

Sheynis, V.N. 1943. Freezing (general cooling). Voprosy patologii i lecheniya. Medgiz, 95 pp.

Shimanskiy, N.K. 1940. Directed change of the nature of spring wheat Erythrospermum 1160 into winter wheat. Yarovizatsiya, No. 4(39).

Shishkov, S.N. 1857. Effect of cold on plants. Zhurn. sadovodstva, No. 3, 345-59

Shkol'nik, M.A. 1950. Significance of trace elements in the life of plants and in agriculture. Izd-vo AN SSSR, 512 pp.

Shmelev, I. Kh. 1935. Frost resistance of fruit trees and methods of determining it. Tr. po prikl. bot., gen. i sel., seriya 3, No. 6, 263-77.

Shmelov, I. Kh. 1937. Frost resistance of Michurin apple varieties according to laboratory data. Za michurinskoye plodovodstvo, No. 6, 39-55.

Shmelov, I. Kh. 1940. Frost resistance of Soviet and foreign winter wheat varieties and the direct laboratory method of determining it. Tezisy dokl. soveshch. po fiziol. rast. Izd. AN SSSR, 161-3.

Shmidt, P. Yu. 1948. Anabiosis. Moscow-Leningrad. Izd-vo AN SSSR, 376 pp.

Shmit, A. 1901. Adverse climatic factors of Russian gardens in comparison with the situation in Western Europe and North America. Plodovodstvo, No. 3, 214-56; No..4, 317-51; No. 5, 406-41; No. 6, 494-518.

Shokhin, M.V. 1951. Artificial sprinkling to combat frosts. Byull. Glavn. bot. sada AN SSSR, No. 10, 70-1.

Shostakovskiy, S.A. 1937. Xerophilia and species formation. Sov. botanika, No. 3, 20.

Shreder, R.I. 1882. Fruit growing. Izd. Russk. ob-va lyubit. plodov i sadovodstva v Moskve, 91 pp.

Shreder, R.I. 1890. Fruit growing in the north. Plodovodstvo, No. 1, 1-9.

Shreder, R.I. 1898. Reciprocal influence of stock and graft and propagation of dwarf fruit trees. Sad i ogorod, No. 4, 51-4 and No. 5, 68-72.

Shreder, R.R. 1937. Increasing the hardiness of the peach. Sots. nauka i tekhnika, No. 9, 41-9.

Shub, D. 1935. Methods of controlling the winterkilling of strawberries. Plodoovoshchnoye khozyaystvo, No. 10, 59-60.

Shub, D. 1936. Control of winterkilling of strawberries. Nauchnoye plodovodstvo, No. 1, 63-75.

Shul'gin, A.I. 1940. Overwintering conditions of farm crops in the high-altitude regions of the Northern Caucasus. Dokl. VASKhNIL, No. 4.

Shul'gin, A. 1940. Role of the top layer of soil in the overwintering of winter crops. Sov. agronomiya, No. 8-9.

Shul'gin, A.I. 1949. Temperature regime of the top layers of soil in winter in the forest steppe of Altai kray. Tr. Tsentr. in-ta prognozov 18, No. 45, 58-61.

Shul'ts, A.D. 1934. Methods of cultivating wheat in the north. Semenovodstvo, No. 6, 25-9.

Shulyndin, A.F. 1951. Hardiness of soft wheat obtained from hard spring wheat. Agrobiologiya, No. 5, 3-7.

Shumkov, I. 1904. Cherry orchards in Nikolayev district, Samarskaya province. Plodovodstvo, No. 9, 692-6.

Sidorin, M.I. 1929. Fall yellowing of leaves. Zhurn. Russ. bot. ob-va 14, No. 4, 459-77.

Sidorin, M.I. 1933. Fading of chlorophyll in direct sunlight in killed plant tissues. Bot. zhurn. SSSR 18, No. 3, 127-36.

Sigalov, B. Ya., and M.V. Shokhin. 1952. Wintering of lawns. Byull. Glavn. bot. sada AN SSSR, No. 12, 73-7.

Simirenko, L. 1898. Winterkilling of roots in the commonest fruit stocks. Plodovodstvo, No. 5, 371-85.

Sisakyan, N.M. 1937. Direction of action of invertase as a sign of drought resistance and early ripening in cultivated plants. Izv. AN SSSR, No. 6, 1770-80.

Sisakyan, N.M. 1937-8. Direction of enzymic action as a sign of drought resistance in cultivated plants. Soobshch. 1 and 2. Biokhimiya, No. 2, 687 and No. 3, 796.

Sisakyan, N.M. 1940a. Biochemical characteristics of drought resistance. Moscow-Leningrad, Izd-vo AN SSSR.

Sisakyan, N.M. 1940b. Enzymic characteristics of plant resistance to drought and frost. Tezisy dokl. soveshch. po fiziol. rast., 152-3. Izd-vo AN SSSR.

Sisakyan, N.M., and others. 1947. Daily pattern of adsorption capacity in plants in relation to enzymic synthesis of sucrose. Dokl. AN SSSR 57, No. 5, 479-80.

Sisakyan, N.M., and T.P. Verkhovtseva. 1948. Aftereffect of different temperatures on the adsorption of invertase on tissues of higher plants. Ibid. 59, No. 1, 107-9.

Sisakyan, N.M., V.K. Karapetyan, and A.M. Kobyakova. 1949. Direction of enzymic conversion of carbohydrates of hereditary spring wheat forms changed into winter forms. Sb. Probl. biokhim. v michurinsk. biol., 102-12.

Sisakyan, N.M., and A.M. Kobyakova. 1947. Direction of enzymic action as a sign of drought resistance in cultivated plants. Biokhimiya, No. 5, 377-82.

Sisakyan, N.M., A.M. Kobyakova, and N.A. Vasil'yeva. 1947. Effect of osmotic concentration on the adsorption and elution of invertase by tissues of higher plants. Ibid. 12, No. 1, 7-18.

Sisakyan, N.M., and A. Kobyakova. 1949. Enzymic activity of proplasmatic structures. Ibid. 14, No. 1, 86-93.

Sisakyan, N.M., and B.A. Rubin. 1944. Cause of age inactivity of peroxidase in apple leaves. Ibid. 9, No. 6, 307-11.

Skarzhinskiy, V.N. 1853. A few words on grass cultivation in Novorossiyskiy kray. Zapiski Ob-va sel'sk. khoz-va Yuzhnoy Rossii, No. 2.

Skhiyereli, V.S. 1938. Effect of the winter of 1934-1935 on woody plants. Tbilisskogo botanicheskogo sada. Tr. Tbilissk. bot. sada 3, 201-15.

Skorobogatov, M. 1937. Experience in agroclimatic zoning. Sov. subtropiki, No. 2(30), 63-4.

Smelov, S.P. 1937. Vegetative reproduction of meadow grasses. Bot. zhurn. SSSR 22, No. 3, 296-325.

Smelov, S.P., and A.S. Morozov. 1939. Localization of reserve plastic substances in meadow grasses. Ibid. 24, No. 2, 157-66.

Sobchanov, V.I. 1864. Short survey of horticulture in Moscow before Peter I. Zhurn. sadovodstva, No. 4, 70-84.

Sofronov, M. 1902. Effect of the stock on the graft and vice versa. Plodovodstvo, No. 10, 723-45.

Sokolov, M.I. 1949. Cultivation of decumbent fruit trees. Sad i ogorod, No. 10, 23-6.

Sokolova, N.P. 1949. Meteorological evaluation of wintering conditions, growth, and development of winter wheat at different periods of winter sowing. Tr. Tsentr. in-ta progn., No. 18(45), 18-35.

Sokolova, N.F. 1935. Hardiness of the olive on the southern shore of the Crimea in relation to the water balance (winter drought). Tr. Gos. Nikitskiy bot. sada 21, No. 1, 1-35.

Sokolova, N.F. 1940. Resistance of the peach and almond to low temperatures. Tezisy dokl. soveshch. po fiziol. rast. Izd-vo AN SSSR, 155-6.

Sokolovskaya, A.P. 1937. Karyogeographic investigation of Agrostis L. Bot.

zhur. SSSR 22, No. 5, 457-80.

Sokolovskaya A.P., and O.S. Strelkova. 1938. The phenomenon of polyploidy in the mountains of the Pamirs and Altai. Dokl. AN SSSR 21, No. 1-2, 68-71.

Sokolovskaya, A.P., and O.S. Strelkova. 1940. Karyological investigation of high-altitude flora of the main Caucasian range and the geographic distribution of polyploids. Ibid. 29, No. 5-6, 413-6.

Sokolovskaya, A.P., and O.S. 1941. Polyploidy and karyological races in the Arctic (an investigation of flora on Kolguyev Island). Ibid. 32, No. 2, 145-7.

Sovetov, A. 1859. Summary of a dissertation for the degree of master of agriculture and forestry. Tr. Vol'n. ekon. ob-va 4, appendix: Zapiski Yarosl. ob-va sel'sk. khoz-va za 1858.

Sovetov, A.V. 1891. Smoky fires as a means of protecting plants from morning frosts. Vest. russk. sel'sk. khoz-va, No. 1, 1-3.

Spichenko, N. 1910. Amateur cultivation of tub fruit plants in the north. Ibid., No. 5, 420-4.

Stebut, A.I. 1916. Anabiosis in connection with the overwintering of winter crops. Vestn. sel'sk. khoz-va. 1939. Experiments with photoperiodism to increase the hardiness of trees in the Urals. Ural'sk. opytn. st. zelen. stroit., No. 1, 67-93.

Stepanov, V.N. 1945. Frost hardiness of farm crops at various stages of development. Dokl. Mosk. s.-kh. akad. im. K.A. Timiryazeva, No. 3, 28-32.

Stepanov, V.N. 1948. Characteristics of farm crops in respect to frost hardiness. Sov. agronomiya, No. 4, 82-7.

Stoletov, V.N. 1948. Some experimental data on the nature of earing in winter crops when planted in the spring. Tr. In-ta gen. AN SSSR 16, 38-59.

Strelkova, O.S. 1938. Karyosystematic description of Alopecurus L. Tr. Petergof. biol. in-ta 16, 135-55.

Stroganov, B.P. 1940. Role of oxidation processes in physiological immunity of plants. Sb. nauchn. rab. komsom.-biologov AN SSSR, 27-47.

Struve, V. 1927. Wintering of meadow grasses in the river valley of the Marusino experimental plant breeding station. Nauchno-agron. zhurn., No. 10, 694-6.

Sukhorukov, K.T., and K. Bol'shakova. 1946. Free and bound hormone of cell division. Dokl. AN SSSR 53, No. 5, 475-8.

Sukhorukov, K.T., and O. Semovskikh. 1946. Action of auxins on plant cells. Ibid. 54, No. 1, 85-9.

Sulukadze, T.S. 1939. Determination of the amount of ice in frozen winter plants. Dokl. AN SSSR 23, No. 4, 370-2.

Sulukadze, T.S. 1940. Determination of the amount of ice in frozen winter plants and the protective function of the sugars. Tezisy dokl. soveshch. po fiziol. rast., 156-7, Izd-vo AN SSSR.

Sulukadze, T.S. 1945. Amount of ice in winter plants at various low temperatures and the protective function of the sugars. Dokl. Vsesoyuzn. soveshch. po fiziol. rast. 2, Izd-vo AN SSSR, 134-46.

Surozh, I. 1890. Oil as a protective substance of trees. VIII S"yezd russk. yestestv. i vrachey v Spb., No. 5, 28.

Tarapukhin. 1893. Sowing winter wheat in November. Vestn. russk. sel'sk. khoz-va, No. 43, 701-15.

Tarachkov, A. 1858. Gardens and gardening in Orlov province. Zhurn.

sadovodstva, No. 6, 311-23.

Tauson, V.O. 1945. Connection of the synthetic processes with respiration. Izv. AN SSSR, seriya biol., No. 5, 514-28.

Tauson, V.O. 1945. Conditions for storage of fat and spore formation in Aspergillus flavus. Ibid., 598-611.

Terpilo, N.I. 1935. Determination of the viability of winter crops. Sots. zern. khoz-vo, No. 4, 88-95.

Terpilo, N.I. 1935. Overwintering of wheat. Ibid., No. 5, 61-75.

Terpugov, D.I. 1948. Effect of periodic thawing on the hardiness of onion bulbs. Dokl. AN SSSR 59, No. 6, 1199-1200.

Tetyurev, V. Cause of low germinating power in freshly harvested wheat seeds. Dokl. VASKhNIL, No. 11-12, 3-10.

Tikhomirov, B.A. 1941. Dynamics of polar and vertical limits of forests in Eurasia. Sov. botanika, No. 5-6, 23-38.

Tikhomirov, F. 1901. Acclimatization of the myrobalan in Peterburg province. Plodovodstvo, No. 11, 874-9.

Timiryazev, K.A. Writings, I-X. 1937-1940. Moscow, Sel'khozgiz.

Timiryazev, K.A. 1865. Short sketch of Darwin's theory. The first edition of the book was called in later editions "Charles Darwin and His Theory." Ibid. VII, 13-654.

Timiryazev, K.A. 1878. Life of plants. 1st ed. Ibid., IV, 11-337.

Timiryazev, K.A. 1890. Factors in organic evolution. In the book: VIII s''yezd russk. yestestv. i vrachey v Spb. [Eighth Congress of Russian Naturalists and Physicians in St. Petersburg], Obshch. otd. 62-9. Ibid. V, 107-42.

Timiryazev, K.A. 1892. The historical method in biology. Ibid. VI, 18-237.

Timiryazev, K.A. 1898. Plant physiology as a basis of rational agriculture. Ibid. III, 48-88.

Timiryazev, K.A. 1906. Agriculture and plant physiology. Ibid. III, 13-368.

Timofeyeva, M.T. 1933. Dynamics of hardiness in winter plants during the winter and characteristics of hardiness in winter wheat and winter rye. Tr. po prikl. bot., gen. i sel., seriya 3, No. 3, 253-72.

Timofeyeva, M.T. 1935a. How to deal with ice crusts. Semenovodstvo, No. 2, 30-31.

Timofeyeva, M.T. 1935b. Hardiness of winter grains in relation to phasic development and hardening of plants. Dokl. AN SSSR 1, No. 1, 61-7.

Timofeyeva, M.T. 1935c. Role of development and hardening in the frost resistance of crops. Sots. rasteniyevodstvo, seriay A, No. 15, 39-52.

Timofeyeva-Tyulina, M.T. 1948. Causes of death of winter grains in the Central Chernozem Belt. Agrobiologiya, No. 5, 78-92.

Timofeyeva-Tyulina, M.T. 1949. Physiological characteristics of hardiness in winter wheat and rye. Selektsiyz i semenovodstvo, No. 2, 27-31.

Titlyakov, A. 1941. Early removal of snow from fields as a farming technique on Kamchatka. Dokl. VASKhNIL, No. 8.

Titlyakov, A.A., and Ye. G. Lebedeva. 1940. Field crops on Kamchatka. Dal'nevostochnyy nauchno-issled. in-t zemledeniya i zhivotnovodstva. Sb. nauchn. rabot, No. 3, 101-26.

Tiunova, K.P. 1936. Causes of winter-spring death of winter wheat. Sb. Voprosy agrotekhniki pshenitsy v nechernozemnoy polose. Izd. In-ta severn. zern. khoz-va, 126-48.

Tokar', L.O., P.P. Sychev, and M.M. Shvetsov. 1936. Use of own-root fruit trees. Saratovskoye krayevoye idz-vo. 144 pp.

Tolmachev, A.I. 1940. Persistence of winter and spring qualities in certain varieties of plants. Sov. botanika, No. 5-6, 342-4.

Toporkov, S. 1899. A contribution to the biology of winter wheat. Sel'sk. khoz-vo i lesovodstvo, CXCII, 1-44, 241-90, 481-523.

Topuridze, Ye. M. 1938. Technique of crossing sour oranges. Sov. subtropiki, No. 2(41), 41-8.

Tovarnitskiy, V.I. 1928. Characteristics of wheat hardiness from the sugar content. Byull. Ivanivskoy dosv. selekts. stantsii, No. 7-8, 41-60.

Tregubenko, M. Ya. 1940. Decrease in alfalfa frost resistance in relation to age. Dokl. VASKhNIL, 23-4.

Tregubenko, M. Ya. 1947. Decrease in cold resistance of alfalfa in relation to aging. Ibid., No. 4, 13-5.

Tregubenko, M. Ya. 1940. Effect of growing conditions on alfalfa frost and winter hardiness. Naukovi zapiski KDU 8, No. 5, 117-34. Izd. Kievsk. gos. un-ta.

Tregubenko, M. Ya., and F.K. Rak. 1946. Frost hardiness, winter hardiness, and yield of clover the first year of life in relation to time of sowing. Dokl. VASKhNIL, No. 5-6, 18-22.

Tregubenko, M. Ya. and F.K. Rak. 1949. Contraction of the alfalfa root. Ibid., No. 2, 9-14.

Tropin, A.V. 1950. The Manchurian walnut at the sources of the Volga. Lesnoye khoz-vo, No. 9, 61.

Trukhina, A.T. 1948. Wheat hardiness in Siberia. Tr. In-ta gen. AN SSSR 16, 60-8.

Tsabel', N. 1862. Plant physiology. Appendix to the journal Vestnik Russkogo ob-va sadovodstva.

Tseplin, K. 1848. Observations on the action of snowless frosts on winter crops of 1847-1848 in Smolensk province. Zhur. sel'sk. khoz-va i ovtsevodstva, No. 1, 82-4.

Tseshevskiy, S. 1911. Burning of fruit trees. Zemledel'ch. gazeta, No. 8-9, 334-50.

Tsitsin, N.V. 1934. Winter crops and perennial wheat. Moscow, Sel'khozgiz, 100 pp.

Tsitsin, N.V. 1935. Winter crops and perennial wheat. Wheat-wheatgrass hybrids. Moscow, Sel'khozgiz, 99 pp.

Tsitsin, N.V. 1951. Wheat-wheatgrass hybrids. Izd-vo Mosk. rabochiy, 27 pp.

Tsivinskiy, V.N. 1894. Protecting young winter crops by freezing of the ground. Ibid., No. 17, 369-70.

Tumanov, I.I. 1931. Hardening of winter plants to low temperatures. Tr. po prikl. bot., gen. i sel. 25, 69-109.

Tumanov, I.I. 1933. Physiological foundations of winter hardiness in winter crops. Semenovodstvo, No. 6, 5-8.

Tumanov, I.I. 1933a. Winter-spring death of winter crops in the nonchernozem belt. Sots. rasteniyevodstvo, No. 9, 151-5.

Tumanov, I.I. 1935. Rapid methods of evaluating plant hardiness. Teoreticheskiye osnovy selektsii 1, 753-82. Moscow-Leningrad, Sel'khozgiz.

Tumanov, I.I. 1937. Survey of recent Soviet and foreign literature on winter hardiness in plants. Vestn. s.-kh. literatury, 6-7, 8 and 9-10.

Tumanov, I.I. 1938. Current status of the problem of winter hardiness in plants. Selektsiya i semenovodstvo, No. 2.

Tumanov, I.I. 1940. Physiological foundations of winter hardiness in cultivated plants. Moscow, Sel'khozgiz, 366 pp.

Tumanov, I.I. 1945. Physiology of fall ripening of fruit trees. Izv. AN SSSR, seriya biol., No. 5, 546-66.

Tumanov, I.I. 1947. Causes of death of orchards. Sad i ogorod, No. 7, 45-52.

Tumanov, I.I. 1947. Physiological properties of cultivated plants in the high-altitude regions of the eastern Pamirs. Tr. In-ta fiziol. rast. im. K.A. Timiryazeva AN SSSR 5, No. 2, 88-118.

Tumanov, I.I. 1951. Main achievements of Soviet science in the field of plant hardiness. Khi timiryazevskoye chteniye. Izd-vo AN SSSR, 54 pp.

Tumanov, I.I., and I.N. Borodina. 1929. An investigation of frost resistance of winter crops by direct freezing and indirect methods. Tr. po prikl. bot., gen. i sel. 22, No. 1, 395-400.

Tumanov, I.I., I.N. Borodina, and T.V. Oleynikova. 1935. Role of snow in overwintering of winter crops (damping off). Ibid., seriya 3, No. 6, 3-57.

Tupenevich, S.M. 1936. Fusarium wilt of cereals. Sb. Glavneyshiye vrediteli i bolezni s.-kh. kul'tur v SSSR (obzor za 1935 g.). Izd-vo VASKhNIL, 155-71.

Tupenevich, S.M. 1939. Sclerotinia on winter grains in Kirov oblast and Udmurt ASSR, Tr. Kir. obl. nauchno-issled. in-ta krayev, No. 16, 32 pp.

Tupenevich, S.M. 1940. Reaction of winter wheat varieties to snow mold (Fusarium nivale) in connection with their phasic development. Vestn. zashchity rast., No. 1-2, 260-7.

Tupenevich, S.M. 1940. The snow mold in damping off of winter grains in spring and basis of control measures. Izv. vyssh. kurs. po prikl. zool. i fitopat., No. 10, 5-108. Leningrad.

Tupenevich, S.M., and V.I. Shirko. 1939. Measures to control the destruction of winter crops in spring by Sclerotinia gramineorum Elen. Zashchita rasteniy, No. 18, 85-98.

Turbin, N.V., and Ya. S. Ayzenshtat. 1949. The preliminary mentor method. Agrobiologiya, No. 2, 72-9.

Tyrina, V.A. 1952. Winter-spring sunburns of apple trees in the Maritime Territory and methods of prevention. Avtoref. diss. kand. biol. nauk. Dal'nevost. filial AN SSSR, Vladivostok.

Ukrainskiy, V.T. 1949. Causes of thinning out of alfalfa and sainfoin after the winter. Sov. agronomiya, No. 4, 36-45.

Ul'yanishchev, M.M. 1948. Increased winter hardiness of orchards and vineyards in Voronezh oblast. Sad i ogorod, No. 3, 7.

Uolles [Wallace], A.R. 1878. Tropical nature. Transl. from the English by I. Puzanov. Moscow-Leningrad, Biomedgiz, 1936, 210 pp.

Ursul, A. 1900. Is mounding trees with snow necessary? Plodovodstvo, No. 2, 106.

Urushadze, D.K. 1939. Overwintering of citrus seedlings. Sov. subtropiki, No. 12, 40-2.

Val'dgeym. 1869. Effect of high and low temperatures on plants. Tr. Vol'n. ekon. ob-va, No. 2, 25-8.

Val'ter, G., and V. Alekhin. 1936. Principles of botanical geography. Biomedgiz, 715 pp.

Valyumar, V. 1939. Soviet pineapples. Sov. subtropiki, No. 12, 69.

Vanin, S.I. 1931. Course on forest phytopathology, pt. 1. Diseases and injuries caused by fungi. Moscow, Sel'khozgiz, 326 pp.

Vanin, S.I. 1933. Course on forest phytopathology, pt. II. Bacterial and non-parasitic diseases of trees. Moscow, Sel'khozgiz, 150 pp.

Varenitsa, Ye. T. 1948. Depth of tillering nodes in winter wheat and rye varieties as an indication of hardiness. Selektsiya i semenovodstvo, No. 1, 43-7.

Varnek, N. 1856. Effect of the winter of 1855-1856 in the environs of Kashira. Zhurn. sadovodstva, No. 2, 131-2.

Vasil'yev, V.F., and V.M. Doltnikova, 1935. Effect of mineral fertilizers on the anatomical structure of the sugar beet root. Sov. botaniki, No. 5, 129-34.

Vasil'yev, I.M. 1927a. Changes in water content in the leaves of wheats differing in drought resistance. Reprint from Tr. Sev.-Kavk. assots. n.-i. in-tov 28, No. 7, 1-15.

Vasil'yev, I.M. 1927b. Effect of insufficient soil moisture on the transpiration of wheats differing in drought resistance. Ibid., 1-7.

Vasil'yev, I.M. 1927c. Effect of air temperature on extent of opening of wheat stomata. Ibid., 1-15.

Vasil'yev, I.M. 1927d. Daily pattern of transpiration in wheat. Ibid., 1-33.

Vasil'yev, I.M. 1929. Investigations of drought resistance in wheat. Tr. po prikl. bot., gen. i sel. 22, No. 1, 147-218.

Vasil'yev, I.M. 1931a. Water regime of plants in the sandy desert of South-eastern Kara-Kum. Ibid. 25, 185-272.

Vasil'yev, I.M. 1931b. Effect of drought on transformation of carbohydrates in wheat. Ibid. 25, 185-272.

Vasil'yev, I.M. 1932. Price of disregarding agrotechnics. Sots. zemledeliye, No. 108 (1016).

Vasil'yev, I.M. 1934. Vernalization of winter crops and hardiness. Dokl. AN SSSR 4, No. 3, 154-7.

Vasil'yev, I.M. 1937. Summary of work on vernalization and photoperiodism of the Laboratory of Plant Physiology, All-Union Institute of Grain Culture. Tr. Mosk. doma uchenykh, No. 1, 99-110.

Vasil'yev, I.M. 1938. Shoot development. Dokl VASKhNIL, No. 3-4 (12-13).

Vasil'yev, I.M. 1939a. Physiological principles underlying the method of vernalizing lupine, vetch, and lentils. Tr. Vsesoyuzn. n.-i. in-ta sev. zern. khoz-va i zernobobovykh kul'tur, No. 2.

Vasil'yev, I.M. 1939b. Low growth rate of winter wheat as compared with that of spring wheat at low temperatures. Dokl. AN SSSR 24, No. 1, 84-6.

Vasil'yev, I.M. 1939c. Growth of wheats differing in hardiness during harden-ing. Ibid., No. 2, 196-9.

Vasil'yev, I.M. 1946a. Wherein lie the causes of partial destruction of winter crops in Mordovian ASSR? Sots. zemledeliye, No. 131 (4424).

Vasil'yev, I.M. 1946b. Sowing times of winter crops. Ibid., No. 160 (4454).

Vasil'yev, I.M. 1946c. Hardiness of winter crops in relation to growth during the hardening period. Dokl. Vsesoyuzn. soveshch. po fiziol. rast., No. 1, 120-7.

Vasil'yev, I.M. 1947. Cultivation of fallow and wintering conditions of winter wheat. Sots. zemledeliye, No. 167 (4733).

Vasil'yev, I.M. 1950. Winter-spring "burns" of fruit trees and control measures. Sad i ogorod., No. 1, 15-7.

Vasil'yev, I.M. 1950a. Cultivation of winter wheat in the Maritime Territory. Krasn. znamya (Vladivostok), No. 197 (9759).

Vasil'yev, I.M. 1950b. Let us push forward with growing large-fruited apples in the Maritime Territory. Ibid., No. 244 (9806).

Vasil'yev, I.M. 1951. Method of continuous fall-winter whitewashing of fruit trees and subtropical plants. Moscow, Izd-vo AN SSSR, 1-20.

Vasil'yev, I.M. 1953. Wintering of ornamental plants under city conditions. Moscow, Izd-vo Min. kom, khoz-va RSFSR, 102 pp.

Vasil'yev, I.M. 1953. Plant hardiness. Moscow, Izd-vo AN SSSR, Nauchno-populyarnaya seriya, 192 pp.

Vasil'yev, I.M., and N.G. Vasil'yeva. 1934. Changes in carbohydrate content of wheat during hardening to drought. Izv. AN SSSR, Otd. matem. i yestestv. nauk, No. 9, 1325-40.

Vasil'yev, P.I. 1930. Winter transpiration of annual shoots of several apple varieties. Nauchn.-agron. zhurn. 7, No. 2, 154-65.

Vasil'yev, Ya. Ya. 1938. Geobotanical prerequisites for the distribution of fruit trees in the Far East. Sov. botanika, No. 4-5, 146-8.

Vavilov, P. 1948. Effect of direction of rows on the development and yield of crops. Sov. agronomiya, No. 7, 77-84.

Vedeneyeva, R.S. 1951. Transformation of winter orchard grass into spring orchard grass. Agrobiologiya, No. 3, 30-33.

Veselovskiy, K. 1871. Development of cherry orchards. Tr. Vol'n ekon. ob-va, No. 2, 412-31.

Vetukhova, A.A. 1933. Effect of chilling on the vigor of photosynthesis in sprouts of different winter wheat varieties. In the collection: Povrezhdeniye ozimykh na Ukraine v 1930/1931 g. i metody opredeleniya sostoyaniya i morozoustoychivosti osimykh [Winter crop injury in the Ukraine in 1930/1931 and methods of determining the condition and hardiness of winter crops].

Vetukhova, A.A. 1938. Internal factors in the hardiness of winter plants. Zhurn. In-ta bot. AN UkSSSR, No. 18-19 (26-27), 57-9.

Vetukhova, A.A. 1939. Strengthening hardiness in winter wheat by treating seeds with chemical solutions. Dokl. AN SSSR 24, 603-6.

Vetukhova, A.A. 1940. Strengthening hardiness in plants by treating seeds with chemical substances. Tezisy dokl. soveshch. po fiziol. rast., Izd-vo AN SSSR, 121-2.

Vil'chinskiy, N.M. 1947. Changing the nature of the tea bush. Sov. agronomiya, No. 6, 80-5.

Vonogradov-Nikitin, P.Z. 1936. The propeller in protection of plants. Sov. botanika, No. 3, 13-6.

Vinogradov-Nikitin, P.Z. 1937. Sunburn of mandarins. Sov. subtropiki, No. 7, 74-6.

Vitkevich, V.I. 1941a. Direction of sowing. Dokl. VASKhNIL, No. 6.

Vitkevich, V.I. 1941b. Direction of rows in sowing crops. Sov. agronomiya, No. 2.

Vitkevich, V.I. 1946. Control of frosts. Ibid., No. 5-6, 26-34.

Vitkevich, V.I. 1946a. Solar energy and heavy yield. Ibid., No. 3, 29-35.

Vlasenko, I.A. 1938. Citrus in the Southern Ukraine. Sov. subtropiki, 3 (43), 29-33.

Voblikova, T.V. 1941. Intensity of photosynthesis and leaf respiration in relation to age. Dokl. AN SSSR 33, No. 1, 76-7.

Vol'f, E. 1917. Observations of hardiness in woody plants. Tr. byuro po prikl. bot. 10, No. 2, 11-156.

Vorob'yev, S.O. 1932. Winter crops, steppe "bottoms" and "saucers". Sots. rasteniyevodstvo., No. 2, 124-8.

Voronov, A.G. 1952. Overwintering of herbaceous plants. Bot. zhurn. 27, No. 2, 173-80.

Voskresenskaya, N.P. 1948. Role of potassium in photosynthesis. Dokl.

AN SSSR 59, No. 2, 359-62.

Vostokova, M.N. 1934. Methods of diagnosing the condition of winter plants. Tr. po sel. Sarat. sel.-gen. stantsii, No. 1, 83-98.

Vostokova, M.N. 1936. Regeneration of winter plants during the winter. Selektsiya i semenovodstvo, No. 1, 39-41.

Voyeykov, A.I. 1872. Effect of snowy surfaces on the climate. Izbr. soch., 2, 11-4. Izd-vo AN SSSR, 1949.

Voyeykov, A.I. 1889. Snow, its effect on soil, climate, and weather, and methods of research. Ibid., 15-157.

Voyeykov, A.I. 1884-1887. Climates of the globe, particularly in Russia. Ibid., vol. I, 161-78.

Voyeykov, A.D. 1916. Viticulture north of the present-day limits of commercial winegrowing. Plodovodstvo, No. 1, 1-61.

Vyatkin, V.V. 1934. Simplified cold apparatus. Sov. botanika, No. 2, 64.

Vyatkin, V.V. 1936. Reactions of the fig to low temperatures. Sov. subtropiki, No. 17, 43-9.

Vyatkin, V.V. 1937. Simplified cold apparatus using ice-salt cooling and results of using them. Sov. botaniki, No. 2, 84-93.

Vyurmzer, R. 1935. Biological oxidation and reduction. Transl. from the French. 362 pp.

Vyust, 1850. Causes of poor rye crops in Northern Russia and means of eliminating them. Tr. Vol'n ekon. ob-va. No. 2, 133-46.

Yablokov, A.S. 1936. Interspecific hybridization of walnuts. Sov. subtropiki, No. 4.

Yachevskiy, A.A. 1902. Parasitic diseases of fruit trees. Plodovodstvo, No. 5, 328-55.

Yachevskiy, A.A. 1922. Note on the snow mold Fusarium nivale Sacc. Zhurn. opytn. agronomii Yugo-Vostoka 1, No. 2, 12-9.

Yakovlev, A.G. 1941. Sclerotinia of winter grains and control measures. Kirovsk. obl. izd-vo. g. Kirov, 28 pp.

Yakovlev, V.I. 1935. Effect of late frosts on winter rye during the earing and flowering periods. Tr. po prikl. bot., gen. i sel., seriya 3, No. 6, 153-61.

Yakusheva, Ye. I. 1940. Hardiness of clover and alfalfa in relation to growing conditions in the preceding vegetation period. Tezisy dokl. soveshch. po fiziol. rast. 163-5. Izd-vo AN SSSR.

Yakusheva, Ye. I. 1945. Hardiness of clover and alfalfa in relation to growing conditions in the preceding vegetation period. Dokl. Vsesoyuzn. soveshch. po fiziol. rast. 2, 134-46. Izd-vo AN SSSR.

Yaroslavtsev, I.M. 1948. Frosts. Leningrad, Gidrometeoizdat, 26 pp.

Yasinskiy, M.A. 1940. Major problems in the cultivation of winter wheat in the east. Soobshcheniye 1-e, Sov. agronomiya, No. 1; Soobshcheniye 2-e, No. 7.

Yelenev, L.K. 1938. Photoperiodism of the tung. Sov. subtropiki, No. 6 (46), 51-2.

Yelenev, L.K. 1939. Physiological condition of the lemon with winter shelter. Ibid., No. 12, 29-33.

Yelizarova, S.S. 1937. Inheritance of enzymic characteristics. Izv. AN SSSR, No. 6, 1781-9.

Yenikeyev, Kh. K. 1948. Growing the apricot further north. Tr. In-ta gen. AN SSSR 16, 89-115.

Yeremeyev, G.P. 1936. Protection of fruit plants from winter drying and frost injury by coating them. Sots. rasteniyevodstvo, No. 20, 128-92.

Yukhimchuk, F.F. 1935. Fertilizer as a factor in increased hardiness of winter grains. Khimizats. sots. zeml., No. 9-10, 103-8.

Yur'yev, V. Ya. 1938. Methods of evaluating varieties for hardiness. Sel. i semenovodstvo, No. 5.

Yur'yev, V. Ya., P.V. Kuchumov, G.N. Linnin, V.G. Vol'f, and B.T. Nikullin. 1950. General selection and seed production of field crops. 2nd ed. Moscow, Sel'khozgiz, 432 pp.

Zagorskiy, P. 1895. Autumn frosts and drought as causes of crop failures in Orlov province in connection with the value of forests in the economy of nature. Sel'sk. khoz-vo i lesovodstvo, mart, 200-16.

Zalenskiy, O.V. 1949. Summary of botanical research in the Pamirs. Bot. zhurn. 34, No. 4, 443-58.

Zalomanov, I. 1848. Effect of earing of grains with which clover is sown on growth of the latter. Sel'sk. khoz-vo i ovtsevodstvo, No. 11, 275-6.

Zalomanov, I. 1850. Means of avoiding winterkilling of clover on chernozems. Tr. Vol'n. ekon. ob-va, No. 12, 109-12.

Zarochentsev, M.T. 1910. Cold in fruit and flower growing. Zapiski Ross. ob-va sadovodov, No. 108, 1-10.

Zarubaylo, T. Ya. 1948. Significance of ripening conditions of seeds for subsequent development of the plants. Sov. botanika, No. 4-5, 22-43.

Zarubaylo, T. Ya., and M.M. Kislyuk. 1948. Conditions of passage through the vernalization stage as a factor in hereditary variability. Agrobiologiya, No. 3, 29-32.

Zaytsev, K.N. 1940. Agrocomplex of winter wheat in the Trans-Volga region after irrigation. Sov. agronomiya, No. 1.

Zaytseva, A.A. 1949. Attempt at sowing winter wheat in Karaganda oblast. Agrobiologiya, No. 2, 21-8.

Zelinskiy, V. 1891. Genealogical and acclimatized wheats as a means of increasing the profitability of southern farms. Vestn. russk. sel'sk. khoz-va, No. 20, 1173-5.

Zhdanova, L.P. 1941. Changes in content of supplementary growth substances in relation to vernalization and photoperiodism of plants. Dokl. AN SSSR 32, No. 8, 584-7.

Zheleznov, N.I. 1851. Observations of the development of buds during the winter (in French). Byull. Mosk. ob-va ispyt. prirody, No. 3, 134-7.

Zheleznov, N.I. 1869. Some observations on fruit growing. Vestn. Russk. ob-va sadovodstva, 473-7.

Zhemchuzhnikov, Ye. A., and F.D. Skazkin. 1927. Daily cycle of assimilation in wheat. Tr. Sev.-Kavk. assots. n.-i. in-tov 28, No. 7, 5-19.

Zholkevich, V.N. 1955. Causes of plant death at low temperatures above zero. Tr. In-ta fiziol. rast. im. K.A. Timiryazeva AN SSSR 9, 9-58.

Zhukov, G. 1904. The best apple varieties for Central Russia. Plodovodstvo 11, 808-27.

Zigmondi, R. 1931. Colloid chemistry. 1. General part. Kiev. Izd. UNIS, 230 pp.

Zorin, F.M. 1950. Training of hybrid citrus seedlings. Agrobiologiya, No. 1, 58-67.

FOREIGN AUTHORS

Akerman A. 1927. Studien über den Kältetod und die Kälteresistenz der Pflanzen nebst Untersuchungen über die Winterfestigkeit des Weizens. Lund. 1-232.

Albert, W.P. 1927. Studies on the growth of alfalfa and some perennial grasses "J. Am. Soc. Agr.", 19, No. 7, 624-655.

Andersson, G. 1935. Auslese von winterfesten Transgressionen bei Wintergerste durch Gefrierversuche. "Züchter", 1, No. 10, 254-260.

Apelt A. 1907. Neue Untersuchungen über den Kältetod der Kartoffel. "Btr. Biol. Pfl.", 11, 215.

Arland, A. 1932a. Kalidüngung und Frostschutzwirkung. "Die Ernähr. der Pfl.", 28, 61-64.

Arland, A. 1932b. Anfälligkeit, Ernährung und Winterfestigkeit in ihren Beziehungen untereinander und zur Transpiration. "Pflanzenbau", 8, 218-223.

d'Arsonval, M. 1901. La pression osmotique et son role de défense contre le froid dans la cellule vivante. C.R., 133, 84-86.

Badalla, L. 1911. Lo sveramento delle piante sempreverdi nel clima del Piemonte. "Ann. di. Bot.", 8, 549-615 (E. Pantanelli B "Bot. Zbl.", 1911, 7, 456).

Barnes, H.T. 1925. Colloidal water and ice. "Coll. Symp. Monogr.", 3, 103-111.

Bartetzko, H. 1909. Untersuchungen über das Erfrieren von Schimmelpilzen. "Jrb., Wiss. Bot.", 47, 57.

Beach, S.A., & Allen F.W. 1915. Hardiness in the apple as correlated with structure and composition. Agric. Exp. Sta. Iowa State Coll. of Agric. a. Mechan. Arts. "Hort. Sec. Res. Bull.", No. 21, 158-204.

Becker, G. 1932. Experimentelle Analyse der Genom- und Plasmonwirkung bei Moosen. III. Osmotischer Wert heteroploider Pfanzen. "Ztschr. Indukt. Abst.- u. Vereb.", 60, 17-38.

Belehradek, J. 1935. Temperature and living matter. "Protopl.-Monogr.", 8, 1-277.

Biebl, R. 1939. Über die Temperaturresistenz von Meeresalgen verschiedener Klimazonen u. verschiedenen tiefer Standorte. "Jrb. Wiss. Bot.", 88, 383-420.

Blisch, M.J. 1920. Effect of premature freezing on composition of wheat. "J. Agric. Res.", 19, No. 4, 181-188.

Bobart, J. 1683. On the effects of the great frost on trees and other plants. "Philos. transact.", No. 165, London, 1809.

Bobertag, O., Feist K. u. Fischer, H. 1908. Über das Ausfrieren von Hydrosolen. "Ber. Dtsch. Chem. Ges". 41, No. 4, 3675.

Boon-Long T.S. 1941. Transpiration as influenced by asmotic concentration and cell permeability. "Ann. J. Bot.", 28, No. 4, 333-342.

Boonstra, A.E. 1937. Winter hardheid. "Maandblad van het nederlandsch Genootschap voor Landbouweretenschap", Jaarg., 49, 600, 479-484.

Boswell, V.R. 1923. Dehydration on certain plant tissues. "Bot. Gaz.", 54. No. 1, 86–94.

Bouyoucos, G.I. & McCool, M.M. 1916. Determination of cell-sap concentration by the freezing-point. method. "J. Am. Soc. Agr.", 8, No. 1, 50–51.

Bowden, W.M. 1940. Diploidy, polyploidy a. winter hardiness relationships in the flowering plants. "Am. J. Bot.", 27, No. 6, 357–371.

Bradford, F.C. 1922. Observations on winter injury. 1. Early and late winter injury. Univ. of Miss. Coll. Agric. "Agric. Exp. Sta. Res. Bull.", 56, 1–16.

Brierly, W.G. 1934. Winter desiccation in the Lathan raspberry. "Proc. Am. Soc. Hort. Sci.", 31, 110–113.

Briggs, D.R. 1932. Water relationships in colloids. II. "Bound" water in colloids. "J. Physic. Chem.", 36, 367–386.

Brink, R.A., Keller, W. & Eisenhart, C. 1939. Differential survival of alfalfa strains under an ice sheet. "J. Agric. Res.", 59, No. 1, 59–79.

Buffon, Duhamel. 1737. Observations des différents effets que produisent sur les végétaux les grandes gelées d'hiver et les petites gelées du printemps. "Mém. Acad. Roy. Paris", 273 (cited from Goppert, 1830).

Buhlert, 1906. Untersuchungen über das Auswintern des Getreides. "Landw. Jrb.", 35, 837–888.

Bull, H.B. 1933. Some methodical errors which may arise in the determination of bound water. "J. Gen. Physiol.", 17, No. 1, 83–86.

Burge, W.E. & Burge, E.L. 1924. Effect of temperature and light on catalase content of Spirogyra. "Bot. Gaz.", 77, 220–224.

Burge, W.E. & Burge, E.L. 1928. A study of the effect of hot and cold weather on the catalase of the plant and animal in relation to their respiratory metabolism. "Am. J. Bot.", 15, No. 7, 412–415.

Busse, W.F. & Buruham, C.R. 1930. Some effects of low temperatures on seeds. "Bot. Gaz.", 90, No. 4, 394–411.

Candolle, C. de. 1895. Sur la vie latente des graines. "Arch. Sci. Phys. et Nat.", 33, No. 6, 497–512.

Cardinell, N.A. 1922. II. An aftermath of winter injury. Univ. Miss. coll. agric. "Agric. Exp. Sta. Res. Bull.", 56, 17–26.

Carroll, J.C. & Welton, F.A. 1939. Effect of heavy and late applications of nitrogenous fertilizer on the cold resistance of kentucky blue grass. "Plant Physiol.", 14, No. 2, 297–308.

Caspary, R. 1854. Auffallende Eisbildung auf Pflanzen. "Bot. Ztg.", 12, 665, 681, 697.

Caspary, R. 1855. Über Frostspalten. "Bot. Ztg.", 13, 449, 473, 489.

Chambers, R. & Hale, H.P. 1932. The formation of ice in protoplasm. "Proc. Roy. Soc.", ser. B, 110, 336–352.

Chandler, R. C. 1941a. Bound water in plant sap and some effects of temperature and nutrition thereon. "Plant Physiol.", 16, No. 4, 785–798.

Chandler, R.C. 1941b. Nature bound water in colloid systems. "Plant Physiol.", 16, No. 2, 273–291.

Chandler, W.H. 1913. The killing of plant tissue by low temperature. "Miss. Agric. Exp. Sta. Res. Bull.", 8, 143–309.

Chibnall, A.C. & Grover, C.E. 1926. The extraction of sap from living leaves by means of compressed air. "Ann. Bot.", 40, 158, 491–497.

Chrysler, H.L. 1934. Amounts of bound and free water in an organic colloid at different degrees of hydratation. "Plant Physiol.", 9, No. 1, 143–157.

Clements, H.F. 1938. Mechanismus of freezing resistance in the needles of

Pinus ponderosa and Pseudotsuga Mucronata. "Res Stud. of the St. Coll. of Washington", 6, No. 1, 3-45.

Constantinescu, E. 1934. Die Kältefestigkeit verschiedenen Wintergersten. "Ztschr. f. Zücht.", Reihe A, 19, No. 1, 439-453.

Coville, F.V. 1920. The influence of cold in stimulating the growth of plants. "J. Agric. Res.", 20, No. 2, 151-160.

Cullen, C.J. & Fabergé, A.C. 1939. The rate of temperature change with the plant. "Ann. Bot.", N.S., 3, No. 11, 759-760.

Curtis, O.F. 1929. Studies on solute translocation in plants. "Am. J. Bot.", 16, No. 3, 154-168.

Dalmer, M. 1895. Über Eisbildung in Pflanzen mit Rücksicht auf die anatomische Beschaffenheit derselben. "Flora", 80, 436-444.

Day, W.R. & Peace, T.R. 1937. The influence of certain accessory factors on frost injury to forest trees. "Forestry", 11, No. 1, 13-29.

Degham, W. 1709. An account of the great frost in the winter of 1708 and 1709. "Philosoph. Transact.", 5, 324, London, 1809.

DeLong, W.A., Beaumont, J.H., & Willman, I.J. 1930. Respiration of apple twigs in relation to winter hardiness. "Plant Physiol.", 5, No. 4, 509-534.

Denny, F.E. 1933. Changes in leaves during the period preceeding frost. "Contr. Boyce Thomps. Inst.", 5, No. 3, 297-312.

Denny, F.E., & Miller, L.P. 1935. Storage temperatures and chemical treatments for shortening the rest period of small cornes and cormels of gladiolus. "Contr. Boyce Thomps. Inst.", 7, No. 3, 257-265.

Detmer, W. 1886. Über Zerstörung der Molekularstruktur des Protoplasma der Pflanzenzellen. "Bot. Ztg.", 44, 513-524.

DeVries, H. 1906. Arten und Varietäten und ihre Entstehung durch Mutation. Berlin, 530 S.

Dexter, S.T. 1932. Studies of the hardiness of plants: A modification of the Newton pressure method of small samples. "Plant Physiol.", 7, No. 4, 721-726.

Dexter, S.T. 1933a. Decreasing hardiness of winter wheat in relation to photosynthesis, defoliation and wintery injury. "Plant Physiol.", 8, 297-304.

Dexter, S.T. 1933b. Effect of several environmental factors on the hardening of plants. "Plant Physiol.", 8, 123-140.

Dexter, S.T. 1934a. Respiratory rate and enzyme activity as related to the hardened condition of plants. "Plant Physiol.", 9, 831-837.

Dexter, S.T. 1934b. Salt concentration and reversibility of ice-formation as related to the hardiness of plants. "Plant Physiol.", 9, 601-618.

Dexter, S.T. 1935. Growth, organic nitrogen fractions and buffer capacity in relation to hardiness of plants. "Plant Physiol.", 10, 149-158.

Dexter, S.T. 1941. Effects of periods of warm weather upon the winter hardened condition of plants. "Plant Physiol.", 16, 181-188.

Dexter, S.T., Tottingham, W.E.,& Graber, L.F. 1930. Preliminary results in measuring the hardiness of plants. "Plant Physiol.", 5, 215-223.

Dexter, S.T., Tottingham, W.E., & Graber, L.F. 1932. Investigations of the hardiness of plants by measurement of electrical conductivity. "Plant Physiol.", 7, 63-79.

Dixon, H., & Atkins, W. 1915. Osmotic pressures in plants. V. Seasonal variations in the concentrations of the cell-sap of some deciduous and evergreen trees. "Scient. Proc. of the Royal Dublin Soc.", 14, No. 34, 445-461.

Döring, B. 1934. Die Temperaturabhängigkeit der Wasseraufnahme und ihre ökologische Bedeutung. "Ztschr. Bot.", 28, 305-383.

Dorsey, M.J. 1934. Ice formation in the fruit bud of the peach. "Proc. Am. Soc. Hort. Sc.", 31, 22-27.

Duhamel du Monceau, M. 1758. La physique des arbres. Paris.

Dunn, S. 1933. Relation of hydrophilic colloids to hardiness in cabbage, brussels sprouts and alfalfa plants as shown by the dye adsorption tests. "Plant Physiol.", 8, 2, 275-287.

Dunn, S. 1937. Factors effecting cold resistance in plants. "Plant Physiol.", 12, No. 2, 519-526.

Eglite, H. 1938. Kodiniet rudzu seklu. Latvijas lauksaimniecibas kamera. "Zemkopibas nodala", 41.

Ewart, A.J. 1898. The action of cold and of sunlight upon aquatic plants. "Ann. Bot.", 12, 363-397.

Famintzin, A., & Borodin I. 1867. Über transitorische Stärkebildung bei der Birne. "Bot. Ztg.", 49, 385-387.

Fischer, A. 1888. Glucose als Reservestoffe der Laubhölzer. "Bot. Ztg.", 46, 405-419.

Fischer, A. 1891. Beiträge zur Physiologie der Holzgewächse. "Jrb. Wiss. Bot.", 22, 73.

Fischer, H.W. 1911. Gefrieren und Erfrieren, eine physiochemische Studie. "Btr. Biol. Pfl.", 10, 133.

Fischer, M.H. 1924. Die Kolloidchemische Theorie der Wasserbedingung im Organismus. "Koll.-Ztschr.", 35, No. 5, 294-302.

Flovick, K. 1940. Chromosome numbers and polyploidy within the flora of Spitzbergen. "Hereditas", 26, 430-440.

Foote, H.W., & Saxton, B. 1916. The effect of freezing on certain inorganic hydrogels. "J. Am. Chem. Soc.", 38, 588-609.

Frank, A.B. 1880-1895. Die Krankheiten der Pflanzen. Breslau (2 ed. 1895).

Freeland, P.O. 1944. Apparent photosynthesis in some conifers during winter. "Plant Physiol.", 19, No. 2, 179-185.

Friedberg, R. 1932. Contribution a l'etude du tallage du ble. Relation entre la profondeur du neud de tallage et la resistance au froid. "Ann. Agr., n.s.", 2, 215-228.

Fuchs, W.H. 1934. Beiträge zur Züchtung kältefester Winterweizen. "Ztschr. f. Zucht.", Reihe A, 19, No. 3, 309-323.

Fukuda, J. 1932. Hydronastic curling and uncurling movement of the leaves of Rhododendron micranthum Turez. with respect to temperature and resistance to cold. "Jap. Journ. Bot.", 6, No. 2, 191-224.

Fukuda, J. 1932. A study of the conditions of completely frozen plant cells with special reference to resistance to cold. "Bot. Mag.", 46, No. 544, 239-246.

Gail, F.W. 1926. Osmotic pressure of cell sap and its possible relation to winter killing and leaf fall. "Bot. Gaz.", 81, 435-445.

Gardner, V.R. 1935. The susceptibility of flower buds of the Montmorency cherry to injury from low temperature. "J. Agric. Res.", 50, No. 6, 563-572.

Gassner, G., & Rabien, H. 1931. Über die Durchführung der Frosthärteprüfungen von Getreidezüchtstämmen. "Zuchter", 3, 1, 297-300.

Gates, K. 1915. The mutation factor in evolution. London.

Gäumann, E. 1927. Der jahreszeitliche Verlauf des Kohlehydratgehaltes im Tannen und Fichtenstamm. "Ber. Dtsch. Bot. Ges.", 45, No. 9, 591-598.

Gehenio, P.M., & Luyet, B.J. 1939. A study of the mechanism of death by cold in the plasmodium of the myxomycets. "Biodynamica", 55, 1–22.

Gerassimow, J.I. 1935. Über die Grösse des Zellkeers. "Beih. Bot. Zbl.", 18,45–118.

Gicklhorn, J. 1936. Gradienten des Erfrierens von Laubblättern. "Protoplasma", 26, No. 1, 90–96.

Goetz, A., & Goetz, S. 1938a. Death by devitrification in yeast cells. "Biodynamica", 43, 1–8.

Goetz, A., & Goetz, S. 1938b. Vertification and crystallization of protophyta at low temperatures. "Proc. Am. Phylos. Soc.", 79, No. 3, 361–387.

Göppert, H.R. 1830. Über die Wärme-Entwicklung in den Pflanzen, deren Gefrieren und die Schutzmittel gegen dasselbe. Breslau.

Göppert, H.R. 1871. Wann stirbt die durch Frost getödtete Pflanze, zur Zeit des Gefrierens oder im Moment des Auftauens? "Bot. Ztg.", 29, 399–402.

Gorke, H. 1907. Über chemische Vorgänge beim Erfrieren der Pflanzen. "Landw. Vers. St.", 65, 149–160.

Gortner, R.A., & Gortner, W.A. 1934. The cryoscopic method for the determination of "bound water". "J. Gen. Physiol.", 17, No. 3, 329–339.

Graber, L.F. 1931. Food reserves in relation to other factors limiting the growth of grasses. "Plant Physiol.", 6, 43–71.

Grahle, A. 1933. Vergleichende Untersuchungen über strukturelle und osmotische Eigenschaften der Nadeln verschiedenen Pinus Arten. "Jrb. Wiss. Bot.", 78, 2, 203–294.

Grauthouse, G.A., & Stuart, N.W. 1937. Enzyme activity in cold-hardened and unhardened red clover. "Plant Physiol.", 12, No. 3, 685–702.

Greely, A.W. 1902. On the analogy between the effects of loss of water and lowering of temperature. "Am. J. Physiol.", 6, 122–128.

Gregory, C.T., & Beeson, K.E. 1926. Note some aspects of freezing injury to wheat in Indiana in 1925. "J. Am.-Soc. Agr.", 18, No. 5, 444–446.

Grünberg, G. 1932. Über die Ursachen des Zelltodes in Anaerobiose. "Planta", 16, 433–466.

Guilliermond, A. 1941. The cytoplasm of the plant cell. 1–247.

Guthrie, J.D. 1933. Changes in the glutatione content of potato tubers treated with chemicals that break the rest period. "Contr. Boyce Thomps. Inst.", 5, No. 3, 331–350.

Hagerup, O. 1931. Über Polyploidie in Beziehung zu Klima, Ökologie und Phylogenie. "Hereditas", Lund, 16, 19–40.

Hales, S. 1748. Statik der Gewächse (transl. from English). Halle.

Handley, W.S.C. 1939. The effect of prolonged chilling on water movement and radial growth in trees. "Am.-Bot.", N.S., 3, No. 12, 803–813.

Hardy, W.B. 1926. A microscopic study of the freezing of gel. "Proc. Roy. Soc. London", ser. A, 47–61.

Harris, H.A. 1934. Frost ring formation in some winterinjured deciduous trees and shrubs. "Am. J. Bot.", 21, 485–499.

Harvey, R.-B. 1918. Hardening process in plants and developments from frost injury. "J. Agric. Res.", 15, 83–112.

Harvey, R.-B. 1923. Cambial temperatures of trees in winter and their relation to sun scald. "Ecology", 4, 261–265.

Harvey, R.-B. 1933. Physiology of the adaptation of plants to low temperature. "Proc. World's Grain Exibit. a. Confer.", 2, 145–151. Regina — Canada.

Hayes, H.K., & Aamodt, O.S. 1927. Inheritance of winter hardiness and growths habit in crosses of Marquis with Minhardi and Minturki wheats. "J. Agr. Res.", 35, 233–236.

Hedlund, T. 1917. Om möjlighetem att at hvetests utbildning pa hösten Sluta sig till de olika sorternas vinterhärdigkeit. "Sonderabdr. Tidskr. Landtman", Lund, 227–234, 247–253.

Heilbrunn, L.V. 1928. The colloid chemistry of protoplasma. "Protopl.-monogr.", 1, 1–356, Berlin.

Heiss, V.R. 1933. Untersuchungen über den Kältebedarf und die ausgefrorenen Wassermengen beim Schellen und beim langsamen Gefrieren von Lebensmitteln. "Ztschr.f.d.g. Kälte-Industrie", 39, No. 7, 97–104; No. 8, 122–128; No. 9, 144–146.

Hemenway, A.F. 1926. Late frost injury to some trees in Central Kentucky. "Am. J. Bot.", 13, No. 6, 364–367.

Hildreth, A.C. 1926. Determination of hardiness in apple varieties and the relation of some factors to cold resistance. "Univ. of Minn. Techn. Bull.", 42, 1–37.

Hill, D.D., & Salmon, S.C. 1927. The resistance of certain varieties of winter wheat to artifically produced low temperatures. "J. Agric. Res.", 35, No. 10, 933–937.

Hoffman, H. 1857. Witterung und Wachstum oder Grundzüge der Pflanzenklimatologie. Leipzig.

Hoffman, W. 1937. Die Winterfestigkeit keimgestimmter Gersten. "Züchter", 11.

Hofmeister, W. 1867. Die Lehre von der Pflanzenzelle. "Handb. der Physiol. bot.".

Iljin, W.S. 1930. Die Ursachen der Resistenz von Pflanzenzellen gegen Austrocknen. "Protoplasma", 10, 379–414.

Iljin, W.S. 1933. Über den Kältetod der Pflanzen und seine Ursachen. "Protoplasma", 20, 105–124.

Iljin, W.S. 1934. The point of death of plants at low temperatures. Laborat. of plant physiol. Charl. Univ. Prague.

Iljin, W.S. 1935. Lebensfähigkeit der Pflanzenzellen in trockenem Zustand. "Planta", 24, 742–754.

Ireland, J.C. 1939. Seasonal sugar variations in alfalfa. "Plant Physiol.", 14, No. 2, 381–384.

Irmscher, G. 1912. Über die Resistenz der Laubmoose gegen Austrocknung und Kälte. "Jrb. Wiss. Bot.", 50, 387–449.

Janssen, G. 1929a. Effect of date of seeding of winter wheat on plant development and its relationship to winter hardiness. "J. Am. Soc. Agr.", 21, No. 4, 444–466.

Janssen, G. 1929b. Effect of date of seeding of winter wheat upon some physiological changes of the plant during the winter season. "J. Am. Soc. Agr.", 21, No. 2, 168–200.

Janssen, G. 1929c. Physical measurements of the winter wheat plant of various stages in its development. "Plant Physiol.", 4, 477–493.

Jardine, W.M. 1916. Effect of rate and date of sowing on yield of winter wheat. "J. Am. Soc. Agr.", 8, No. 3, 163–167.

Jensen, A.B. 1941. Studien über die Kälteresistenz von Pflanzenzellen. "Protoplasma", 36, 195–203.

Jensen, I.J. 1925. Winter wheat studies in Montana with special reference to winter killing. "J. Am. Soc. Agr.", 17, No. 10, 630–631.

John, I.L. 1931. The temperature at which unbound water is completely frozen in a biocolloid. "J. Am. Chem. Soc.", 53, 4014–4019.

Jones, F.R. 1928. Winter injury of alfalfa. "J. Agric. Res.", 37, No. 4, 189–212.

Jones, J.D., & Gortner, D.A. 1932. Free and bound water in elastic and non-elastic gels. "J. Physic. Chem.", 36, 387–436.

Jones, W. 1942. Respiration and chemical changes of the papaya fruit in relation to temperature. "Plant Physiol.", 17, No. 3, 481–486.

Kärcher, H. 1931. Über die Kälteresistenz einiger Pilze und Algen. "Planta", 14, No. 2, 515–516.

Karsten, H. 1861. Über die Wirkung plötzlicher, bedeutender Temperatur-veränderungen auf die Pflanzenwelt. "Bot. Ztg.", 40, 289–292.

Kessler, W. 1935. Über die inneren Ursachen der Kälteresistenz der Pflanzen. "Planta", 24, 312–352.

Kessler, W., & Ruhland, W. 1938. Weitere Untersuchungen über die inneren Ursachen der Kälteresistenz. "Planta", 28, 159–204.

Kihlman. 1890. Pflanzenbiologische Studien aus Russisch-Lapland. "Acta Soc. pro fauna et flora Fennica", 6, No. 3.

Klages, K.H. 1926a. Relation of soil moisture content to resistance of wheat to low temperatures. "J. Am. Soc. Agr.", 18, No. 3, 184–192.

Klages, K.H. 1926b. Metrical attributes and the physiology of hardy varieties of winter wheat. "J. Am. Soc. Agr.", 18, No. 7, 529–566.

Klebs, G. 1913. Fortpflanzung der Gewächse. "Handwörterbuch der Naturw.", 4, 276–296.

Klebs, G. 1914. Über das Treiben der einheimischen Bäume spezielle der Buche. "Abh. Heidelb. Akad. wiss. Math.-naturw. Klasse", 3, 1–113.

Klemm, P. 1895. Desorganisationserscheinungen der Zelle. "Jrb. Wiss. Bot.", 24, No. 4, 627–700.

Kochs, W. 1892. Über die Vorgänge beim Einfrieren und Austrocknen von Tieren und Pflanzensamen. "Biol. Zbl.", 12, 330–339.

Kokkonen, P. 1926. Beobachtungen über die Struktur des Bodenfrostes. "Acta Forest Fenn.", 30.

Kokkonen, P. 1929. Über das Verhältnis der Winterfestigkeit des Roggens zur Dehnbarkeit seiner Wurzeln. "Acta Forest. Fenn.", 33, 1–45.

Krabbe, G. 1896. Über den Einfluss der Temperatur auf die osmotischen Processe lebender Zellen. "Jrb. Wiss. Bot.", 29, 3, 441–498.

Kramer, P.J., & Wetmore, T.H. 1943. Effects of defoliation on cold resistance and diameter growth of broadleaved evergreens. "Am. J. Bot.", 30, No. 6, 428–430.

Kramer, P.K. 1937. Photoperiodic stimulation of growth by artificial light as a cause of winter killing. "Plant Physiol.", 12, No. 3, 881–883.

Kraus, 1874. Die winterliche Färbung grüner Pflanzentheile. "Bot. Ztg.", 32, No. 26, 406–408.

Kraus, C. 1908. Die Lagerung der Getreide. Stuttgart, 426 S.

Kuhn, A. 1924. Überblick unserer jetzigen Kenntnisse über Wasserbindung in Kolloiden. "Koll.-Ztschr.", 35, No. 5, 275–294.

Kühne, W. 1864. Untersuchungen über das Protoplasma und die Contractivität. Leipzig, 158 S.

Kunisch, H. 1880. Über die tödliche Einwirkung niederer Temperaturen auf die Pflanzen. Breslau.

Kuster, E. 1929. Pathologie der Pflanzenzelle. Teil I. Pathologie des Proto-plasmas. Berlin.

Kylin, H. 1917. Über die Kälteresistenz der Meeresalgen. "Ber. dtsch.

Bot. Ges.", 35, 370-384.

Laude, H.H. 1937a. Comparison of the cold resistance of several varieties of winter wheat in transition from dormancy to active growth. "J. Agric. Res.", 54, 919-926.

Laude, H.H. 1937b. Cold resistance of winter wheat, rye, barley and oats in transition from dormancy to active growth. "J. Agric. Res.", 54, No. 12, 899-919.

Langham, D.G. 1941. The effect of light on growth habit of plants. "Am. J. Bot.", 28, 951-956.

Lepeschkin, W.W. 1910a. Zur Kenntnis der Plasmamembran. I. "Ber. Dtsch. Bot. Ges.", 28, 91-103.

Lepeschkin, W.W. 1910b. Zur Kenntnis der Plasmamembran. II. "Ber. Dtsch. Bot. Ges.", 28, 383-393.

Lepeschkin, W. 1924. Kolloidchemie des Protoplasmas. "Protopl. Monogr.", 7, Berlin, 228 S.

Lepeschkin, W.W. 1930. My opinion about protoplasm. "Protoplasma", 9, No. 2, 268-297.

Lepeschkin, W. 1937. Zell-Nekrobiose u. Protoplasma-Tod. "Protopl.-Monogr.", 12, 198 S.

Lettermoser, A. 1908. Über das Ausfrieren von Hydrosolen. "Ber. Dtsch. Chem. Ges.", 41, No. 4, 3976-3979.

Leukel, W.A. 1927. Deposition and Utilization of reserve foods in Alfalfa plants. "J. Am. Soc. Agr.", 19, No. 7, 596-624.

Levitt, J. 1939. The relation of cabbage hardiness to bound water, unfrozen water and cell contraction when frozen. "Plant Physiol.", 14, No. 1, 93-112.

Levitt, J. 1941. Frost killing and hardiness of plants. A critical review. Minneapolis, Minn., 211 p.

Levitt, J., & Scarth, G.W. 1936a. Frost-hardening studies with living cells. I. Osmotic and bound water changes in relation to frost resistance and the seasonal cycle. "Canad. J. Res.", 14-267-284.

Levitt, J., & Scarth, G.W. 1936b. Frost-hardening studies with living cells. II. Permeability in relation to frost resistance and the seasonal cycle. "Canad. J. Res.", 14, 285-305.

Levitt, J., Scarth, G., & Gibbs, R. 1936. Water permeability of isolated protoplasts in relation to volume change. "Protoplasma", 26, No. 2, 237-248.

Lewis, F.J., & Tuttle, G.M. 1920. Osmotic properties of some plant cells at low temperatures. "Ann. Bot.", 34, 135, 405-416.

Lidforss, B. 1896. Zur Physiologie und Biologie der wintergrünen Flora. "Bot. Zbl.", 68, 33.

Lidforss, B. 1907. Die wintergrüne Flora. "Lunds Univ. Arska.", N.F. Afd. 2, 2, No. 13, 78 S.

Link, H.F. 1807. Grundlehren der Anatomie und Physiologie der Pflanzen. Gottingen.

Lipman, C.B. 1936. Normal viability of seeds and bacterial spores after exposure to temperature near the absolute zero. "Plant Physiol.", 11, No. 1, 201-205.

Lipman, C.B. 1939. On the difference on resistance of various types of cells to extremely low temperatures. "Biodynamica", 45, 1-4.

Lipman, C.B., & Lewis, G.W. 1934. Tolerance of liquid-air temperatures by seeds of higher plants for sixty days. "Plant Physiol.", 9, No. 2, 391-394.

Loeb, J. 1924. Regeneration. 143 p.

Loew, Q. 1885. Über den verschiedenen Resistenzgrad im Protoplasma. "Arch. Ges. Physiol. Mensch. u. Tiere", 35, 509-516.

Löve, A. 1942. Cytogenetic studies in Rumex. III. Some notes on the scandinavia species of the genus. "Hereditas", 28, 289-296.

Löve, A. 1944. Cytogenetic studies on Rumex sulgenus acetosella. "Hereditas", 30, 136 S.

Lubimenko, B.N., & Shseglova, O.A. 1932. Über den Einfluss des Protoplasmareizes auf die Photosynthese. "Planta", 18, 1/2, 383-404.

Luyet, B.J. 1937. The vitrification of organic colloids and of protoplasm. "Biodynamica", No. 29, 14 p.

Luyet, B.J., & Gehenio, P.M. 1937. The double freezing point of living tissues. "Biodynamica", No. 3, 1-123.

Luyet, B.J., & Gehenio, P.M. 1938a. The lower limit of vital temperatures. A review. "Biodynamica", No. 33, 1-92.

Luyet, B.J., & Gehenio, P.M. 1938b. The survival of moss vitrified in liquid air and its relations to water content. "Biodynamica", No. 42, 1-7.

Luyet, B.J., & Gehenio, P.M. 1939. The physical states of protoplasm of low temperatures. "Biodynamica", No. 48, 1-128.

Luyet, B.J., & Gehenio, P.M. 1940a. Life and death at low temperatures. "Biodynamica", 341 p.

Luyet, B.J., & Gehenio, P.M. 1940b. Effect of the rate of cooling on the freezing point of living tissues. "Biodynamica", No. 3, 65, 157-169.

Luyet, B.J., & Gehenio, P.M. 1940c. The mechanism of injury and death by low temperature. "Biodynamica", 3, No. 60, 1-99.

Luyet, B.J., & Gibbs, M.C. 1937. On the mechanism of congelation and of death in the rapid freezing of epidermal plant cells. "Biodynamica", No. 25, 1-18.

Magistad, O.C., & Trong, E. 1925. The influence of fertilizers in protecting corn against freezing. "J. Am. Soc. Agr.", 17, No. 9, 517-526.

Mallery, T.D. 1934. Comparison of the heating and freezing methods of killing plant material for cryoscopic determination. "Plant Physiol.", 9, No. 2, 369-377.

Martin, J.N. 1934. The relative growth rates and interdependence of tops and roots of the biennial sweet clover, Melilotus alba Dess. "Am. J. Bot.", 21, No. 3, 140-159.

Matruchot M., & Molliard, M. 1902. Modifications produites par le gel dans la structure des cellules végétales. "Rev. Génér. Bot.", 401-420, 463-482, 522-538.

McCool, M.M., & Bouyoucos, G.I. 1929. Causes and effect of soil heaving. "Michig. Agric. Exp. St. Spec. Bull.", No. 192, 1-11.

McDermott, J.J. 1941. Changes in chemical composition of twigs and buds of yellow poplar during the dormant period. "Plant Physiol.", 16, No. 2, 415-418.

Megee, C.R. 1935. A search for factors determining winter hardiness in alfalfa. "J. Am. Soc. Agr.", 27, No. 9, 685-698.

Meyen, F.J.F. 1841. Pflanzen-Pathologie. Berlin, 330 S.

Meyer, B.S. 1928. Seasonal variations in the physical and chemical properties of the leaves of the pitch pine, with special reference to cold resistance. "Am. J. Bot.", 15, 449-472.

Meyer, B.S. 1932. Further studies on cold resistance in evergreen, with special reference to the possible role of bound water. "Bot. Gaz.", 94, 297-321.

Mez, C. 1905. Neue Untersuchungen über das Erfrieren eisbeständiger Pflanzen. "Flora", 94, 89-123.

Michaelis, P. 1934a. Ökologische Studien an der alpinen Baumgrenzen. IV. Zur Kenntnis des winterlichen Wasserhaushaltes. "Jrb. Wiss. Bot.", 80, No. 2, 169-247.

Michaelis, P. 1934b. V. Osmotischer Wert und Wassergehalt während des Winters in den verschiedenen Höhenlangen. "Jrb. Wiss. Bot.", 80, No. 3, 337-362.

Mitchell, J. W. 1944. Winter hardiness in Guayule. "Bot. Gaz.", 106, No. 1, 95-102.

Möbius, M. 1907. Die Erkältung der Pflanzen. "Ber Dtsch. Bot. Ges.", 25, 67-70.

Mohl, H. 1848. Über das Erfrieren der Zweigspitzen mancher Holzgewächse. "Bot. Ztschr.", 6, 6-8.

Mohl, H. 1860. Über die anatomischen Veränderungen des Blattgelenkes, welche das Abfallen der Blätter herbeiführen. "Bot. Ztg.", 18, No. 1, 1-7, 9-17.

Molisch, H. 1896. Das Erfrieren von Pflanzen bei Temperaturen über dem Eispunkt. "Sitzungsber. Kais. Adad. wiss. Math.-naturw. Klasse". 1, 82-95.

Molisch, H. 1897. Untersuchungen über das Erfrieren der Pflanzen. Jena.

Molisch, H. 1910. Abstr. of articles by Bartetzko and Voigtländer. "Ztschr. Bot.", 2, 211.

Moran, T. 1926. The freezing of gelatin gel. "Proc. Royal. Soc.", ser. A, 112, 30-46.

Moran, T. 1935. Bound water and phase equilibria in protein systems: Egg albumin and muscle. "Proc. Royal Soc.", ser. B, 118, 811, 548-559.

Mothes, K. 1931. Zur Kenntnis des N-Stoffwechsels höherer Pflanzen. "Planta", 12, 686-731.

Mothes, K. 1933. Die natürliche Regulation des pflanzlichen Eiweisstoffwechsels. "Ber. Dtsch. Bot. Ges.", 51, 31-46.

Mudra, A. 1932. Zur Physiologie der Kälteresistenz des Winterweizens. "Planta", 18, 435-478.

Müller-Thurgau, H. 1880. Über das Gefrieren u. Erfrieren der Pflanzen. I. "Landw. Jrb.", 9, 133-189.

Müller-Thurgau, H. 1882. Über Zuckeranhäufung in Pflanzentheilen in Folge niederer Temperature. "Landw. Jrb.", 11, 751.

Müller-Thurgau, H. 1886. Über das Gefrieren und Erfrieren der Pflanzen. II. "Landw. Jrb.", 15, 453-610.

Müller-Thurgau, H. 1894. Über das Erfrieren des Obstes. "Schweizer. Zeit. für Obst- und Weinbau. (cited from Molisch, 1897).

Murneek, A.E. 1929. Hemicellulose as a storage carbhohydrate in woody plants, with special reference to the apple. "Plant Physiol.", 4, No. 2, 251-265.

Navashin, M. 1929. Studies on polyploidy. 1. Cytological investigations on triploidy in Crepis. "Univ. Calif. Publ. Agric. Sc.", 2, No. 14, 377-400.

Nelson, R. 1926. Storage and transportational diseases of vegetables due to suboxidation. Agric. Exp. Sta. Michig. "Techn. Bull.", 81, 1-38.

Newton, R. 1922. A comparative study of winter wheat varieties with special reference to winter killing. "J. Agric. Sci.", 12, 1-19.

Newton, R. 1924a. Colloidal properties of winter wheat plants in relation to frost resistance. "J. Agric. Sci.", 14, 178-191.

Newton, R. 1924b. The nature and practical measurement of frost resistance in winter wheat. "Univ. of Alberta Res. Bull.", 1, 53.

Newton, R., & Anderson, J.A. 1931. Respiration of winter wheat plant at low temperature. "Canad. J. Res.", 5, 337–354.

Newton, R., & Brown, W. 1931a. Catalase activity of the wheat leaf juice in relation to frost resistance. "Canad. J. Res.", 5, 333–336.

Newton, R., & Brown, W. 1931b. Frost precipitation of proteins of plant juice. "Canad. J. Res.", 5, 87–110.

Newton, R., Brown, W., & Anderson, J. 1931. Chemical changes in nitrogen fractions of plant juice on exposure to frost. "Canad. J. Res.", 5, 327–332.

Newton, R., & Gortner, R.A. 1922a. Determination of moisture content of expressed plant tissue fluids. "Bot. Gaz.", 74, 308–313.

Newton, R., & Gortner, R.A. 1922b. A method for estimating the hydrophilic colloid content of expressed plant tissue fluids. "Bot. Gaz.", 74, 442–446.

Nightingale, G.T., Robbins, W.R., & Schermerhorn, L.G. 1927. Freezing as a method of preserving plant tissue for the determination of nitrogenous fractions. "New Jersey Agric. Exp. Sta. Bull.", 448, 1–16.

Niklewski, B. 1906. Untersuchungen über die Umwandlung einiger stickstoffreien Reservestoffe während der Winterperiode der Bäume. "Beih. z. Bot. Zbl.", 19, 68–117.

Nilsson-Ehle, H. 1913. Zur Kenntnis der Erblichkeitsverhaltnisse der Eigenschafft Winterfestigkeit beim Weizen. "Ztschr. f. Pflanzenzucht.", 1, 3–12.

Northen, H.T. 1938. Effect of drought on protoplasmatic elasticity. "Plant Physiol.", 13, No. 3, 658–660.

Oserkowsky, J. 1942. Polar and apolar transport of auxin in woody stems. "Am. J. Bot.", 29 (10), 858–868.

Pantanelli, E. 1918. Su la resistenza delle piante al fredda. "Atti R. Avad. Lincei 27", ser. V, 126–130, 148–153.

Pantanelli, E. 1919. Alterazioni del ricambio e della permeabilita cellulore a temperature prossime al congelamento. "Atti R. Acad. Lincei", ser. V, 28, 205–209.

Pantanelli, E. 1920. Influenza della nutrizione e dell'attivita radicale sul collasso e il disseccamento prodotti dal freddo. "Atti R. Acad. Lincei", 29, 66–71.

Peach, K. 1935. Experimentelle Studien über die Anaerobiose höherer Pflanzen. "Planta", 24, No. 4, 529–551.

Pekarek, J. 1933. Absolute Viskositätsmessungen mit Hilfe der Brownschen Molekularbewegungen. "Protoplasma", 18, No. 1, 1–53; 20, No. 2, 251–278; 20, No. 3, 359–375.

Pekarek, J. 1935. Absolute Viskositätsmessungen mit Hilfe der Brownschen Molekularbewegung. VIII. Mitteilung: Die Zellsaftviskosität in ihrer Abhängigkeit von Temperatur und Licht. "Protoplasma", 24, No. 1, 128–173.

Peltier, G.L., & Tysdal, H.M. 1931. Hardiness studies with 2-year-old alfalfa plants. "J. Agric. Res.", 43, 931–955.

Peltier, G.L., & Tysdal, H.M. 1932. A method for the determination of comparative hardiness in seeding alfalfa by controlled hardening and artifical freezing. "J. Agric. Res.", 44, 429–444.

Petit-Thouars. 1817. Le verger français.

Pfeffer, W. 1904. Pflanzenphysiologie. Leipzig.

Phillis, E., & Mason, T.G. 1941. On the expression of sap by low pressure. "Ann. Bot.", 17, 15-24.

Phillis, E., & Mason, T.G. 1945a. The effect of extreme desiccation on the viability of cotton seed. "Ann. Bot.", 36, 353-359.

Phillis, E., & Mason, T.G. 1945b. Studies of filiar hydration on the cotton plant. VI. A gel theory of cell water relation. "Ann. Bot.", 36.

Platenius, H. 1942. Effect of temperature on the respiration rate and the respiratory quotient of some vegetables. "Plant Physiol.", 17, No. 2, 179-197.

Platt, A.W. 1937a. The effect of freezing temperatures and of defoliation on the subsequent growth of wheat plants. "Sci. Agric.", 17, No. 7, 420-430.

Platt, A.W. 1937b. The effect of soil moisture, hardening, endosperm condition and variety of the frost reaction of wheat, oat and barley seedlings. "Sci. Agric.", 17, No. 10, 616-626.

Pojarkova, A. 1924. Winterruhe, Reservestoffe und Kälteresistenz bei Holzpflanzen. "Ber. Dtsch. Bot. Ges.", 42, 420-429.

Prillieux, M.E. 1869. Sur la formation de glaçons à l'interieur des plantes. "Ann. Sci. Natur.", 5 série, Bot., 12, 125.

Prillieux, M.E. 1872. Coloration en bleu des fleurs de quelques orchidées sous l'influence de la gelée. "Bull. Soc. Bot. France", 19, 152-157.

Rahm, P.G. 1920. Einwirkung sehr niederer Temperatur auf die Mossfauna. Köningl. Akad. van Wetensh. te Amsterdam. "Wis-en Natuurkundige Afdeeling", 29, 14. R. Matthaci B "Ztschr. d. Allg. Physik", 1923, 20, 20.

Rahm, P.G. 1922. Biologische und physiologische Beiträge zur Kenntnis der Moosfauna. "Ztschr. f. Allg. Phsiol.", 20, 1/2, 1-34.

Rein, R. 1908. Untersuchungen über den Kältetod der Pflanzen. "Ztschr. f. Naturw.", 80, No. 1-2, 1-38.

Rigg, G.B., & Cain, R.A. 1929. A physico-chemical study of the leaves of three medical plants in relation to evergreenness. "Am. J. Bot.", 16, No. 1, 40-58.

Rosa, J.T. 1921. Investigation of the hardening process in vegetable plants. "Miss. Agric. Exp. Sta. Res. Bull.", 48, 1-97.

Rudorf, W. 1938. Keimstimmung und Photoperiode in ihrer Bedeutung für die Kälteresistenz. "Züchter", 10, 238-246.

Russow, F. 1882. Über Tüpfelbildung und Inhalt der Bastparenhymund Baststrahlzellen der Dicotylen und Gymnospermen, sowie über den Inhalt der parenchymatischen Rinde in Stamm und Wurzel der einheimischen Lignosen. "Sitz. d. Dorpater Naturforsch. Ges.", 350, S. (cited from "Bot. Zeit., 13, 1883).

Sachs, J. 1860a. Krystallbildungen bei dem Gefrieren und Veränderung der Zellhäute bei dem Aufthauen saftiger Pflanzenteile. "Ber. d. math.-phys. Klasse d. Kgl. Sächs. Gesell. d. Wissensch.", 2, 1-40. Cited from Sachs J., Gesammelte Abhandlungen der Pflanzen. 1892, 1, 3-48.

Sachs, J. 1860b. Untersuchungen über das Erfrieren der Pflanzen. "Landw. Versuchs-Stationen", 2, 167-201.

Sachs, J. 1860c. Das Erfrieren bei Temperaturen über null Grad. "Bot. Zeit.", 19, No. 14, 123-126.

Sachs, J. 1864. Über den Einfluss der Temperatur auf das Ergrünen der Blätter. "Flora", 22, No. 32, 497-506.

Sachs, J. 1865. Handbuch der experimentalen Physiologie der Pflanzen. Handb. der Physiol. Bot., "Flora", 22, 32, 497-506.

Sachs, J. 1892. Gesammelte Abhandlungen über Pflanzenphysiologie, 1.

Salmon, S.C. 1916. Seeding winter grains in furrows to prevent winterkilling. "J. Am. Soc. Agr.", 8, No. 3, 176-187.

Salmon, S.C. 1917. The relation of winter temperature to the distribution of winter and spring grain in the United States. "J. Am. Soc. Agr.", 9, No. 1, 21-24.

Salmon, S.C., & Fleming, F.L. 1918. Relation of the density of cell sap to winter hardiness in small grains. "J. Agric. Rec.", 13, No. 10, 497-506.

Scarth, G.W. 1941. Dehydration injury and resistance. "Plant Physiol.", 16, No. 1, 171-180.

Scarth, G.W., & Levitt, J. 1937. The frost hardening mechanism of plant cells. "Plant Physiol.", 12, No. 1, 51-78.

Scatchard, G. 1921. The hydration of sucrose in water solution as calculated from vapor-pressure measurements. "J. Am. Chem. Soc.", 43, No. 11, 2406-2418.

Schacht, H. 1856-1859. Lehrbuch der Anatomie und Physiologie der Gewächse. Berlin.

Schaffnit, E. 1910. Studien über den Einfluss niedriger Temperaturen auf die pflanzliche Zelle. "Mitt. d. K.W. Inst. f. Landw. in Bromberg", 3, 93-144.

Schaffnit, E. 1912. Der Schneeschimmel und die übrigen durch Fusarium nivale Sacc. hervorgerufenen Krankheitserscheinungen des Getreides. "Landw. Jrb.", 43, 1-128.

Schaffnit, E., u. Lüdtke, N. 1932. Beiträge zur Kenntniss von Kältewirkungen auf die pflanzliche Zelle. II. Über den Stoffwechsel landwirtschaftlicher Kulturpflanzen bei verschiedenen Temperaturen und wechselnder Ernährung. "Phytopath. Ztschr.", 4, 329-386.

Schaffnit, E., & Wilhelm, A. 1933. Beiträge zur Kenntnis von Kältewirkungen auf die pflanzliche Zelle. (III Mitt.). Kühlversuche mit verschiedenen ernährten Pflanzen und Untersuchungen über deren Stoffwechselphysiologie. "Phytopath. Ztschr.", 5, No. 6, 505-566.

Schander, R., & Schaffnit, E. 1919. Untersuchungen uber das Auswintern des Getreides. "Landw. Jrb.", 52, 1-66.

Schellenberg, H.C. 1905. Hemicellulosen als Reservestoffe bei unseren Waldbaumen. "Ber. Dtsch. Bot. Ges", 23, 36-45.

Schlösser, L.A. 1936. Frostharte und Polyploidie. Zuchter, 8, No. 3, 75-80.

Schübler, & Halder. 1827. Beobachtungen über die Temperatur der Vegetabilien. Diss., Tübingen. (cited from Göppert, 1830).

Schübler, & Neuffer. 1829. Untersuchungen über die Temperaturveränderungen der Vegetabilien und verschiedene damit in Beziehung stehende Gegenstände. Diss., Tubingen. (cited from Göppert, 1830).

Schultz, C.H. 1823. Die Natur der lebendigen Pflanze. Berlin.

Sellschop, J.P.F., & Salmon, S.C. 1928. The influence of chilling, above the freezing point, on certain crop plants. "J. Agric. Res.", 37, No. 6, 315-338.

Senebier, J. 1800. Physiologie végétale. Genève.

Shull, C.A. 1916. Measurement of the surface forces in soils. "Bot. Gaz.", 62, No. 1, 1-31.

Shutt, F.T. 1903. On the relation of moisture-content to hardiness in apple. "Royal Soc. Canada Transact.", sect. 4, 141-153.

Sidorin, M.J. 1932. Eine neue Lebensreaction "Btr. Biol. Pfl.", 20, 1-6.

Siminovitch, D., & Scarth, G.W. 1938. A study of the mechanism of frost injury to plants. "Canad. J. Res.", 16, No. 11, 467-481.

Siminovitch, D., & Levitt, J. 1941. The relation between frost resistance and the physical state of protoplasm. II. The protoplasmatic surface. "Canad. J. Res.", 19, No. 1, 9-20.

Simon, S. 1906. Untersuchungen über das Verhalten einiger Wachstumsfunktionen sowie der Atmungstätigkeit der Laubholzer während der Ruheperiode. "Jrb. Wiss. Bot.", 43, No. 1, 1-48.

Simonds, A.O. 1942. Histological study of freezing, desiccation and winter injury of raspberry canes. "Bot. Gaz.", 104, 356-361.

Slater, C.S., & Hopp, H. 1949. The action of frost on the water-stability of soils. "J. Agric. Res.", 78, No. 10, 341-346.

Smart, H.F. 1935. Growth and survival of microorganisms at sub-freezing temperatures. "Science", 82, 2135, 525.

Sorauer, P. 1901. Der Schneeschimmel. "Ztschr. Pflanzenkrankh.", XI, 217-228.

Sorauer, P. 1906. Experimentelle Studien über die mechanischen Wirkungen des Frostes bei Obst-und Waltbäumen. "Landw. Jrb.", 35, 469-526.

Stark, A.L. 1936. Unfrozen water in apple shoots as related to their winter hardiness. "Plant Physiol.", 11, No. 4, 689-712.

Steinberg, 1929. Beobachtungen über die Frostschutzwirkung von Kalisalzdüngung bei Wintergetreide. "Die Ernähr. d. Pf.", 25, No. 19, 449-450.

Steiner, M. 1933. Zum Chemismus der osmotischen Jahresschwankungen einiger immergruner Holzgewächse. "Jrb. Wiss. Bot.", 78, No. 4, 564-622.

Steinmelz, F.H. 1926. Winter hardiness in alfalfa varieties. "Univ. Minn. Agric. Exp. Sta. Tech. Bull.", 38, 1-32.

Stiles, W. 1930. On the cause of cold death of plants. "Protoplasma", 9, No. 3, 459-467.

Stocker, O. 1928. Der Wasserhaushalt ägyptischer Wüsten- und Salzpflanzen. Jena.

Strausbaugh, P.D. 1921. Dormancy and harding in the plum. "Bot. Gaz.", 71, No. 5, 337-357.

Strömer, M. 1749. Gedanken über die Ursachen, die Bäume bei starkem Winter erfrieren etc. (transl. from Swedish). Hamburg (cited from Göppert, 1830).

Thoenes, F. 1925. Untersuchungen zur Frage der Wasserbindung in Kolloiden und tierischen Geweben. "Bioch. Ztschr.", 157, 174-186.

Thouin, A. 1805. Observations sur l'effet des gelées précoces qui ont eu lieu les 18, 19. et 20 vendémiaire an XIV (11, 12 et 13 octobre 1805). "Ann. Museum d'Hist. Natur., par les profess. de cet Etabliss.", 7, 85-114, Paris.

Tottingham, W.E., Shands, R.G., & Delwiche, E.D. 1931. Tests of Chibnall's method of extraction for investigating winter hardiness of plants. "Plant Physiol.", 6, 167-176.

Treviranus, L.C. 1838. Physiologie der Gewächse, 2, 808 S.

Turkey, H.B., & Carlson, R.F. 1945. Morphological changes in peach seedlings following after-ripening treatments of the seeds. "Bot. Gaz.", 106, No. 4, 431-440.

Tuttle, G.M. 1919. Induced changes in reserve materials in evergreen herbaceous leaves. "Ann. Bot.", 33, 130, 202-210.

Tuttle, G.M. 1921. Reserve food materials in vegetative tissues. "Bot. Gaz.", 71, No. 2, 146-151.

Tysdal, H.M. 1934. Determination of hardiness in alfalfa varieties by their enzymatic response. "J. Agric. Res.", 48, No. 3, 219-241.

Tysdal, H.M., & Salmon, S.C. 1926. Viscosity and winter hardiness in the small grains. "J. Am. Soc. Agr.", 18, No. 12, 1099-1100.

Ullrich, H., & Mäde, A. 1940-1941. Studien über die Ursachen der Frostresistenz. II. Untersuchungen über den Temperaturverlauf beim Gefrieren von Blättern und Vergleichsobjekten. "Planta", 31, 251-262.

Ulmer, W. 1937. Über den Jahresgang der Frosthärte einiger immergrüner Arten der alpinen Stufe, sowie der Zirbe und Fichte. Unter Berücksichtigung von osmotischen Wert, Zuckerspiegel und Wassergehalt. "Jahrb. Wiss. Bot.", 84, No. 4, 553-592.

Vegis, A. 1932. Über das Frühtreiben Winterknospen von Hydrocharis morsus ranal L. durch hochtemperierte Wasserbäder. "Jrb. Wiss. Bot.", 75, No. 5, 726-770.

Verdoorn, F. 1945. Plants and plant science in Latin America. "Waltham, Mass. USA", 383 p.

Vogel, A. 1820. Über die Veränderung, welche einige Stoffe des organischen Reiches beim Gefrieren erleiden. "Gilbert's Ann. der Physik", 64, 167.

Voigtländer, H. 1909. Unterkühlung und Kältetod der Pflanzen. "Btr. Biol. Pfl.", 9, No. 3, 359-414.

Walter, H. 1924. Plasmaquellung und Wachstum. "Ztschr. Bot.", 16, No. 7, 353-429.

Walter, H. 1929a. Die Winterschäden an unseren immergrünen Pflanzen während der Kälteperiode January—Marz 1929 und ihre Ursachen. "Naturwiss", 44, 854-859.

Walter, H. 1929b. Die osmotischen Werte und die Kälteschäden unsere wintergrünen Pflanzen während der Winterperiode. 1929. "Ber. Dtsch. Bot. Ges.", 47, 338-347.

Walter, H. 1931. Die Hydratur der Pflanzen. 1-170. Jena.

Wartenberg, H. 1929. Über primäre und sekundäre Kälteresistenz bei Bohnensippen. "Planta", 7, No. 2-3, 347-381.

Wartenberg, H. 1953. Kälte und Hitze als Todesursasche der Pflanze und als Ursache von Pflanzenkrankheiten. Handb. der Pflanzenkr., 6, Aufl., 475-592.

Wassiljew, I.M. 1932. Untersuchungen über die Dynamik der Kohlehydrate beim Weizen. "Arch. Pflanzenbau", 8, No. 3, 565-578.

Webber, H.J. 1946. The citrus industry, I, 1028 pp. "Univ. Calif. Press".

Welsmann, O. 1938. Eine theoretische und experimentelle Kritik der "Bound Water-Theorie", "Protoplasma", 31, 27-68.

Wettstein, F. 1924. Morphologie und Physiologie des Formwechsels der Moose auf genetischer Grundlage. I. "Ztschr. Indukt. Abst.-n. Vereb", 33, 1-236.

Wiegang, K.M. 1906. Some studies regarding the biology of buds and twigs in winter. "Bot. Gaz.", 41, 6, 373-424.

Wilhelm, A.F. 1933. Experimentelle Untersuchungen über die Kälteresistenz von Reben und Obstgehölzen. "Gartenbauwiss.", 8, 77-114.

Wilhelm, A.F. 1935a. Untersuchungen über die Kälteresistenz winterfester Kulturpflanzen unter besonderer Berücksichtigung des Einflusses verschiedener Mineralsalzernährung und des N-Stoffwechsels. "Phytopath. Ztschr.", 8, No. 2, 111-156.

Wilhelm, A.F. 1935b. Studien über die Bedeutung der Lipoide, insbesondere der Phosphatide, für die Frostresistenz der Pflanzen. "Phytopath. Ztschr.", 8, No. 3, 225-236.

Wilhelm, A.F. 1935c. Untersuchungen über das Verhalten sogenanter nicht einsbeständiger Kulturpflanzen bei niederen Temperaturen, unter besonderer Berichtigung des Einflusses verschiedener Mineralsalzernährung und des N-Stoffwechsels. "Phytopat. Ztschr.", 8, No. 4, 335-362.

Willaman, J.J., & Brown, W.R. 1930. Carbon dioxide dissolved in plant sap and its effect on respiration measurements. "Plant Physiol", 5, No. 4, 535-542.

Winkler, A. 1913. Über den Einfluss der Aussenbedingungen auf die Kälteresistenz ausdauernder Gewächse. "Jahrb. Wiss. Bot.", 52, 467-506.

Zacharowa, T.M. 1925. Über den Einfluss niedriger Temperaturen auf die Pflanzen. "Jahrb. Wiss. Bot.", 56, No. 1, 61-87.